THE NATURE OF
WYRE

a wildlife-rich forest in the heart of Britain

Edited by Brett Westwood, Peter Shirley, Rosemary Winnall & Harry Green

Main authors
Mike Averill (dragonflies and damselflies)
John Bingham (flora, fungi, beetles)
Mick Blythe (flies)
Chris Bradley (deer)
Gary Farmer (grasshoppers, bush-crickets and their allies)
Fran Flanagan (bats)
Harry Green (habitats, hidden worlds, other insects, birds)
Graham Hill (watercourses, aquatic crustaceans)
Rosemary Hill (molluscs)
Jenny Joy (butterflies)
Mark Lawley (mosses and liverworts)
Susan Limbrey (geology, soil)
John Partridge (spiders and harvestmen)
Graeme Peirson (fish)
David Poyner (history)
Phil Rudlin (deer, Hazel Dormouse)
Sylvia Sheldon (reptiles)
Peter Shirley (galls)
Tony Simpson (moths)
Geoff Trevis (bees, wasps, ants, sawflies and woodwasps)
Brett Westwood (introduction, bugs)
Mike Williams (butterflies)
Rosemary Winnall (amphibians, lichens, plant fossils, other mammals)

with contributions from
Johnny Birks (mammals)
Mike Bloxham (hoverflies, Parasitica)
Trevor Duke (lichens)
John Robinson (amphibians, birds, mammals)
Ian Wallace (caddisflies)

Supported by

Worcestershire

Published by

Published 2015 by Pisces Publications

First published 2015.

British-Library-in-Publication Data
A catalogue record for this book is available from the British Library.

ISBN 978-1-874357-69-8

Designed and published by Pisces Publications

Visit our bookshop
www.naturebureau.co.uk/bookshop/

Pisces Publications is the imprint of NatureBureau, 36 Kingfisher Court, Hambridge Road, Newbury, Berkshire RG14 5SJ
www.naturebureau.co.uk

Printed and bound in the UK by Gomer Press Ltd

MIX
Paper from
responsible sources
FSC® C114687
www.fsc.org

COVER PHOTOGRAPHS
Front cover **Dowles Brook** [Bob Kemp]
 Narrow-leaved Helleborine [Rosemary Winnall], **Pearl-bordered Fritillary** [Rosemary Winnal], **Hawfinch** [John Robinson]
Back cover **Aerial view of the Wyre Forest** [Forestry Commission]

MAIN CHAPTER PHOTOGRAPHS
Chapter 1 **Aerial view looking south across the Wyre Forest, Dowles Brook valley and Lodge Hill Farm** [Forestry Commission]
Chapter 2 **Mixed woodland in Longdon** [John Bingham]
Chapter 3 **Knowles Mill 2003** [Rosemary Winnall]
Chapter 4 **Ramsons** *Allium ursinum* **along Baveney Brook** [Peter Creed]
Chapter 5 **Waterfall on Bow Brook, Hitterhill Coppice** [Peter Creed]
Chapter 6 **Common Bonnet** *Mycena galericulata* **on deadwood** [John Bingham]
Chapter 7 *Ophegrapha atra* **lichen on Hazel, Park Brook valley** [Rosemary Winnall]
Chapter 8 **Oak Apple gall, Callow Hill** [Rosemary Winnall]
Chapter 9 **Black-and-Yellow Longhorn Beetle** *Rutpela maculata* **and the hoverfly** *Eristalis tenax*, **Longdon** [Rosemary Winnall]
Chapter 10 **Lemon Slug** *Malacolimax tenellus*, **New Parks** [Rosemary Winnall]
Chapter 11 **River Severn south of Bewdley** [Rosemary Winnall]
Chapter 12 **Grass Snakes have been seen swimming across the River Severn** [Wendy Carter]
Chapter 13 **Dippers can be seen along the Dowles Brook all year** [Matthew Lissimore]
Chapter 14 **Fallow buck, black colour form, New Parks** [Phil Rudlin]
Chapter 15 **Conservation of the Wyre Forest's wildlife and heritage is important for future generations** [Rosemary Winnall]

ENDPAPER PHOTOGRAPHS
Front **As main chapter photographs**
Back **Early morning in New Parks** [Phil Rudlin]

Contents

Acknowledgements

To embark on a book about the Wyre Forest would have been impossible without the encouragement and the deep knowledge of a host of people. These pages contain the results in many cases, of lifetimes of appreciation and understanding of the Forest's wildlife. All the people involved have given their expertise freely and enthusiastically and we thank them sincerely for their contributions.

Particular thanks must go to the authors of the individual chapters, all of them specialists, amateur or professional. Wyre has sometimes been able to lead the way nationally in the studies of certain creatures and we are lucky to be able to include Sylvia Sheldon's detailed studies of adders, Phil Rudlin's and Roger Trout's work on dormice and Graham and Ann Hill's work on native crayfish. But we have been able to include so much detailed information on all aspects of Wyre's structure, history and natural history, thanks to the combined expertise of the following chapter authors, all of whom have been gathering records and information about Wyre for many years: Mike Averill (dragonflies and damselflies), John Bingham (flora, fungi, beetles) Mick Blythe (flies), Chris Bradley (deer), Gary Farmer (grasshoppers, bush-crickets and their allies), Fran Flanagan (bats), Harry Green (habitats, birds, other insects, hidden worlds), Graham Hill (watercourses, aquatic crustacians), Rosemary Hill (molluscs), Jenny Joy (butterflies), Mark Lawley (mosses and liverworts), Susan Limbrey (geology, soil), John Partridge (spiders and harvestmen), Graeme Peirson (fish), David Poyner (history), Phil Rudlin (deer, Hazel Dormouse), Sylvia Sheldon (reptiles), Peter Shirley (galls), Tony Simpson (moths), Geoff Trevis (bees, wasps, ants, sawflies and woodwasps), Brett Westwood (introduction, bugs), Mike Williams (butterflies) and Rosemary Winnall (amphibians, lichens, plant fossils, other mammals). These were ably assisted with contributions from Johnny Birks (mammals), Mike Bloxham (hoverflies, Parasitica), Trevor Duke (lichens), John Robinson (amphibians, birds, mammals) and Ian Wallace (caddisflies), all of whom contributed sections within the text.

The Wyre Forest is fortunate in attracting highly-talented photographers who either live in the area or visit regularly and we are immensely grateful for the use of their images which add so much to the attraction of this book. All the photographers have allowed us to use their outstanding images without charge. The principal photographers whose work is included here are; Mike Averill [MA], John Bingham [JB], Patrick Clement [PCl], Peter Creed [PC], Bob Kemp [BK], Kevin McGee [KMcG], Matthew Lissimore [ML], John Robinson [JR], Phil Rudlin [PR], Oliver Wadsworth [OW] and Rosemary Winnall [RW]. Images were also received from Mick Blythe [MB], Stewart Carter [SC], Wendy Carter [WC], Gary Farmer [GF], Fran Flanagan [FF], Alonza Garbett [AG], Harry Green [HG], Dave Grundy [DG], Susan Limbrey [SL], Craig Reed [CR], Sylvia Sheldon [SS], Brett Westwood [BW], David Williams [DW] and we were able to obtain a few from the late Neville Wilde's slide library [NW]. Mark Boulton [MB], Paul Brock [PB], Daniel Hargreaves [DH], Peter Walkden [PW] and Roger Waseley [RWa] generously responded to requests to use their excellent images to illustrate particular sections of the text. Help with sourcing historical photographs came from Sue Holmes [SH], Charles Purcell (CP Bewdley Historical Research Group), Wyre Forest District Council's Bewdley Museum [BM] and Worcestershire County Council's Kidderminster Library Service [KLS]. For all these we are very appreciative.

As we planned the book, a daunting cloud of problems and questions arose, but we are especially grateful to the many people who helped the fog to clear. In some technical areas we needed specialist advice and would like to single out Andy Grubb and Graham Hill for their help with GIS mapping, and Adam Mindykowski (Historic Environment advisor, Worcestershire County Council) for information about LiDAR. We also thank Charles Purcell and Stuart Davies for sharing their knowledge, always generously given over the years, on aspects of Wyre's history. Fossils were a potentially tricky area and we thank Daniel Lockett (Ludlow Museum Resource Centre) for advice and for permission to use Angela Gladwell's attractive drawings. Brian Stephens was a mine of information on Wyre's orchards which could have provided several volumes of their own.

Some of the animal groups required extra information and for answering questions and providing details about Wyre's mammals, we are grateful to Johnny Birks, Jason Ford, Albert Link, Richard Parsons, Sally Pendergast and Brenda Rea. John Robinson provided specialised knowledge about Wyre's birds, amphibians and as well as mammals, and his knowledge of Wyre's wildlife has been invaluable. Val Lambourne and Phil Rudlin allowed us to feature their newt survey work and David Dewsbury kindly provided his illustration of his innovative newt trap called the Dewsbury Box. Nigel Hand (Central Ecology) has helped Sylvia Sheldon to shine a new light on adders in Wyre through the adder telemetry project. Caddis flies are still a specialist's area for many and we are especially grateful for the expertise of Ian Wallace from the Freshwater Biological Association in providing more information about them.

Field trips are a vital part of the Wyre Forest Study Group's calendar and we are grateful to all landowners and managers for allowing access. In particular we would like to thank John and Linda Iles from the Guild of St George, Cedric and Thelma Quayle, and James Tibbetts and family, all of whom regularly allow access onto their land. Local personnel from Natural England (John Bingham prior to his retirement, Fran Flanagan and Saul Herbert) have encouraged us in our studies. We are indebted to the Forestry Commission for much ongoing help, especially Ian Hickman (before his retirement), Richard Boles and Phil Rudlin. Their support and housing of the Wyre Forest Records Room at Callow Hill have greatly assisted our work.

Recording is the lifeblood of any natural history group and there are many other active recorders in addition to the chapter authors and those already mentioned, and we would like to thank them for their companionship and expertise in many subjects. Though not all are still regular visitors to Wyre, they have in a professional or amateur capacity increased our knowledge of the Forest and its natural history. They are Paul Allen, Andrew Allott, David Antrobus, Dave Barnett, Denise Bingham, Ted Blackwell, Steve Bloomfield, Godfrey Blunt, Pete Boardman, Joe Botting, Ron Boyce, Alan Brown, Nigel Cane-Honeysett, Tessa Carrick, Wendy Carter, Jon Cartwright, Ian Cheeseborough, Patrick Clement, John Cox, Steve Davies, John Day, John Dodgson, Nicki Farmer, Roy and Frances Finch, Lorna Fraser, Cherry Greenway, Dave Grundy, Ann Hill, Godfrey Jones, Nigel Jones, Bob Kemp, Frank and Pat Lancaster, Cody Levine, Matthew Lissimore, David Long, Scott Martin, Kevin McGee, John Meiklejohn, Mervyn Needham, Mark Peacock, Ross Piper, Ellen Pisolkar, Colin Plant, Jane Pope, David Pryce, Paul Reade, Craig Reed, Bert Reid, Joy Ricketts, Dave and Jane Scott, Malcolm Smart, David Smith, Brian Stephens, Nigel Stone, Mike Taylor, Joe Turner, Oliver Wadsworth and Will Watson. In fact we would like to thank anyone who has sent in records—please don't stop!

A number of expert naturalists, sadly no longer with us, have enriched this book with their explorations and discoveries about Wyre's wildlife in past times. We are indebted to them for their work and for providing inspiration not just for this book, but also for the generations who will visit Wyre in the future: the late Fred Fincher, Edwin George, David Harding, Norman Hickin, Noel King, Roy Mantle, Jim Martin, Simon Walker and Neville Wilde.

Many organisations have provided information, data or images for this book and we would particularly like to thank: Birmingham Museums Trust (Dr Luanne Meehitiya), British Arachnological Society (data from Spider Recording Scheme), British Geological Survey (geology maps), British Plant Gall Society (Janet Boyd and Tom Higginbottom), Butterfly Conservation, Conchological Society of Great Britain and Ireland (records), the Environment Agency (data), Forest Research (LiDAR Peter Crow and dormice data Roger Trout), Guild of St George (John Iles and Cedric Quayle), Natural England (Saul Herbert), Staffordshire Ecological Record (Craig Slawson), Shropshire Ecological Data Network (Robin Mager), Worcestershire Biological Records Centre (Simon Wood), Worcestershire Recorders, Worcestershire Wildlife Trust, Wyre Community Land Trust, the Wyre Forest Society and, of course, all our colleagues in the Wyre Forest Study Group.

The Wyre Forest Study Group (with help from their legacy from Grow With Wyre), has supported the concept of writing this book from the beginning, and helped substantially with funding the project. We are grateful also to the Worcestershire Wildlife Trust which has provided significant help towards the cost of publication.

We have especially enjoyed working with Pisces Publications and we are indebted to our publisher Peter Creed for working his unique magic on the book's design and layout. Professor Chris Baines has provided us with a stirring and thoughtful foreword and we thank him for his support and encouragement.

If we have left anyone out, we apologise and sincerely thank them all.

Last, but by no means least, the book has been made possible by the foundation of The Wyre Forest Study Group. Initially called the Wyre Forest Research Group, it was started in 1991 by Peter Hobson together with founder members Mike Averill, Mike Taylor, Frank and Pat Lancaster, John and Denise Bingham, Sylvia Sheldon, Chris Bradley, and Rosemary Winnall. In those early days one of our aims was to publish the findings of our studies. Although an annual Review has been produced annually since 2000, many reports written, and much information presented on the website **www.wyreforest.net**, it has taken us until now, in the 24th year since the group was formed, to write the book to celebrate the special place that is Wyre. The spirit of sharing information and expertise has always been the main aim of the Group and through this book, it is a pleasure to share that spirit with our readers.

The Editors
19 August 2015

Foreword

The Wyre Forest is extraordinary! Its complex pattern of ancient woodlands, conifer plantations, stream valleys, orchards and pastures provides habitats for a quite exceptional abundance of wild plants and animals.

My own love of Wyre dates back 40 years. When I moved to the West Midlands I was lucky enough to get to know Norman Hickin. He was an exceptional amateur naturalist, a writer, illustrator and a successful businessman with a lifelong passion for the Wyre Forest. He lived in Bewdley and through his eyes I learned to see the Forest as a complex reflection of the soils below, the streams and rivers that flow through it and the centuries of human activity that have shaped it. The Forest's location at the very heart of the country makes it all the more interesting as an ecological crossroads between north and south, east and west, and Norman devoted a long lifetime to exploring, understanding and explaining this very special place. That tradition clearly continues in the safe hands of today's Wyre naturalists.

There is no corner of the Wyre that is truly wild. Throughout the forest there are echoes of its hard-working history, from cherry orchards to railway tracks and from charcoal hearths to water mills. Without exception each of these interventions has added a new natural dimension to the mosaic of wildlife habitats. The ancient cherry trees may no longer yield a crop to match the trainloads of fruit that once supplied the nearby towns and cities. Nevertheless the orchards still offer an ideal range of habitats for some of England's rarest insects and a happy hunting ground for Wyre's Green Woodpeckers. The railway that ran through the main area of woodland was dismantled long ago, but its cuttings and embankments still carve strips of sunny woodland-edge through the high forest, providing ideal conditions for Wyre's famous fritillary butterflies.

Making the most of Wyre will demand knowledge, skill and imagination far into the future. Most importantly it will need a wide range of enthusiastic individuals with complementary expertise, keen to embrace a long-term vision for the Forest and eager to work creatively together. This book and the information it contains will be a cornerstone of that sustainable future. Its contents are a testament to the hard work of the present generation of Wyre's dedicated and knowledgeable naturalists and it is rare to find such breadth and depth of knowledge concentrated in one place.

In the past, wildlife in the Wyre Forest and places like it has been little more than a happy accident. No-one planned for fritillary butterflies or Nuthatches or Bluebells. They thrived or struggled in response to the impact of a working landscape. Wyre still needs to pay its way, to contribute to the local economy and to provide enjoyable breathing spaces for people. What is relatively new is the idea that the Forest can be actively managed for nature conservation at the same time. In the past, Wyre's diversity of wildlife habitats may have evolved by chance. Now we can look forward to a future forest that is actively encouraged to become even better for wildlife. This wonderful book shows why that matters, and how it can best be achieved.

Professor Chris Baines
Chair of the Wyre Forest Landscape Partnership
September 2015

Springtime in Wyre is cause for celebration with flowers in bloom, insects emerging and birdsong overhead [RW]

Chapter 1

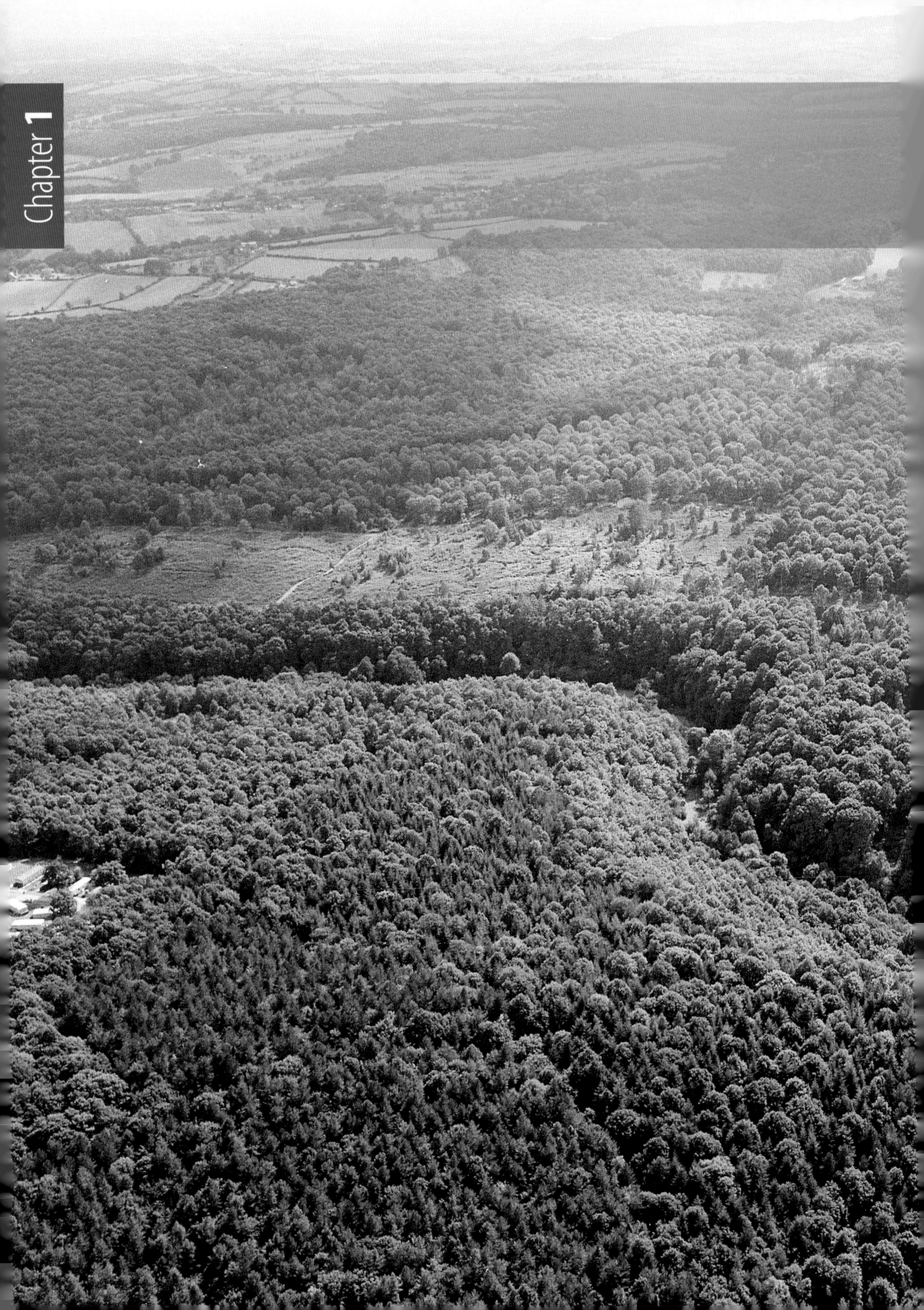

Wyre: An Introduction

It's mid-March. The first warm sunshine of spring strikes a bank of bracken whose cushions of crisp fronds crackle underfoot. Overhead, bumble bees drone among sallow blossom. The larvae of the tiny Land Caddis *Enoicyla pusilla* stumble like animated twigs over the sunlit leaves. A blur of ginger resolves into a Dark-edged Bee-fly *Bombylius major* which settles on a bank near an ammonite coiled tightly among the roots of a young birch. This is no fossil. The Adder *Vipera berus* twitches slightly, and flattens its body to soak up the sun's rays.

Fast forward a few weeks and Bluebells *Hyacinthoides non-scripta* flood the valley of the Dowles Brook. Pearl-bordered Fritillaries *Boloria euphrosyne* glowing like embers flicker above them. Nearby a Wood Warbler *Phylloscopus sibilatrix* is shivering in ecstatic song. A Dipper *Cinclus cinclus* whirrs downstream, calling sharply above the babble of rippling water. On a sunny slope, a raiding party of Slavemaker Ants *Formica sanguinea* scurries past a snowy spike of a Narrow-leaved Helleborine *Cephalanthera longifolia*.

There is nowhere else in the British Isles where this combination of wildlife exists. This is remarkable enough, but all the more extraordinary when you realise that the Wyre Forest is only 25 miles from the centre of Birmingham and less than 12 miles from the Black Country, a crucible of activity during the Industrial Revolution. In a rapidly changing landscape the survival of this mosaic of woodland, orchards, old meadows and fast-flowing streams seems like a modern miracle.

The proximity of manufacturing industry to the relative wilderness of Wyre, and its inhabitants, fascinated the Black Country writer, Francis Brett Young. In his novel *Far Forest*, published in 1936, he describes 'Werewood' as a mysterious, if rather forbidding place where "searching light beat down through an inky filigree of bared branches on to the Forest's rusty floor, its deep mould releasing the summer heat in which slow-worms and adders had been born". With a naturalist's eye Brett Young deftly captures the essence of Wyre. In the depths of the spring woodland, "wild cherry trees rose like puffs of smoke or hung tangled like fallen cloud" and "antheaps, accumulated, twig on twig, by the minute labours of summers unnumbered". But industry was hard to forget. In winter, easterly winds carried "in millions those fine particles of carbon which the Black Country breathes into the sky above it", staining the Forest fogs yellow (Brett Young 1936).

Modern Wyre is much more accessible, nuzzled by Bewdley, networked with forest tracks and fringed by carparks, but its mystery remains. Although it is one of the largest tracts of ancient oakwood in England and within easy reach of millions of people,

Dipper *Cinclus cinclus* [ML]

Dark-edged Bee-fly *Bombylius major* and Wood-sorrel *Oxalis acetosella* [PC]

Adder *Vipera berus* [ML]

it is much less well-known than say, the New Forest or Epping Forest. Wyre guards its secrets well and it will take several visits over many years to see and appreciate the wide range of wildlife that lives here. The aim of this book is to reveal its nature and history, its extraordinary variety of habitats and wildlife and to celebrate the value and richness of a very special place.

In doing so, we tread in the wake of notable naturalists. The Worcestershire Naturalists, or 'Lookers-out' as they were known, made regular excursions into the Forest and its surrounds and their records shine a light into the glories of Victorian Wyre. Their regular pilgrimages to the descendants of Wyre's famous Whitty Pear or True Service-tree *Sorbus domestica* are faithfully recorded in the Transactions, which include subjects as varied as fossils, sedges, Glow-worms *Lampyris noctiluca* and tantalising glimpses of the last Black Grouse *Tetrao tetrix*. Other prominent naturalists include the entomologist W.G. Blatch, who was active 1870–1890, and recorded many new beetles as well as the elusive Shining Guest Ant *Formicoxenus nitidulus* which lurks in the nests of Southern Wood Ants *Formica rufa*. Brunsden Yapp was a pioneer of woodland bird study who conducted much of his research in the Forest. In the 1920s Wyre was the open-air laboratory of Edgar Chance who, with Oliver Pike, was the first person to film female Cuckoos *Cuculus canorus* laying eggs in the nests of their hosts

at Pound Green Common near Button Oak. The stories of some of these early naturalists are told elsewhere in these pages.

One naturalist has probably encouraged more modern wildlife enthusiasts to visit Wyre than any other. Born in Birmingham in 1910, Norman Hickin was a professional entomologist who wrote about the Forest's wildlife in a series of articles for the *Kidderminster Times*, later published in 1971 as *The Natural History of an English Forest* (Hickin 1971). Hickin knew Wyre intimately and had a house here. His descriptions of its wildlife are still an inspiration, whether of crab spiders *Misumena vatia* lurking in the flowers of Wood Spurge *Euphorbia amygdaloides* or the churring of Nightjars *Caprimulgus europaeus* at dusk. His main claim to entomological glory came with the rediscovery while camping in the Forest 1957 of the Land Caddis, a rare and very local insect nationally, but common in Wyre. Throughout this book are references to Hickin's studies in Wyre: modern naturalists owe him the debt of inspiration.

Following in Norman Hickin's footsteps is a growing number of local naturalists, many of them members of the Wyre Forest Study Group, whose findings have both increased our knowledge of the Forest and provided information for its conservation managers. In addition to their regular programme of field meetings, the Group and its members supervise

In some areas of Wyre, especially where oak/beech woodland has been thinned, Bluebells *Hyacinthoides non-scripta* flood the Forest floor in April and May. Here, as in other places in the British Isles, they grow in ancient woodland on light acidic soils. Plants take five years to develop from seed to flower-bearing plants. [RW]

or assist with a range of projects and regular surveys, some of them long running. Because Wyre lies across the border between Shropshire and Worcestershire, the Study Group also acts as a collator of records for the whole site area and publishes an annual *Review* as well as contributing to studies by Wyre's two principal public landowners, the Forestry Commission and Natural England. The chapters in this book have been written by expert naturalists, most of them Study Group members, who value the sheer variety of Wyre's wildlife.

Naturalists in the know visit Wyre for the surprising mix of species it contains, especially outlying colonies of those commoner outside the Midlands. Northern plants such as Mountain Melick grass *Melica nutans* and Wood Crane's-bill *Geranium sylvaticum* grow here alongside primarily southern species like Chaffweed *Centunculus minimus* and Violet Helleborine *Epipactis purpurata*. The western oakwood trio of Pied Flycatcher *Ficedula hypoleuca*, Redstart *Phoenicurus phoenicurus* and Wood Warbler all breed but are very rare farther east. In Wyre live scarce and local species whose distribution is highly fragmented; these include the Slavemaker Ant and the Strawberry Spider *Araneus alsine* which are found on southern heaths and in open Scottish woods, but hardly anywhere in between. The Six-spotted Longhorn Beetle *Anoplodera sexguttata* is a distinctly rare southern species, but has recently turned up in Wyre. It is this unexpected potential which makes the area so enticing, and new species are always in the offing as habitats change.

A walk in the woods

The Wyre Forest is a large area to explore, but a walk in late spring or summer along the river from Bewdley to the Dowles, following the brook upstream and returning along the old railway line will show you the variety of habitats and wildlife. Heading north along the Bewdley quay where Rue-leaved Saxifrage *Saxifraga tridactylites* grows, look out for Kingfishers *Alcedo atthis* and Mandarin Ducks *Aix galericulata* on the river: in winter Goosanders *Mergus merganser* even come into the centre of town. Along the riverbank comfrey *Symphytum* spp. buzzes with bees and in early summer Common Clubtail dragonflies *Gomphus vulgatissimus* sit on bankside leaves.

At Dowles Brook head into the Forest, crossing the road near the old railway line. Following the lower path near Dowles Manor you may see Grey Wagtails *Motacilla cinerea* on the brook and, in May and June, the rare hoverfly *Chalcosyrphus eunotus* basking on sunlit logs in the stream channel. Where the path joins a stone track near an old mill, keep the brook on your left, where there are Dippers and listen for Wood Warblers. In April Toothwort *Lathraea squamaria* grows on the roots of brookside Hazels *Corylus avellana* here. Soon you reach Knowles Mill and one of a series of valley meadows, popular with fritillary butterflies and sooty Chimney Sweeper moths *Odezia atrata*. Beautiful Demoiselles *Calopteryx virgo* flash cobalt and turquoise as they defend territories along the Dowles. Near Cooper's Mill, heathy banks support butterflies, solitary bees

Six-spotted Longhorn Beetle *Anoplodera sexguttata* [PB]

Knowles Mill in the heart of Wyre is now owned by the National Trust [JB]

Dowles Brook, the boundary between Shropshire and Worcestershire for most of its length, flows through the Forest [BK]

Map 1 General map of the area covered in this book, woodland shown in green

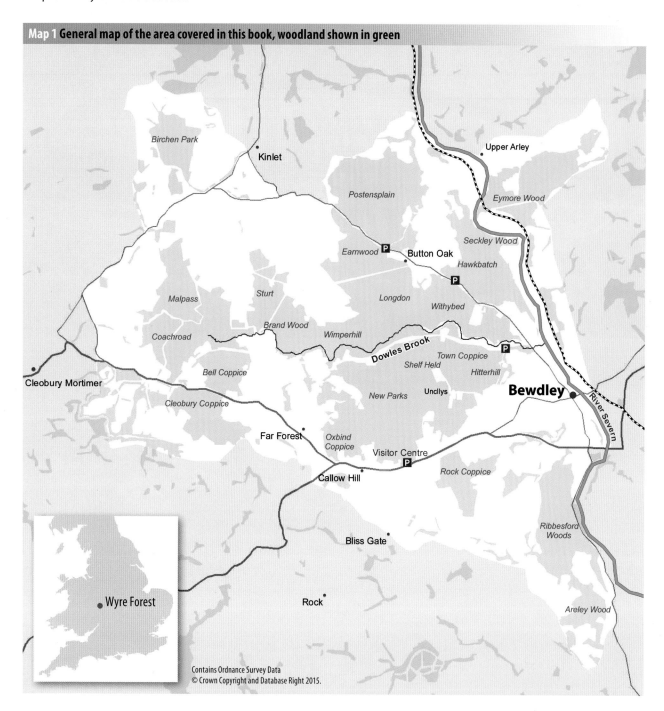

Contains Ordnance Survey Data
© Crown Copyright and Database Right 2015.

and spiders including the Green Huntsman Spider *Micrommata virescens*. Tree Pipits *Anthus trivialis* and Redstarts sing in the open oakwoods here.

At Cooper's Mill there's a chance of seeing White Admiral butterflies *Ladoga camilla* in June and July, and Buzzards *Buteo buteo* wheeling high above the trees. Across the bridge it's a steep climb to the disused railway line which takes you back to Bewdley via Dry Mill Lane carpark. There are basking Common Lizards *Zootoca vivipara* on the well-drained banks, and listen for Fallow Deer *Dama dama* moving through the trees and Ravens *Corvus corax* croaking overhead. This cross-section of wildlife and habitats is only a hint of Wyre's riches and their presence and survival here are the subjects of this book.

Location

Throughout this book the term Wyre Forest or Wyre is used to refer, not only to the woodlands, but also the orchards, meadows, arable land and urban areas of Bewdley town which are shown on the map. This area (75 square kilometres) has been chosen to reflect the nature of the underlying geology which is crucial to understanding the history and wildlife of Wyre, and so excludes the sandstone areas around Kidderminster and Stourport-on-Severn.

This is not to be confused with the considerably larger area of Wyre Forest District, a local government region including the towns of Stourport-on-Severn, Bewdley and Kidderminster together with other outlying parishes in north Worcestershire. References throughout the book to 'the Forest' are meant to denote the 2,600 ha of woodland only.

The Wyre Forest straddles the modern county boundary between Shropshire to the north and Worcestershire to the south. However, if vice-counties are considered (which some wildlife recording schemes use), in addition to VC37 (Worcestershire) and VC40 (Shropshire), Wyre has a Staffordshire VC39 arm coming in from the north-east to include Arley, Pound Green and Hawkbatch.

A large part of the Forest, some 1,753 ha has been notified as a Site of Special Scientific Interest (SSSI) by Natural England. This includes the Wyre Forest National Nature Reserve consisting of 650 ha, most of which is owned or leased by Natural England and the Forestry Commission. Near Stourport lies Areley Wood SSSI, some 64 ha in extent and considered as part of the Wyre Forest complex. There are a number of smaller SSSIs found within the Wyre Forest area: one geological (Eymore Railway Cutting) and six unimproved grasslands sites, all in private ownership. The Worcestershire Wildlife Trust has five Nature Reserves in the area: Knowles Coppice, Button Oak Meadow (in conjunction with Shropshire Wildlife Trust), Pound Green Common, Brown's Close Meadows and The Betts Reserve. Although all the public land within the Forest has open access, private land can only be accessed via public rights of way.

Studying the Forest

In 1974 the Wyre Forest Society was formed, bringing together people interested in the Forest, its wildlife, history, conservation and management. This society continues to run a programme of talks and walks throughout the year.

The Wyre Forest Study Group's formation in 1991 brought wildlife recorders together and increased the collection of data. Members used field meetings, surveys and projects enable members to exchange information and undertake studies. Thanks to the Forestry Commission and funding from 'Grow With Wyre' (see below), the Group now has a Records Room in the Community Discovery Centre at Callow Hill. This is used for computerising biological records in conjunction with the Worcestershire Biological Records Centre, training, meetings, and the preparation of reports, articles and an annual Review. There is also regular input onto their website **www.wyreforest.net** which includes species lists for many of the groups (plants, animals and fungi) so far recorded from Wyre.

'Grow with Wyre'

'Grow with Wyre' was a £4 million Landscape Partnership Scheme led by the Forestry Commission in conjunction with Natural England, Shropshire County Council, Bewdley Development Trust, Butterfly Conservation, Worcestershire County Council, Wyre Forest Study Group, Wyre Community Land Trust, Wyre Forest District Council, and The National Trust between 2008 and 2012, funded by the Heritage Lottery Fund and others. The aim was to conserve, enhance and restore the distinctive landscape heritage of the Wyre Forest, and 18 projects were delivered across greater Wyre. These included: the construction of a new community forest centre; restoration of traditional orchards and the setting up of a fruit juicing plant; a grazing animal project and training in a range of countryside skills; management and surveys to help fritillary butterflies and veteran trees; planting and gapping-up of hedges; crayfish and reptile surveys; restoration of two mills; and the production of woodchip and installation of woodchip boilers for use in local businesses.

LiDAR (see Chapter 2, pages 14–15) helped to reveal and promote landscape archaeology in the area, and volunteer groups were set up to support this project and others across the area with the help of the Wyre Community Land Trust. Grow with Wyre has been followed up by the formation of the Wyre Forest Landscape Partnership to create a sustainable future for the Forest with consideration to wildlife, heritage, conservation, recreation, tourism and heritage, with profitable forestry and links to the local economy and community.

Members of the Wyre Forest Study Group studying aquatic invertebrates in the River Severn near the Dowles Brook confluence. The stanchions in the background show where the railway once crossed the river before entering the Forest on its way to Cleobury Mortimer and beyond. [RW]

Chapter 2

The Landscape

The best way to understand the structure and landscape of Wyre Forest is to fly over it slowly. Such opportunities are rare so a balloon flight was organised in 2010 as part of the Grow with Wyre Project, its potential was seized enthusiastically. Phil Rudlin from the Forestry Commission made the flight with Susan Jones, contracted to carry out filming for the Grow with Wyre project, and project Officer Chris Mansell. Phil's pictures tell us a lot about Wyre Forest (Rudlin 2010) and these and others can be seen on Youtube together with the video:

- **www.youtube.com/watch?v=dN8FU51kgmo** many aerial images
- **www.youtube.com/watch?v=cqHQfm2mVDg** the Grow with Wyre documentary.

For those of us who cannot fly, useful substitutes are the images on Google Earth and the Ordnance Survey 'Explorer' map number 218. Wyre Forest is irregular in shape and fits roughly into a rectangle 9 × 6 km on the west bank of the River Severn with additional woodland on the east bank and to the north and south of the main block, all near Bewdley. The map shows in blue the Dowles Brook, running east through the Forest within a moderately steep-sided valley to its outflow at the River Severn.

A walk in the Forest leads along narrow paths and forestry tracks, sometimes by streams. In places there are small fields and orchards carved from the woodland, sometimes surrounding solitary cottages or small hamlets.

At the time of the balloon flight on the 7 November 2010, the oaks still retained their brown autumn leaves. From the air these trees stand out as brown bands along rides, dissecting and even surrounding dark-green conifer blocks, almost hiding the latter from walkers. In other areas, the autumnal browns reveal the large expanses of oak forest. Summer pictures taken from an aircraft show an undulating, almost featureless, mass of green treetops dissected by narrow passageways marking the rides, paths and the Dowles Brook.

Forest tree cover from the air

Conifer plantation in Dinglespout Coppice [PR]

Oak and Beech woodland in Postensplain [PR]

Looking east across the Forest to the River Severn, shadows pick out the valleys deeply incised by Dowles Brook. Lodge Hill Farm and meadows are seen perched above Dowles Brook and Woodlands Park Homes are conspicuous on the opposite bank. Many of the conifers seen here have been removed since 2010 as Wyre is becoming restored to broadleaved woodland. [RW]

LiDAR

The exact nature of the waterways and structure of the ground beneath the trees of Wyre has recently been revealed through the use of modern technology, the remote-sensing laser technique used to create LiDAR (Light Detection and Ranging) images (see maps). This Grow with Wyre-funded project (led by Worcestershire County Council) involved an aerial survey in March 2007. During this harmless laser beams were bounced back to measuring equipment on the aircraft giving information about location and height. Computer software was then used to filter out the tree canopy revealing the land surface in fine detail. It was possible for the first time to see how the natural landscape has been modified by both environmental processes and cultural practice ranging from late prehistory to the present day. Over

2,000 surface features of archaeological potential were mapped from the LiDAR imagery over an area covering 100 square kilometres. Volunteers were allocated survey areas of one kilometre square, which they visited to carry out more detailed and contextual recording of the archaeological features present. Many new archaeological sites were discovered in this way, as well as more information about known sites. For example, several prehistoric enclosures located on promontories and riverside locations, and an ancient medieval field system, were discovered in Earnwood Copse. The full extent of a large area of 17th century coal mining was found in Seckley Wood and a deserted village found near Button Bridge.

These remarkable LiDAR pictures (maps 2 and 3) reveal the underlying nature of the ground beneath the trees. They clearly show the central Dowles Brook

Map 2 LiDAR map of Wyre showing tree cover

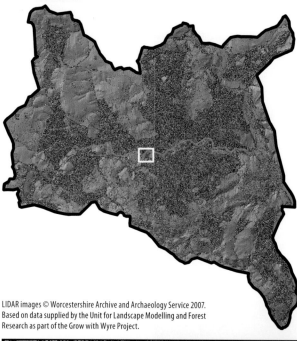

LIDAR images © Worcestershire Archive and Archaeology Service 2007. Based on data supplied by the Unit for Landscape Modelling and Forest Research as part of the Grow with Wyre Project.

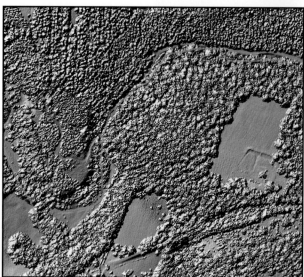

Map 3 LiDAR map of Wyre with tree cover removed

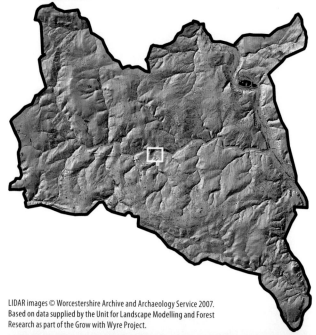

LIDAR images © Worcestershire Archive and Archaeology Service 2007. Based on data supplied by the Unit for Landscape Modelling and Forest Research as part of the Grow with Wyre Project.

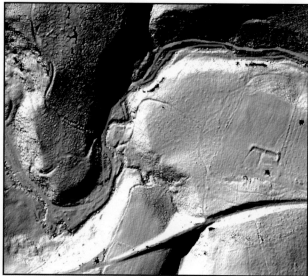

valley running from higher ground in the west through the Forest to the River Severn and fed by several large western tributaries, the Lem, Mad and Baveney Brooks. These brooks run in small valleys and LiDAR reveals that on either side they, and the Dowles Brook itself, are supplied by a multitude of small streams and rivulets running in from surrounding higher ground and cutting their own small valleys. Beneath the trees the terrain is often very uneven. Clearly, LiDAR shows that the Forest is in a small water catchment area draining east to the Severn.

The bare landscape left by the last ice age around 10,000 years ago has been slowly incised by eroding watercourses. It was eventually naturally clothed with vegetation and populated by animals. This landscape in turn has been adapted for farming and forestry. All this is described in the following pages.

Habitats of Wyre

Most of the area featured in this book is woodland. Other habitats include unimproved herb-rich grasslands, heath, cultivated land, wetlands (the River Severn, streams, pools, and wet ground), orchards, hedges, gardens and innumerable 'wildlife patches' near houses or on roadside verges. Many of these are referred to directly in watercourses in this chapter and in the chapters on flora and the history of the Forest.

Orchards deserve special mention as relatively small but important features, glorious with blossom in spring and laden with fruit in summer. Many are remnants of planting over the last 200 years. Some of the old ones have been renovated under Grow with Wyre to prolong the life of old trees by restorative pruning and replanting in gaps where trees have died, and to seek modern uses for the fruit. The old traditionally

Woodland landscape through the seasons in Wyre

Dowles Brook valley from Hitterhill [PC]

Dowles Brook valley from Knowles Coppice [RW]

Beech woodland, New Parks [JB]

Douglas Fir trees, New Parks [PR]

Other Wyre landscapes

Bell Coppice meadow, near Far Forest [RW]

Brown's Close meadow, Bewdley [RW]

Old railway line, New Parks [JB]

Roadside verge, Hedgewick Common, Far Forest [JB]

Heathland, Pound Green Common [RW]

The Great Bog, New Parks [JB]

Carex flush, Cold Harbour Coppice [JB]

Shingle bar, River Severn [JB]

Historic photograph showing the Ribbesford Cherry Orchard that was removed in the 1960s. [BM]

managed orchards are a version of wood-pasture, often seen on a grander scale in parklands, and containing ancient trees. Like parklands, orchards have a high biodiversity value and are especially important for invertebrates which require naturally decaying wood. This was clearly shown by a detailed study of three orchards at Bowcastle Farm in 2004 undertaken by the Wyre Forest Study Group working closely with English Nature (now Natural England) (Smart & Winnall 2006). During the study 1,868 species of plants, fungi and animals were identified from 16,900 specimens. In addition many very small flies, parasitic hymenoptera and some microlepidoptera sampled during this survey remain to be identified.

These three orchards (5.3 ha overall) contained 159 cherry, 55 apple, 28 pear and 18 damson trees, and most showed features of veteran trees such as hollow trunks and fissured bark. Major parts of the orchards were planted or re-planted in the 1930s but some pear trees were well established long before then. Of the species identified by the survey, 224 are specialists dependent on natural wood-decay including fungi, flies, beetles, hymenoptera and lepidoptera. This survey provided important evidence towards a Habitat Action Plan for traditional orchards published in 2007 within the national Biodiversity Action Plan (see **jncc.defra.gov. uk/default.aspx?page=2183&q=orchards**).

Evidence from old maps and other sources show that orchards have long been a feature of the Wyre Forest many being established around 1800. More were created before the forest railway opened in 1870, in anticipation of this providing transport to market (Stephens 2009). For instance a record of trees severely damaged by a 'hurricane' (actually a tornado), on 6 July 1845, implies extensive commercial orchards, even before the opening of the railway at Bewdley in 1861. Catastrophically, 2,478 trees were severely damaged or uprooted: most were fruit trees together with oak, elm, ash and other trees. Amongst them were mature pear trees (Stephens 2011).

Nowadays the remaining orchards of Wyre contain many old varieties of fruit trees, especially cherries. Brian Stephens is collecting information in an on-going study on cherries and DNA investigation is planned to name and rescue old varieties before they are lost—an urgent task. (Stephens 2006a, 2006b, 2008, 2011, 2012, 2014).

Wyre orchards

Old apple tree, Lodge Hill Farm [PC]

Cherry orchard, Bowcastle Farm [RW]

The rocks—geology

Wyre is thin skinned in places and outcrops of rock often occur where the ground is disturbed. The rushing waters of Dowles Brook scour bare rock beds. Forest hollow-ways are lined in places by stony shelves: the geology of the Forest is fundamental to its natural and human history.

If you walk from east to west through Wyre you traverse rocks which are parts of four great geological eras: Triassic, Carboniferous, Devonian and Silurian. The Carboniferous extends well to the north and the Devonian and the Silurian to the south and west, but today almost all of the Forest lies on the Upper Coal Measures. These rocks determine the characteristics of the landscape and the very fact that it is still forest. Whereas the surrounding sandstones and mudstones of the Triassic, and of the Devonian and the Silurian

are relatively uniform on the farm and field scale, the thin sandstones and siltstones of our part of the Carboniferous allow easy passage of water. In places impeded by accompanying clays and mudstones. As a result seepages wash out softer materials and undermine overlying strata, leading to collapse and the formation of steep-sided stream valleys. These conditions make difficult terrain for farming.

Wyre's Carboniferous rocks are outliers of the extensive areas of the Pennines and West Midlands. Deposition did not start here until the time of the Pennine Formation (Productive Coal Measures) (Whitehead & Pocock 1947; Mitchell *et al.* 1961). The name derives from the thick coal seams exploited in the major mining areas. There is though much less coal under Wyre, where grey shales and sandstones only contain very thin traces of coal in small areas. These

---

Map 4 Geological map of Wyre and surrounding area

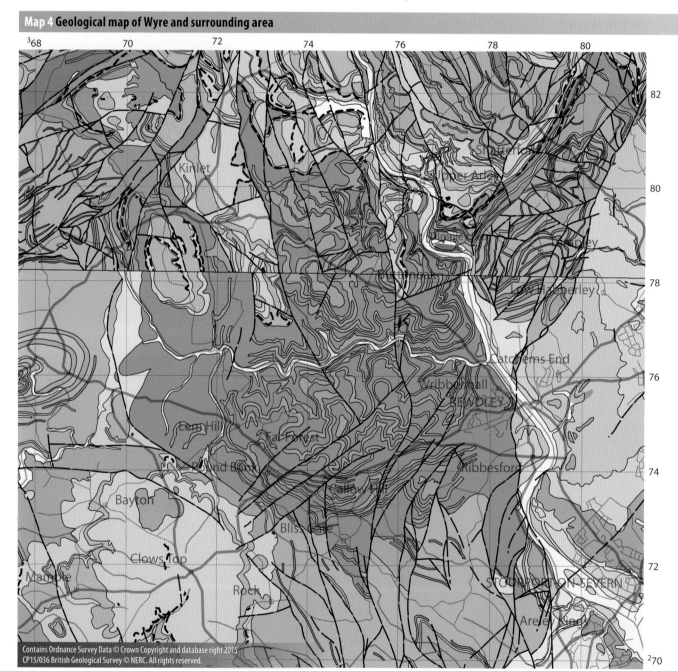

include between North Wood and Crundall's Farm east of the Severn, at Maxfield Coppice, Malpass Wood and Weston Plantation, the south end of Ribbesford Woods, and in the bottom of Dowles Valley.

Later, input of coarser sediments from the eroding Devonian Red Sandstone produced the sandstones, siltstones and clays of the main areas of the Forest. Fossils show these rocks are correlated with the Etruria Formation (Old Hill Marl, which is siltstone, not clay) of Staffordshire. We see them in the Forest's valley sides, with occasional traces of coal from eroding earlier formations and, often, plant fossils.

The Wyre Forest Coalfield lies mainly outside today's Forest (Poyner & Evans 2000). A period of both erosion and deposition resulted in the sandstones, siltstones, mudstones and coals of the Halesowen Formation (Highley Beds) where conditions led to less

small-scale surface variation. There are down-faulted outcrops of Halesowen Formation in Hawkbatch, and in the Winwoods-Kingswood and Meaton areas in the north west of the Forest. The first, very small, is under forest today, but the other two are largely farmland, like the Halesowen Formation around Prizely, Stagborough Hill and the area from Bayton and Mamble to Abberley. Once or twice shallow seas encroached and thin limestones were deposited: these crop out in the small Hawkbatch inlier within the Forest itself, in the Prizely and Ribbesford Woods areas, and around Mamble. Mining settlements from medieval times onwards had to clear forest for subsistence and the topography and soils of the Halesowen Formation were better for farming than the Etruria Formation.

Uplift, folding and faulting of the rocks continued so that today the Coal Measures' strata are mostly gently tilted. Much of the Forest lies on a dome, bisected by Dowles Brook, with persistent sandstones outcropping in rings broken up by faults. North-south trending faults account for the detached inliers of Halesowen Formation within the Forest. Another period of deposition laid down breccias (Clent Breccia, now allocated to the Permian Era), broken up from earlier rocks, on top of the Halesowen Formation, the most noticeable remaining patch capping Church Hill near Clows Top. Later the desert dune sands of the Triassic Red Sandstone were deposited right across the Carboniferous and Devonian landscape. After that no more rock-forming sediments were laid down here.

The relatively thin and young glacial sediments deposited in the Pleistocene ice ages were never compressed and consolidated to form rock. The last glaciation stopped just north and east of here, so that patches of boulder clay are found within 3 km west, south and east of Bridgnorth and across to Wolverhampton. Glaciers blocked the original course of the Teme through the Aymestry Gap and its northern tributaries around the Long Mynd. The Severn, carrying meltwater from its valley glacier, could not follow its former course across the Shropshire–Cheshire plain and burst through to create the Ironbridge Gorge, dropping a vast load of boulders and gravel.

After the glaciers retreated, milder and extremely cold periods alternated, triggering very active slope movements caused by thawing and freezing of the ground. We can see disrupted rock strata particularly clearly here, where thin layers of sandstone and clay were jumbled up. They provided areas of deeply softened and fractured substrates for root penetration and soil formation in the period which followed.

After this late-glacial period gentler stream erosion, hill slope processes and soil development produced today's landscape. Relative stability while forest cover predominated meant that the Severn flowed in shifting interconnected channels, with sandbanks and backswamps. It only laid down the floodplain sediments flanking a single meandering channel after farming began to disrupt the soils, and expose them to erosion by winter rains.

... to the geology of Wyre

Rock type	Geological formation	Former terminology	Geological Era
Superficial deposits			
Silt, clay, sand, gravel	alluvium	alluvium	Post-glacial
Sands and gravels	river terraces	river terraces	Pleistocene
Bedrock			
Sandstone	Kidderminster	New Red Sandstone, Bunter	Triassic
Sandstone	Bridgnorth		
Breccia	Clent	Clent Breccia (Triassic)	Permian
Mudstone, siltstone, sandstone			
Sandstone	Halesowen	Highly Beds	
Limestone			
Mudstone, siltstone	Etruria	Old Hill Marls	Upper Carboniferous
Sandstone			
Mudstone, siltstone, sandstone	Pennine	Productive Coal Measures	
Sandstone			
Clays			
Conglomerate	St Maughams	Old Red Sandstone	Devonian
Limestone			
Siltstone and mudstone	Raglan		Silurian

Paper maps and memoirs use the older terms. The digital map reproduced here largely resolves correlation problems across a sheet boundary. For more information: **www.BGS.ac.uk**

Rock exposure, Park Brook, Shelf Held Coppice. Tufa has formed on these rocks where lime-rich water has flowed down from springs above. [RW]

Plant fossils in Wyre's rocks

A delve amongst the stones in some of Wyre's streams, a search amongst rock exposures, or a scrabble around in some of the old forest quarries may, with luck, result in the find of a fossilised plant formed within the hot, humid, tropical swamps of Carboniferous times. Such a discovery gives a fascinating insight into life in this area over 300 million years ago, and there is something very special about splitting a piece of shale and being the first person ever to look at this buried treasure from the past.

Worcestershire Naturalists' Club recorded a number of their walks through Wyre in the 1860s when plant fossils were collected (Worcestershire Naturalists' Club 1847–1896). Specimens were found easily in those days as there were many more rock exposures. Cuttings excavated for the new Severn Valley Railway line built between 1858 and 1862, and several small worked quarries along the Dowles valley provided good fossil collecting sites. An article in the Midland Naturalist in 1883 describes a fossiliferous shale bed near Dowles Brook: "This bed is absolutely full of plant remains, principally consisting of ferns and calamites" (Atkins 1883).

In the search for coal many boreholes were drilled in the mid to late 1800s and early 1900s but no workable seams were discovered under the Forest. Many plant fossils were found and documented during these searches (Newell Arber 1913). A large collection of plant fossils from Wyre was purchased by the British Museum in 1861 from Mr G.E. Roberts, Mr T Baugh and others of Bewdley (Newell Arber 1913): attempts to relocate this collection have so far failed. Dr Robert Kidston and colleagues collected and identified large numbers of plant fossils in the early 1900s (Kidston 1917). There are fewer fossil collectors around nowadays, but the enthusiast can still find specimens from all the groups described below.

The Lycophytes or Lycopsids are related to present day clubmosses and quillworts: they include some of the largest plants that have ever lived, growing up to a height of 40 m (Wills & McElwain 2014). Several different *Sigillarias* belonging to this group have been identified from Wyre. These grew up to a height of 30 m and are distinguished by the distinctive leaf scars or 'leaf cushions' on the bark, some reminiscent of the patterning on the outside of a pineapple. Syringodendron is the name given to the trunk of *Sigillaria* from which the bark has fallen off, and an example of this was discovered in Withybed Stream in 2011 (see photograph). The underground parts of the plant are called stigmaria and fossils of these 'roots' can also be found.

Sphenophytes such as *Calamites* are like huge versions of the horsetails *Equisetum* spp. that grow in Wyre today. These Carboniferous giant horsetail trees grew up to 18 m high. They had creeping rhizomes from which large aerial trunks arose bearing whorls of branches and leaves (Wills & McElwain 2014) (see drawing). The fossil plant stems still show the vertical ribbing and transverse segments (see photograph) as seen now on bamboo stems. The leaves at the end of the branches appeared in whorls known as annularia (see photograph).

There were many different types of ferns in Carboniferous times, including Filocopsids (tree ferns) and some beautifully delicate fossil ferns can be found today, looking very similar to extant forms. Some tree ferns grew up to 10 m high (Wills & McElwain 2014). There were also Pteridosperms (seed ferns) which had fern-like foliage but reproduced by seed. Several different species have been found in Wyre.

Cordaites are extinct Gymnosperms, seed-bearing plants related to our present day conifers. They grew to 30 m, with trunks up to one metre in diameter, and had wide, distinctive strap-shaped leaves (Wills & McElwain 2014). The trunks are not often found, but the leaves, with many parallel veins, were probably tough and leathery and survived well. They can be seen, particularly in shales near the bridge over Dowles west of the Experimental Pool.

There is one geological Site of Special Scientific Interest within Wyre known for its palaeontological interest called the Eymore Railway Cutting, although there is no public access, and it is currently overgrown and in unfavourable condition (Natural England 2014).

Plant fossils. Left to right: a cordaite, giant horsetail, tree fern, clubmoss.
[Drawings by Angela Gladwell with permission from Ludlow Museum Resource Centre]

Some of the plant fossils found in Wyre's rocks

Calamites was a type of giant horsetail with ribbed stems; they grew to 18 m [RW]

Syringodendron, decorticated *Sigallaria* clubmoss [RW]

Leaves of *Cordaites*, an extinct Gymnosperm [RW]

Part of a seed fern, Pteridosperm [RW]

Annularia, the whorls of *Calamites*, a giant horsetail [RW]

Soil—the basic support for plants and animals

Most of the rocks of Wyre, apart from limited outcrops of limestone, are derived by erosion from weathered landscapes, and so are short of elements such as potassium and calcium. These neutralise acidity and are needed in large quantities for plant growth. The soils developed in the warm, moist post-glacial period, from rocks which included sandstones, siltstones and clays, and rocks fragmented and disturbed during glacial periods. Further fragmentation and disturbance was caused by root penetration, incorporation of organic matter, hydrolysis and other processes. Distinct horizons formed from the surface downwards (see Table 1). Understanding the Forest's ecology requires detailed soil study directed at points of particular significance. The very intricate small-scale pattern of soil types in the Forest, resulting from varied rock types, steep slopes, and seepages, was demonstrated by Margaret Oliver's exercise in mapping and classification in a 6 km² area in the southeast part of the Forest (Oliver 1995).

The nutrient cycle only keeps basic elements within the soil-plant system to a limited extent. Progressive leaching occurs during winter rain when there is no root uptake. Nutrients lost must be replaced by weathering of minerals in the soil, but Wyre's rocks are short of the minerals which yield these elements. It is therefore inevitable that soils become increasingly acid. These conditions lead to relatively slow plant growth favouring species adapted to these conditions, for example oaks *Quercus* spp., Heather *Calluna*

A thin podzol: black O, traces of grey E, and iron-enriched Bfe horizons (scale unit 10 cm) [SL]

Iron oxide deposited on a tufa wall [RW]

Tufa formed around *Palustriella* moss in a wet flush [RW]

Tufa-rich layer
19–39 cm

Surface layer
0–15 cm

A core showing a tufa deposit from a flush in Shelf Held Coppice [MB]

vulgaris and Bracken *Pteridium aquilinum*. Conifers also thrive in these conditions. Tough leaf surfaces and toxic substances, such as polyphenols, are produced by these plants to give some protection against animals and micro-organisms which might feed on them as they grow. The toxins also inhibit decay, so further slowing the release of nutrients back into the soil. Polyphenols washing into the soil attack clays and mobilise iron and aluminium, moving them down through the soil. The resulting soil is called a 'podzol' and in much of the Forest there are incipient or very thin podzols, together with acid brown earths. Erosion on slopes tends to prevent the full development of a podzol, so the distinct horizons are not developed even though the processes are active, and here we have brown podzolic soils. Where clays occur in well-drained locations, soils are gleyed brown earths.

The counterpart of leaching, where drainage is good, is 'flushing' where nutrient-enriched water emerges in springs and seepages. These occur where permeable sandstone or siltstone and impermeable clay meet. Often there is a steep slope or step in the harder rock, out of which water emerges and washes away the softer clays, forming a gentler slope which remains flushed. Here we have base-rich, or even calcareous, heavily gleyed soils with thin, peaty, organic horizons over a considerable depth of clay. In some of these flushes tufa (precipitated calcium carbonate) forms.

With exploitation of the Forest, and the activities of burrowing animals, disruption and erosion of soils has occurred. In places on ridge tops and steep slopes solid rock is very close to the surface, while on lower ground deep deposits of eroded soils are found. These processes rejuvenate soils and limit the more extreme effects of leaching and impoverishment.

The steep and narrow stream valleys generally have small sections of floodplain receiving fine deposits and enriched water; these can be swept away by extreme flood events, such as those of 2007. Dowles Brook however has quite well-developed floodplains, with base-rich alluvial soils. Through much of the post-glacial period, beavers were probably responsible for controlling water flow and sediment deposition. With the spread of agriculture, erosion of soils disrupted by cultivation and grazing yielded greatly increased sediment from the upper part of the Dowles catchment, building up floodplains, as we see continuing today.

Apart from the small areas of limestone in the Highley Beds and the Old Red Sandstone all the soils of the surrounding farmland have a tendency to acidity,

but farming practices reverse or limit its progression. Grazing speeds up the nutrient cycle and, while export of animal products removes nutrients, there is a history of liming in some areas. Arable land has also received inputs of industrially produced fertilisers containing nitrogen, phosphorus and potassium in recent years, instead of the older practices of folding sheep on fallow and use of crop rotations.

Farming has therefore inhibited the spiral into podzolisation. Indeed, 'heath' place names, for example Gorst Hill, indicate that some areas have a history as heathland, with podzolic soils reclaimed for farming in periods of land-hunger. At these times there must have been labour available for transport of lime and other nutrient resources. It is worth noting also that within living memory, on the steeper sandstone lands, where soil has moved downslope until impeded by a hedge, people would pack soil into baskets and carry it back up to the top of the field.

Table 1 Nomenclature and characteristics of soil horizons commonly found in the Wyre Forest

Horizon	Predominant characteristics and processes
O	Top soil in which organic material is slowly broken down by arthropods and fungi, acid, no earthworms, poor in plant nutrients; black. Characteristic of podzols and brown podzolic soils.
A	Top soil in which organic material is rapidly incorporated into mineral soil by earthworms and broken down by bacteria, neutral to basic, richer than O horizon in plant nutrients; dark brown. Characteristic of brown earths.
E	Lies below an O horizon. Depleted of organic material and iron oxides because of chemical processes in acid conditions in the O horizon; pale grey to white. Characteristic of podzols.
Bw	Sub-soil in which clay is formed and iron is oxidised, holds moisture and plant nutrients. Rock structure has given way to soil structure, but contains rock fragments; light brown, yellowish brown. Characteristic of brown earths.
Bfe	Sub soil in which iron oxides accumulate as a result of chemical processes in upper horizons and down-washing; bright rusty colour. Characteristic of podzols, lying below O and E horizons, and brown podzolic soils, lying below O horizon.
Bh	Sub soil in which humus accumulates, as a result of chemical processes above and down-washing; black. May be combined with Bfe (Bhfe) or separate. Characteristic of podzols and brown podzolic soils.
G	'Gleyed' horizon, sub soil in which waterlogging causes stagnation, oxygen is depleted and iron oxides reduced, resulting in grey or mottled grey and rusty colours.
Bg	Sub soil in which gleying has occurred, causing mottling, characteristic of gleyed brown earths.
C	Parent material of the soil, with some degree of disruption of rock but its structure still being obvious, allowing root penetration of cracks, channels for percolation of water.
Cg	C horizon affected by gleying, commonly in soils on clay, or at least seasonally affected by groundwater.

Watercourses

Dowles Brook and its streams drain most of Wyre Forest, running through steep-sided valleys to the River Severn. The streams are relatively small but attractive: who can fail to appreciate a clear babbling brook, casting dappled shade, and enlivened by a Kingfisher *Alcedo atthis*, Grey Wagtail *Motacilla cinerea* or Dipper *Cinclus cinclus*? The Severn, by contrast, is a grander watercourse, very different in character, but pleasing and powerful. Only a few of the Wyre watercourses have names in common use; others have been given names for reference in this book as indicated on Map 5.

Natural watercourses have been used and abused by mankind for millennia, for transport, drinking water, resources for industry, opportunities for recreation, and receptors for waste. The Severn has been an important transport route for hundreds of years, although boat traffic now is primarily for leisure. Over the centuries Dowles Brook has been harnessed to provide power for several mills, and their construction has changed the physical nature of the channel (Booth 2010). Although some mill buildings and associated works still remain, the Brook has reclaimed its channel so it now exhibits a wide range of natural features. In many places, for example downstream of Knowles Mill, beside the Worcestershire Wildlife Trust's Knowles Coppice Reserve, the stream has eroded through several metres of alluvium down to the underlying bedrock.

Wyre watercourses range in size and all drain into the River Severn (Map 5). The larger Lem, Baveney and Mad Brooks join at Furnace Mill to form Dowles Brook at the start of its eight kilometre journey through the Forest to the Severn. These brooks and their tributaries drain a catchment of about 49 km². Dowles Brook has modest flows, particularly in the summer months averaging 0.364 m³ per second compared with 60.781 m³ per second in the Severn (National River Flow Archive 2012a & 2012b). However, unlike the Severn, Dowles Brook responds very quickly to rainfall, rapidly rising after a storm and falling back almost as quickly. During the drought summer of 1976 flow in Dowles Brook fell to only 20 litres, or a couple of bucketfulls each second (NERC, 2003), whilst after torrential rain of between 100 and 125 mm on 19 June 2007 it was flowing at a rate of just over 25 m³ per second (Marsh & Hannaford 2007; Averill 2007).

Dowles Brook has cut a valley which deeply dissects the Forest and for much of its journey is sheltered by overhanging trees: its name derives from the Welsh 'dulas' meaning dark which is likely to come from its dark shale bedrock. This shady environment produces a water temperature lower than one might expect, even in the height of summer. This allows higher oxygen saturation and therefore a greater abundance of aquatic life. At intervals along its course it is fed by smaller streams: Park Brook, Bell Brook and Forest Lodge Stream. The areas drained by Mad, Baveney and Lem Brooks include farmland, and so these streams contribute eroded soil and pollution. Nevertheless Wyre watercourses are rich in aquatic life, containing a wide range of species from single-cell organisms, through large and small aquatic invertebrates, to large fish. The streams that drain forested catchments—Bell Brook and Forest Lodge Stream—are clearer and support the more sensitive fauna, such as the native White-clawed Crayfish *Austropotamobius pallipes* (see Chapter 10, pages 192–193).

Baveney Brook rises in farmland at an altitude of 190 m near to Bagginswood and flows south-east for six and a half kilometres. From a small valley it passes close to the site of Wall Town Roman fort, through a small ravine, which usually has a substantial flow of water, and a stone-faced culvert beneath the road. Beyond this it enters a series of man-made pools shaded by trees. Leaving these it flows through the deeper shade of Maxfield's Coppice, through Malpass Wood, Coachroad Coppice and Breakneck Bank, to be joined by Mad Brook just before Furnace Mill. It drops more than 100 m along the way. At Furnace Mill the course of Baveney Brook was altered to allow it to flow through the grounds of the house which now stands there. The original course, although overgrown, is still easily discernible. The old mill pools, being unused, silted up years ago and since then fishing pools have been created on the same site. These can be seen from the public footpath which runs across the back of Furnace Mill. In its upper reaches the brook flows rapidly over a shallow and stony bed, but for about a mile above Furnace Mill it is deep, slow flowing and heavily silted.

The stream which becomes Lem Brook rises near Clows Top at an altitude of 220 m and runs down through a steep valley where, in the bed of the stream east of Woodside Farm, the base of the coal measures of the Wyre Forest coalfield is exposed. A small stream

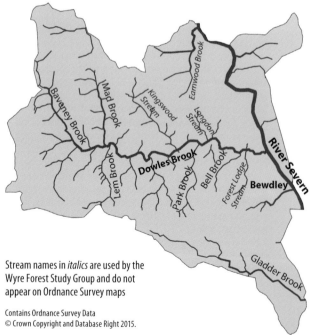

Map 5 Drainage pattern of the streams within Wyre

Stream names in *italics* are used by the Wyre Forest Study Group and do not appear on Ordnance Survey maps

Contains Ordnance Survey Data
© Crown Copyright and Database Right 2015.

Wyre's watercourses

River Severn and Bewdley [RW]

Dowles Brook [JB]

Waterfall, Withybed Wood [JB]

Baveney Brook [PC]

running through Tanners Coppice flows into the stream, which then runs alongside the road before being joined from the south-east by a small stream, culverted under the road, near to Lem Hill. From here it is called Lem Brook and it flows steadily on to join the combined Mad and Baveney Brooks at an altitude of 71 m at the Worcestershire Wildlife Trust Betts Nature Reserve. In the course of just over 5 km from sources to Furnace Mill, the brook falls 150 m. The amount of water in most seasons is small, but erosion of the banks suggests that at times considerable flows occur. Over most of its length the bed is stony, but where the gradient lessens waters deepen and flow is reduced.

Mad Brook rises at an altitude of 125 m at Bradley Farm near Kinlet, and flows south towards Baveney Brook. Mad Brook's valley is at first shallow but rapidly becomes steeper as it descends. After being joined by several minor streams it flows into a man-made pool

where the footpath between Winwoods and Silligrove crosses it. It then flows steadily towards Furnace Mill and before reaching it passes under the road through a large culvert. The dry weather flow of the brook is small but, as with the other streams, erosion of the banks in places shows that during periods of heavy rain large volumes of water are carried. Over its length of 3 km the Brook falls 50 m.

Many other streams flow through greater Wyre— including Gladder Brook and Dick Brook in the south, and the river Rea in the west.

The River Severn, more than 50 m wide and with depths of several metres, carries water from a large part of mid-Wales and Shropshire to the Bristol Channel. Although changes in water level generally occur slowly, it is renowned for its frequent floods, which inundate the floodplain. This used to include parts of Bewdley town before the installation of demountable barriers following the flooding in 2000.

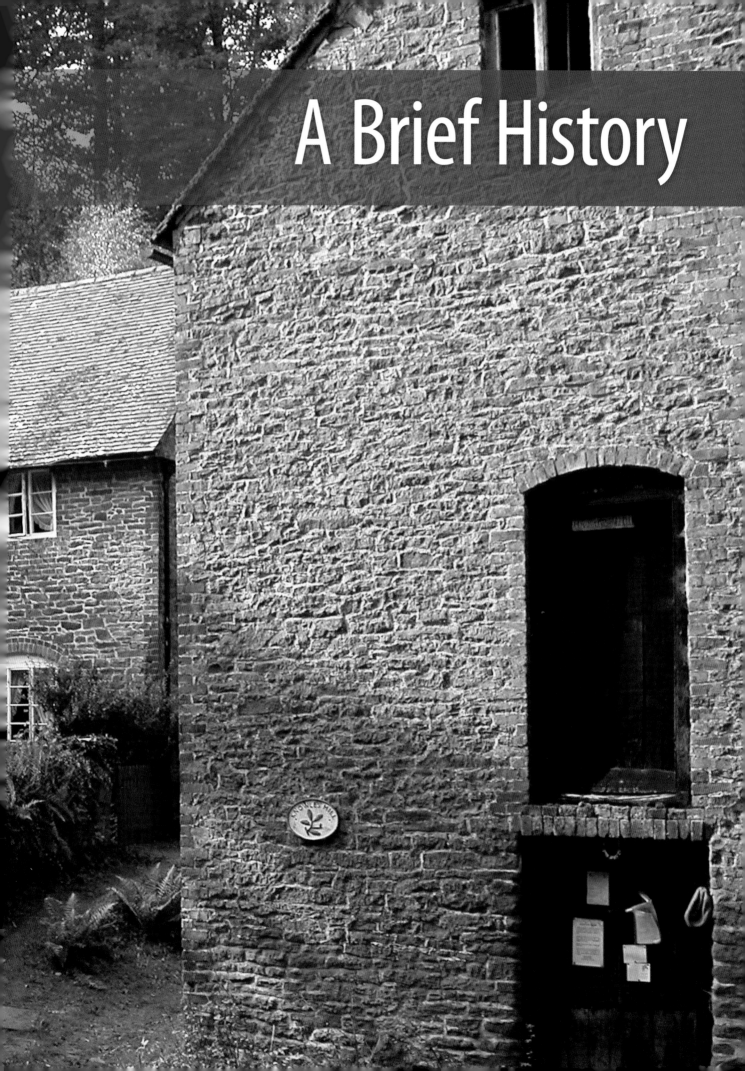

Chapter 3

A Brief History

To understand any landscape we need to have information about past land use. This chapter provides the historical context, suggesting how people would have affected the Forest and its surroundings.

Pre-history to pre-medieval

From about 9,000 years ago small groups of people lived here, hunting, fishing and gathering wild food such as nuts and berries. This was in the Mesolithic period after the last ice age. The people were probably very mobile, using different camp sites according to the seasons and local conditions. At Lightmarsh one of their camp sites has been discovered, dating to around 8000BC. The finds there include traces of possible shelters, evidence of fires and hazelnut shells (Jackson & Dalwood 2007).

As far as the vegetation is concerned pollen analysis from Cookley tells us that the area was first dominated by birch *Betula* spp. and then by Scots Pine *Pinus sylvestris*. These were succeeded by oak *Quercus* spp., lime *Tilia* spp., Alder *Alnus glutinosa* and Hazel *Corylus avellana* (Pearson 2007).

The first farmers arrived and started clearing parts pf the Forest for agriculture and settlement around 4000BC. This activity gradually increased in intensity throughout the remainder of the prehistoric period. Few traces now exist but a possible Iron Age fort has been described at Kingswood, and east of the Severn there are traces of an enclosure in Arley Wood which may be from this period.

The Romans left much more tangible remains, most notably a fort on the edge of the Forest at Wall Town. This underwent several phases of building from about 50 to 150AD (Walker 1994). Roman Britain was generally prosperous, with a peak population comparable to that of the late Middle Ages. The earthworks of two rectilinear enclosures have recently been identified, deep within what is currently forest,

at Trimpley and Kingswood. Whilst the age of these is not known, they are typical of farms of the Romano-British period. If they are, they demonstrate that these areas must have been cleared for fields and that the boundaries of the Forest in Roman times may have been different from today.

The flourishing economy of the Roman period seems to have ended in the fourth century with the abandonment of isolated farms and a population decline. The pattern of pollen records of the Birmingham area for the post-Roman period may well be relevant to Wyre. They demonstrate succession from an open area, through scrub, to mature oak woodland; clearly land was being abandoned and reverting to woodland (Hooke 2007). If the enclosures at Trimpley and Kingswood are Roman, then it is easy to imagine that they too were abandoned at this period or in the succeeding centuries.

The history of the Forest at this time is obscure. All that is certain is that by the mid-7th century the Forest lay within an area controlled by the Anglo-Saxons. Place names give clues as to what was happening to the landscape. It is possible to identify areas of woodland as settlements because such places frequently end in '-ley', from the Old English, 'leah'. Whilst the precise meaning of this changed with time, in most place names it indicates a woodland clearing or perhaps wood-pasture. By contrast, settlements where there was little woodland typically end in '-ton'. The village of Rock gets its name from Middle English *atter oke* 'by the oak' (Gelling 1984).

As might be expected, -ley place names extend outwards from the current boundaries of Wyre, although this is much more marked to the north than to the south. In particular it appears that woodland extended up to Glazeley in the north. To the east there were woods connecting Wyre with Morfe and Kinver Forests. There were also wooded areas stretching from Kinlet into Stottesdon and Neen Savage and to the

Rock church and medieval earthworks are on the edge of the present day village. The word Rock comes from the Middle English *atter oke* meaning 'by the oak'. [Both RW]

south of Cleobury Mortimer. Whilst these extend well beyond current areas of woodland, the distribution of -ton names show that in the west of the region, from the Rea valley to the Clee Hills, woodland was rare. There is also evidence of cleared areas immediately south of the Forest around Bayton and Rock, although woodland place names soon resume with Areley, Astley and Abberley. In turn, these connect with Shrawley, Shelsey and Hanley and so eventually to Worcester.

The Wyre Forest itself perhaps first appears in the historical record as the Weogorena Leage, the Forest of the Weogorena, in a charter of 816. The Weogorena tribe were first mentioned in 691 and they gave their name to Worcester (Poulton-Smith 2003) from where the Forest lay to the north and west. Whilst it is unlikely to have been continuous woodland from Worcester to the Wyre, there was probably enough tree cover for it to stand out compared to cleared land stretching south and east. There is clearly a connection between the name 'Weogorena' and 'Wyre', but it does not necessarily mean that the Weogorena had any territorial claim over Wyre Forest; the bulk of it would have been in the territory of their neighbours, the Magonsaete. It is perhaps more likely that both derive from the same Celtic root; possibly a word meaning 'winding' (Poulton-Smith 2003). This might possibly refer to the winding course of the river Severn, and Wyre is an old Celtic river name.

Charters that record the sale or transfer of land give us a direct insight into the Anglo-Saxon landscape. In the absence of maps estate boundaries were often described in enough detail to allow them to be walked and identified on the ground. A charter for Upper Arley from c.1000 describes the boundary between Arley and Alveley largely in terms of hedges and crofts; a landscape of fields, not woods (Sawyer 1380a). The charters show woodland interspersed with large areas of cleared land, even in places which had -ley place names which must once have had heavy tree cover. The characteristic landscape of small hamlets and isolated farms surrounding much of the Forest has its origins in the clearances (assarts) instigated by the Saxons and continued throughout much of the medieval period.

The uses of the Forest in Saxon times were probably similar to those documented in the later Middle Ages. It would have been remarkable if the various owners, whether nobility or royalty, did not use it for hunting and it is likely to have been a royal Saxon hunting forest. Woodland however was a vital community resource. In 866 a charter specified the uses allowed for woodland at Seckley (Sawyer 1380b) which provided an insight into what was happening in the Forest. The wood was considered to be common land providing food for 70 pigs. This was the right of pannage and reflected autumn conditions when herds of pigs would be allowed to roam and root for acorns. The wood was also to supply five cart loads of rods, one oak tree a year for building, and as much firewood as needed.

The grazing, building materials and fuel supplied were essential for any community and were worth a lot of money. There may well have been a thriving market for wooded estates that could send their resources to wood-poor lands many miles away. Finally of course the Forest also represented land that could be granted to a retainer, to be cleared and used for pasture or crops; this in turn would provide new cash in rent payments or labour services. It is likely that the Saxons were aware that a balance needed to be struck between woodland clearance for agriculture and woodland preservation for timber and hunting. Regardless of the exact use made of the Forest, it was a valuable resource for its owner.

The medieval Forest

At the time of the Domesday Survey in 1086 most of the Shropshire portion of Wyre was owned by the Mortimer family or their tenants; they and their descendants retained ownership for the entire medieval period. They were the single largest owners of land in the Forest, the rest being split between a number of lay and monastic owners.

By the end of the 13th century the Mortimers had established deer parks at Cleobury, Bewdley and Earnwood. They attempted to keep most of the rest of the Forest as their private chase for hunting. By 1296, Nicholas de Segrave, Earl of Warwick and owner of Stottesdon, had his own deer park at Kingswood (National Archives, Calendar of the Patent Rolls). At the same time the population that expanded in Saxon times continued to do so. The Mortimers, the Segraves, and their tenants had to balance hunting with farming for their growing manors; the size of the Forest made this possible.

The Mortimer's deer park at Earnwood, a manor not mentioned in Domesday and where, since the early 13th century they also had a hunting lodge, is an interesting case in point. It may have been counted as part of the woods that belonged to Cleobury or it may have been in extra-manorial woodland reckoned of no monetary value. It was considered sufficiently remote to be used as a prison later in the century and as a retreat when Edmund de Mortimer wanted to scheme with his fellow Marcher lords remote from the eyes of King Edward I (Blakeway 1908).

Yet there were also people living on the manor. In 1251, Roger de Earnwood and his wife sold half a virgate of land at "Maubeg, near the great park of Wyre" to Lucas le Marcescall. Roger must have been a freeholder, a man who owned land in his own right. Both freeholders and the lords of the manor would have been keen to clear woodland to bring more land into cultivation. Between 1304 and 1332, the amount of arable land owned by the Mortimers in Earnwood increased from 48 to 80 ha (National Archives, Calendar of Inquestiones Post Mortum). It seems that the wood was maintained to the east, where the park was, and also extended south to the boundaries with Arley and Kingswood. The manor farm and the open fields were in the north west, around what is today Birch Farm. In the south west was Winwoods and probably other farms owned by freeholders who had cleared the Forest.

If the population had continued to grow unchecked the Mortimers and others would eventually have had to choose between deer and rent income. A series of natural disasters in the first half of the 14th century saved them the decision. From 1315 to 1322 there was a run of terrible harvests, and in 1348/9 the Black Death struck: the population was probably halved. There are no surviving records from the immediate aftermath of the Black Death, but good manorial accounts do survive from the end of the 14th century. In 1373 at Earnwood, the auditor noted that there were either no rents or reduced rents from 13 holdings. For eight of these there were no tenants, one was let at a reduced rent and four were now either in the 'Chace of Wyre' or had been enclosed in the park (National Archives SC6/967/3). The latter items are particularly interesting as they show these holdings had been permanently abandoned and turned over to woodland.

Whilst the crises of the first part of the 14th century were certainly traumatic and had far-reaching consequences, it would be wrong to assume that they set the tone for 150 years of misery. The economy showed itself to be resilient and adaptable. Thus, whilst the auditor mournfully noted the loss of revenue to Earnwood of 11s 10d, this had to be set against an actual rent income of £11 4s 2d. Individual farms were abandoned, but there is no evidence locally for any significant community vanishing. Evidence from the late 15th century shows that the expansion of farmland

was again the dominant theme (National Archives SC6/966/14).

Details of the way Wyre was managed in the 14th century comes from the accounts for Earnwood and Cleobury parks, which record the attention given to the deer (National Archives SC6/965/14, 27, 966/3, 7 (Cleobury Park); SC6/967/3, 5, 14, (Earnwood)). Fencing was renewed around the parks, in winter ivy was cut for fodder and large amounts of hay were brought in. It seems, however, that it was not just the deer that benefited from the parks: grazing rights were leased out or considered to be a tenant's right. In 1307 the inhabitants of Wall Town annually paid 12 hens for the grazing rights in Kinlet Wood (National Archives C134/9).

The presence of deer in medieval times provided temptation and individual acts of poaching were doubtless commonplace, and were dealt with by local manor courts where the individuals were usually fined. In 1364 however Richard Nowel, parker of Earnwood and a priest, and Roger de Foxcote were pardoned for assaulting Robert de Cleeton and taking away his sword, shield, purse, girdle and bow and arrow. They may have suspected that Robert had been using deer for target practice with the last two items. Nowel was dismissed as parker in 1382 when suspected of helping himself to deer (National Archives, Calender of Patent Rolls).

Cattle and sheep were let on to largely tree-free areas of grassland, the lawns, or areas where trees were pollarded to protect them from grazing. In

Ancient trackways and timber extraction routes using horses (known locally as 'tushing ditches') are found within the Forest [BK]

the Mortimer-held parks of Earnwood and around Cleobury horses were grazed in the parks. There was still a right of pannage, a direct connection with the Domesday woods, reckoned by the number of swine which could be supported. At Earnwood and Bewdley the parks also housed rabbit warrens (National Archives, C133/114); at Kinlet the parker had regularly to spend money on tar for the bases of fruit trees in the manorial orchard, to stop them being "wickedly eaten" by the rabbits (National Archives, SC6/967/3). Wild bees were another bonus that came with parks, the lord being entitled to the honey (National Archives, SC6/967/3).

Woodland also of course provided wood in several forms. One was underwood, used for fuel, hurdles and wattle. In the Mortimer-owned woods this belonged to the Lord and was sold (National Archives, SC6/967/14), the tenants being entitled to take dead wood for firewood. The 1373/4 accounts for Earnwood record money spent on enclosing a "vallet" (National Archives, SC6/967/3); another word for a coppice, indicating that there was managed underwood production. There was also timber for building. Any substantial tree that was blown over was usually sold for this purpose but, if required, trees could be felled to supplement this.

There was also industry in the Forest. In 1384 ironstone was mined in Cleobury Park. Henry le Collier, a freeman of Earnwood in 1304, was probably a charcoal burner, perhaps providing fuel for the local iron industry. At the same time William Sawier of Upper Arley was cutting wood for either fuel or timber (National Archives, C133/114). By 1472 there were coal mines in Cleobury Park, albeit unworked at that date (National Archives, SC6/966/13).

The post-medieval Forest

At the end of the medieval period, the Mortimers' holdings came into the hands of the Crown when King Edward VI inherited their lands through his grandmother, the last Mortimer heiress. The monarchs took little or no interest in the Forest, instead appointing a number of officials as Masters of Game to look after their interests.

In the early Tudor period, woodland management largely followed the pattern of medieval times. The parks were maintained for deer, with the grazing rights being leased out. In April 1537 Sir Edward Croft requested two deer from the Wyre Forest, as he found that "the flesh of a red deer [was] much restorit" to him in his old age (National Archives, Calendar of State Papers 1537).

The problem of poaching continued: in 1613 Thomas Potter from Bayton and five others entered "the park of our Lord the King, now in the tenure of Sir William Walshe, Knight at Rock… and hunted and killed with an arrow from a cross bow one doe feeding there" (Worcestershire Record Office, Quarter Sessions, 1/1/4/43/37). The rights of communities to collect wood continued and there is also more evidence for coppices or vallets, to keep animals out to allow the regeneration

of cut wood. At some period between 1550 and 1650 Wyre was legally disafforested. This meant that various rights therein were lost, there was no longer any protection of the hunting forest and more commercial activities could now take place.

In the second half of the 16th century, the traditional pattern of forest use started to come under threat. There was growing pressure on landowners to maximise income from their assets with agricultural land giving a better return than woodland. The parks were particularly vulnerable to conversion to farmland, as significant parts were already managed as grassland for either pasture or hay. A survey of Earnwood Park in 1566 recorded that two-thirds of the 255 acres (103 ha) were arable land. Whilst 530 oaks remained only 100 were mature and 330 were considered fit only for firewood. These were probably in the third of the park considered "rough ground with wood and bushes and very mossy" (National Archives, SP12 Vol 36, f1). Of all the Mortimer parks only Bewdley Park still seems to have been functioning in some form as a park in the early 17th century.

Intensification of agriculture also led to overgrazing in the main part of the Forest. In Earnwood Benn's Vallets and Corbet's Oak Vallets collectively covered 44 acres (19 ha) and should have ensured a regular crop of timber. The 1566 survey however complained that most of underwood was spoilt by cattle because the fences around the regenerating trees had not been maintained (National Archives, SP12 Vol 36, f1).

Wyre survived the Middle Ages as woodland partly because much of the underlying soil was too poor to support sustained agricultural use. Though marginal land could be used for houses which would bring in rent. The occupants could provide useful labour and another market for farm produce. Conversion of forest land to settlements was of course not new, but it became particularly apparent in the early 17th century. In 1616 the parishioners of Rock claimed that they were suffering "divers wrongs by the erecting of cabins… in a wood called Alton's Wood" (Thompson, 1986).

Whilst the area of woodland was decreasing, the demand for wood itself was increasing. This included cleaved wood for craftsmen and grew with the gradual increase in trade throughout the late 16th and 17th centuries. There were constant claims in the early 1600s that the woods around Bewdley were being overexploited. In 1623 a complaint was made to the Council of the Marches that "Many of the magistrats of the town [of Bewdley], that should help to right the king against these apparent wrongs, do trade much in laths and clapboards and such commodities wrought out of these blackpoles and stolen wood and continue the malefactors in their wrong doing" (Thompson 1986).

A second factor was the need for wood for fuel, a shortage resulting in Worcester Corporation acquiring the lease of a coal mine at Pensax in 1575. This may have just been a temporary problem, but a combination of a rising population, an expanding economy and fuel needed for manufacturing meant that the pressures increased (Hatcher 1993). This was to become especially acute in the Forest in the late 16th century, when it became a centre for iron making.

As noted earlier, iron smelting had been taking place around the fringes of the Forest since medieval times. The furnaces concerned however were small bloomeries requiring only a limited supply of wood. In 1563 Queen Elizabeth granted the manor of Cleobury and the associated parts of Wyre to Robert Dudley, Earl of Leicester. By 1571, Dudley had introduced the new technology of blast furnaces to the Forest. A blast furnace could easily produce ten times more iron than a bloomery but it also needed correspondingly more charcoal.

Dudley built two furnaces on Baveney Brook and two forges (which also needed charcoal) on the Rea at Cleobury. These worked until at least 1600. By the time they closed more furnaces and forges had started work within a 10-mile radius and their numbers grew throughout the next century (Baldwin 1994). A typical blast furnace needed around 160 ha of wood to sustain its production. Whilst this was only a small fraction of the total area of the Forest, when combined with all the other problems, and especially if there was a lack of management to ensure the re-growth of coppices, it is easy to understand why contemporaries considered that Wyre was in crisis. This was most strikingly expressed by the poet Michael Drayton writing in 1612:

> "When soon the goodly Wire that wonted was so hie
> Her stately top to reare, ashamed to behold,
> Her strait and goodly trees into the furnace sold:
> And looking on herself, by decay doth see
> The miserie wherein her sister forests be".
> (Drayton 1612)

Whilst not all the "strait and goodly" trees of Wyre were sold into the furnace, it is very likely that the Forest did radically change in nature around the start of the 17th century, as it ceased to be managed for deer and hunting. Henceforth mature trees only had value as a source of building timber and represented a long-term investment. In 1677 Andrew Yarranton may have been accurate when he claimed that there was not more than 40 ha of good timber (Thompson 1986). What took its place were tightly managed coppices to ensure regular production of cordwood (short lengths of wood a few inches in diameter) for charcoal, with occasional sales of other coppice products such as poles for fencing and hurdles. The sale of cordwood was profitable and the ironmasters had every incentive to ensure that there were sufficient coppices to sustain their works for an indefinite period. Thus access to the Forest was significantly curtailed to protect charcoal production.

From the 17th to the 19th centuries, there are abundant records of coppicing in Wyre. The ironmaster Philip Foley acquired coppices to provide wood for charcoal. In the early 1670s he purchased coppices from Lord Newport in Dowles for £420, and took out

a 32-year lease on the woods in Upper Arley belonging to Sir Henry Littleton. In 1679 a schedule drawn up for these coppices since 1654 indicated that they were felled in rotation, beginning with Shatterford. The felling interval in individual coppices varied from 13 to 18 years (George 1987). The average coppice size was just under 20 ha. Seckley Wood was 113 ha and was cut over three consecutive years so that the wood-cutters never had more than 40 ha to fell in a year. In around 1680 Foley took on coppices in New Park belonging to Andrew Yarranton, himself an ironmaster and engineer. He settled on a 19-year coppice cycle. This meant that the coppices were fenced, keeping both animals and people out.

The decline in stands of mature trees meant that there were no longer fallen boughs for firewood and repairs. This of course led to tensions with those who lost their traditional rights. It is said that following the enclosures of the New Parks by the Walsh family, the customary tenants of Abberley agreed to accept the enclosures only if Andrew Yarranton could create new jobs for the poor (Thompson 1986). The adoption of coal as the domestic fuel of choice in the second half of the 17th century eased the situation; some wood was still sold for faggots, but this was only a minor product (Hatcher 1993).

Once the trees had been cut, the wood that was to be used for charcoal had to be converted to cordwood or blockwood. In 1674, William Childe of Kinlet sold 4,000 cords of blockwood from his lands in Kinlet and Cleobury for £1,800 to Foley. The sale specified that the wood was to be cut into two-foot lengths (Herefordshire Record Office E12/VI/KC/55) and it would have been stacked into heaps; the 'cords'.

Between falls very little needed to be done in a coppice. Accounts from 1675 to 1677 show the expenditure on Conningsby Coppice in Kingswood, jointly owned by Thomas Foley and Lady Blount, possibly Mary Blount, the heiress of the Blount family of Kidderminster (Herefordshire Record Office E12/VI/KC/103). The biggest single item of expenditure was the rates for the maintenance of the local church and other such items. The coppice was also assessed for Ship Tax, introduced by Charles II to expand the navy. The main expenditure on the coppice itself was for maintenance of the boundary hedge and repair of its gates, with a little money also spent on ditching.

There are extensive records of the working of the Kinlet estate from 1777 to 1834 with ledger entries from 1810 illustrating the management of the Forest (Childe estate ledgers, Kinlet Hall). The estate owned almost all of the Forest in Kinlet, Neen Savage and Cleobury Mortimer, as well as woods in Alton. There were three woodmen responsible for operations and based at Kinlet, Cleobury and Alton. Spring was a busy time for them, as it was traditional to cut oak at this time of year, just as the sap was rising as this is when the bark could be peeled easily.

Oak bark, used by tanners, was a valuable by product of the felling operations. In 1810 it was worth

Old corn mills along Dowles Book

Remains of old leats (watercourses) that diverted water to run the waterwheels of the corn mills can be found hidden along the Dowles Brook valley. Knowles Mill (pictured top left and right [both JB]), owned by the National Trust, is the best preserved example where the waterwheel and mill mechanism can still be seen. Cooper's Mill (bottom left [NW]) has been renovated (bottom right [RW]) and is now managed by the Frank Chapman Centre for outdoor learning. Old grasslands and orchards formerly associated with the mills are now part of the characteristic landscape of Dowles valley.

around one-third of the price of a typical timber tree. In April 1810 David Jones was paid one shilling for the "setting [of the] peeling of the bark" in Cleobury Coppice. There were numerous tanners in Bewdley and other local towns who would buy it. By 1810 coal was widely used as a fuel for iron production but there were a number of specialist iron works in the vicinity that continued using charcoal. John Ennis was paid £3 for hauling materials to charcoal burners in Weston's Coppice, near Cleobury Mortimer. It was not just the product of one season's coppicing that was used for charcoal. In 1800 there had been a big fall of mature timber and the broken branches from this were finally sawn up and hauled to the charcoal burners in 1810 (Childe estate ledgers).

The other part of the woodcutters' work was felling trees: in the same year 13,000 poles were cut from Alton and 35,000 from Earnwood. Compared to this a mere 49 mature oaks were felled in Bell Coppice near Cleobury. For these there was the additional work of 'butting' and 'topping', squaring the bottom of the trunks and removing the branches. The poles (71,000 in total) were gathered and stacked at Bar Gate, on the banks of the Severn, before being auctioned and sent down the river.

There were also occasional sales of mature timber which, although a long-term investment, could give handsome sums for the landowner fortunate enough to sell it. On 26 April 1804 there was a sale of 301 mature oaks at Mawley. The Navy Board estimated that there

Overgrown coppiced oak with galled trunk [JB]

was a total of 50 tons, which with bark and cordwood would be worth £3,200. Word had however reached other buyers of their interest and they were outbid, the oaks eventually selling for £3,520. The navy buyers had to content themselves with discussing terms for buying from local timber merchants (Crimmin 2008).

The Kinlet estate accounts show that the woods were extremely important, typically accounting for around a quarter of the income, second in importance only to tenants' rents. They also provide evidence of changing fashions in woodland management. By the end of the 18th century the estate had its own tree nurseries, providing new saplings to establish plantations. Some of these may have been developed into coppices but it is likely that in many cases the intention was that all the trees would be allowed to form high forest before felling. Thus was modern forestry introduced. The account books also provide the first evidence for conifer plantations. Conifers and high forest were eventually to be the way forward for much of the Forest.

John Ruskin (1819–1900) had a lasting influence locally in the Wyre Forest. Ruskin was a remarkable man: polymath, visionary, artist and arbiter of good taste, a social and political economist, and an acute observer of nature and society (Wardle and Quayle 1989). He grew up in a privileged family, travelled widely and was educated at Christ Church, Oxford. He had a social conscience, which was shared with George Baker, a Quaker and prominent Birmingham business man. Baker had purchased some woodland and farmland near Bewdley in the 1870 Crown sale and he invited Ruskin to view this land. The Wyre Forest captured Ruskin's imagination, and Baker was moved to give him 20 acres, which is still known as Ruskin Land. In 1878 Ruskin formed the Guild of St George, a charitable education trust formed to focus on the educational needs of the working man. Ruskin donated this land to the Guild, with the idea of creating a museum, although this was never realised. He also had the idea of having some agricultural communities living and working in the Forest and five families moved down from Liverpool between 1889 and 1914 to live by the principles that Ruskin set out. Three families moved into St John's Lane, one into St George's Farm and the other into Uncllys Farm. In 1929 Shelf Held Coppice was sold to the Guild by Peter Adam (the carpet manufacturer), so now the Guild of St George owned 35 ha of woodland (now all SSSI and NNR), in addition to St George's Farm, Uncllys and St George's bungalow and the fields associated with these buildings.

The Forest in the 20th century

In the early 1900s Wyre was superficially little changed from the 1700s. In 1901 there were seven woodmen and woodcutters living in Kinlet. Traditional craftsmen such as basket and besom makers could still be found in Button Oak and Bewdley, albeit their numbers were falling, and charcoal production continued to

Forest crafts in the early 20th century

Swill basket making [KLS]

Wisket making, using birch twigs [KLS]

Peeling oak bark for local tanneries [BM]

Stacking dried oak bark [KLS]

Stacked timber for a charcoal burn [BM]

Charcoal burning: topping with a soil covering [KLS]

decline. In the spring men and women continued to be employed peeling bark from freshly fallen trees for sale to tanners (Crowther 2003). The tipping point came in the aftermath of the First World War. It became apparent that nationally far too few woods were being managed for timber, with many simply being managed for game. This resulted in the establishment of the Forestry Commission, with a brief to acquire woodland and manage it according to best practice for the production of timber and other wood products (James 1981). The opportunity for the Forestry Commission

to act in the Forest ultimately came in 1919 from the sale of large parts of the Kinlet Estate, including all of the Wyre holdings. In 1925/6 much of this land was acquired by the Commission and they announced a five-year programme to replant around 323 ha of oak coppice with European Larch *Larix decidua* and Douglas Fir *Pseudotsuga menziesii* (Baily's Magazine 1926).

A 1925 survey reported that whilst Mawley, Chamberlain and Ribbesford woods were managed as high forest, elsewhere coppicing was still practiced,

Dowles Manor, a small timber-framed Elizabethan manor house with the year 1560 over the door, was burnt down in 1982 [NW]

Albert Link was one of the last bark peelers in Wyre until around 1996

Peeling bark with a spade [RW]

Bark peeling spade and spoons [RW]

Old railway line through the Forest at Lodge Hill. Opened in the early 1860s, closed in 1963 and the rails removed. Now Sustrans cycle route.

[Photographer unknown]

typically on a 16–18 year rotation (19 years on the Kinlet Estate; Salisbury 1925) and charcoal production was unlikely to be the main driver of forestry operations. Instead large quantities of wood went for pit props and the coppicing process grew more complicated. Trees were left at different stages of their development, so that a whole range of products of different diameters would eventually come from felling a coppice.

Coppicing work before the Second World War has been well described by the late Edwin George (George 1987). As well as pit props the main products were penny poles, refinery poles (both used in refining iron) and rustic oak. George recollected a 25-year coppice cycle. The standing timber in each coppice was sold to one or two timber merchants who would be responsible for felling and extracting. Felling was still predominantly by hand; horses and lorries were both used to remove the timber. A typical annual fall would be something like 20–40 ha of coppice. There was still significant demand for the bark from the felled trees.

Elsewhere in the Forest coppice stools were reduced to a single trunk (singled) and allowed to develop into false standards (Packham *et al.* 1996). Whilst the quality of the resulting timber was not as good as genuine standards grown from acorns it rapidly converted coppice to high forest. Whilst significant areas of the Forest remained, and still remain, in the hands of private estates, the techniques practised in these areas for commercial timber production were very similar to those of the Forestry Commission.

The Second World War made a direct impact on the Forest, with a US army camp on its margins at Sturt in Kinlet. This was abandoned soon after D-Day in 1944 as the US forces moved on. In 1953 Imperial Chemical Industries established a small rocket motor testing facility deep in the Forest at Button Oak. The demand for timber in the Second World War emphasised the

need for modern techniques. In the years that followed there was whole-scale mechanisation, with chain saws replacing axes and tractors replacing horses. Once the initial Larch plantations matured they were felled and replaced by a more varied pattern of conifers. The total area of conifers was increased and high forestry virtually eliminated coppicing as a way of managing oak and the small quantities of other hardwoods. Traditional charcoal making in earth clamps had already been abandoned and commercial production of charcoal effectively ceased in the 1950s.

The government, through the Nature Conservancy Council (NCC), began to purchase land in the Wyre Forest in the mid 1970s, and 1978 saw 214 ha of the Forest declared a National Nature Reserve (NNR). The area owned or leased by the NCC (later English Nature) increased in the 1980s and 1990s, and the NNR was extended in stages to 650 ha. Around this time there was a growing appreciation in the Forestry Commission of the importance of the Forest for its wildlife and leisure activities. The Forestry Commission opened the Wyre Forest Discovery Centre at Callow Hill in 1991. This day centre catered for students of all ages and especially for National Curriculum-based programmes in schools which soon resulted in around 10,000 students visiting each year.

During the 1980s and 1990s an increase in awareness of the need for conservation and restoration of ancient woodland resulted in the UK Biodiversity Action Plan's Native Woodland Habitat Action Plans. In 1994 this included targets for restoring Plantations on Ancient Woodland Sites (PAWS) to native woodland by the year 2020. To achieve this the Forestry Commission and Natural England have started removing introduced conifer and beech, substantially changing the nature of the woodland, and together with the creation of more open space and heathy areas, have significantly benefited many species.

Chapter 4

The Forest Flora

For botanists who come to Wyre for its floral specialities, the Forest can be a challenging place. Among its woods, meadows and orchards is a rich variety of unusual and exciting plants, but they can be elusive. Even the 'special' species such as the Whitty Pear *Sorbus domestica* can be tricky to track down, while others such as Wood Crane's-bill *Geranium sylvaticum* are mercurial plants, appearing and disappearing at certain sites from year to year. But the potential of finding their pinkish-violet flowers in a quiet dingle or discovering a spike of Narrow-leaved Helleborine *Cephalanthera longifolia* by a woodland track makes a visit to the Forest irresistible.

Wyre's vegetation is particularly distinctive because of the Forest's position at the boundary of the English uplands and lowlands in the Welsh Marches, and because it shares many characteristics with Welsh upland oak woodland. Different botanical associations meet here; northern and western species grow alongside those usually associated with southern and eastern woodland. While this provides something special and unusual, the populations of particular plants can be small and localised. Over large areas of the Forest, plant diversity can seem poor and it may need a visit to the Dowles Brook valley to find flowers such as Bluebells *Hyacinthoides non-scripta*, Primroses *Primula vulgaris* and Wood Anemones *Anemone nemorosa* in any numbers.

Wyre's history tells us why large areas of woodland are relatively poor for plants. It was a Saxon hunting forest and then a Norman chase so much of the area was grazed by domestic livestock, or used for deer parks, to the detriment of more palatable plants. In later years, from the 17th century, the woods were intensely managed to favour oak coppice that provided charcoal and tannin-rich bark: few other trees and shrubs remained in the resulting "forest of oak poles".

In the 1930s Beech *Fagus sylvatica* and conifers were under-planted into many former oak woods or after clear-felling. In places their dense shade almost eliminated the remaining ground flora.

In Wyre oak reigns supreme. Oak is a variable tree widely introgressed with fertile hybrids and Wyre is certainly a place for a botanist to admire this variation. Whilst Wyre oak seems to be generally Sessile, most are hybrids between Sessile Oak *Quercus petraea* and Pedunculate Oak *Quercus robur*. The oaks of lowland Britain are typically Pedunculate, but to the north and west in more upland areas Sessile Oak dominates. Wyre lies in a broad geographic zone between the range of these two species and here the Hybrid Oak *Quercus × rosacea* occurs. Whilst Wyre oak is typically Sessile, having leaves with a long stalk and acorns that are stalkless, a closer examination of the leaves and acorns will reveal characteristics of both species of tree. Some foresters even maintain that the Wyre Forest oak has its own particular shape. Even so, pure Sessile Oak is rare in the Forest, but good examples of Pedunculate Oak grow in the stream valleys and along the Severn.

Oaks are well known for being some of the most productive trees for wildlife. They can support over 400 species of insects and mites, and only willows do better with 450. This diversity of species provides food for birds and other animals. Although oak is abundant here, Wyre has few really ancient trees. At Mawley, there was an exceptionally large pollarded Sessile Oak, a venerable landmark which was probably 450 years old when it finally fell apart in October 2001: its hulk still remains at the roadside as valuable deadwood habitat. Some fine majestic oaks still remain in the grounds of Mawley Hall, and at Goodmoor Grange there is an impressively large Sessile Oak with a girth of 5.7 m and a height of over 26 m. Although there are

Many of the grasslands around the Forest have woodland flowers present in the sward indicating that these fields were cleared and taken from the Forest (assarted) perhaps a few hundred years ago. [JB]

few sizeable veteran oaks in the Forest, many of the old coppice stools are ancient, 300–400 years old or more, having been coppiced many times throughout their lifetimes.

Oaks are hardy trees and can survive even when surrounded by competing planted conifers. Their stools re-grow when light levels increase as conifers are thinned or removed. It is now Government policy to revert ancient woodlands back to native broadleaf trees, known as PAWS (Plantations on Ancient Woodland Sites). The return of conservation coppicing and the restoration and creation of wood pasture should herald a new era for the special plants of Wyre.

Woods within woods

No two woods are the same and becoming a connoisseur of woodlands is rather like appreciating fine wines. The National Vegetation Classification (NVC) is a standard applied to habitat types which help conservationists to read the landscape botanically (Rodwell 1991; 1992) (see box on page 43). A journey through Wyre's woodlands reveals their subtle varieties and characteristic plants.

There are two main woodland types in Wyre, both of them oak woodlands. Most of the oak woodland is NVC W10, whilst the other main type is NVC W16. W10 woodland contains several sub-divisions; some are species-poor and contain little ground flora other than Creeping Soft-grass *Holcus mollis*, Bracken *Pteridium aquilinum* and Bramble *Rubus* spp. Typically these oakwoods occur on the deeper, often acid sandy-shale, soils on level ground. If the canopy is widely open, Bracken can become dominant and Bramble may be rampant. Under Bracken and Bramble, more delicate plants are harder to find, but include Bluebell, Wood Anemone, Common Dog-violet *Viola riviniana*, Early Dog-

Sessile Oak *Quercus petraea* [PC]

violet *V. reichenbachiana*, Bugle *Ajuga reptans*, Foxglove *Digitalis purpurea*, Honeysuckle *Lonicera periclymenum* as a ground cover plant, and Broad Buckler-fern *Dryopteris dilatata*.

As coppicing declined the coppice oak stools were 'stored'; the best stems were allowed to grow on and the rest removed leaving a single trunk. Many of the larger

The Mawley Oak was a massive pollarded Sessile Oak that eventually declined with old age and now provides valuable deadwood habitat for invertebrates. [NW]

surviving oaks date from around 1900 when coppicing was already in decline; by 1940 it had virtually finished. During the Second World War some trees were felled when the woods were thinned for timber, creating an age class of trees or coppice from around this date.

As a result of past coppicing for bark, charcoal and timber, the modern oak woods are almost pure with few other species of trees or shrubs. However they often have a scattering of sombre Yews *Taxus baccata,* which are easier to pick out in winter. Yews were often allowed to remain by foresters, not through sentimentality, but probably because their hard wood made them difficult to clear. Maybe they also held a special place in the minds of woodsmen as revered trees.

Wyre Yews deserve more attention. Here on the poor soils and with competition from other trees, they are slow growing and may be much older than we think. Some may have notched up their first millennium and even most of the smaller trees are likely to be several hundred years old. In Longdon Orchard there are some particularly fine specimens

and elsewhere small groves and single trees are widespread. Yews have a remarkable talent for re-inventing themselves. One fallen Yew in Cleobury Coppice has regrown so that each branch on its upper side has developed into a new trunk, creating a line of new trees. The dark leathery foliage of Yews is the favourite habitat in the Forest for the rare Triangle Spider *Hyptiotes paradoxus* and Yew berries are a lure for winter thrushes and Hawfinches *Coccothraustes coccothraustes.*

Holly *Ilex aquifolium* is the main understorey shrub in the W10 oak woodlands, but its presence is fitful, and depends on former management. In the past, from medieval times until the 19th century, it was cut as winter food for livestock and deer. Some areas, such as Oxbind Coppice, contain thickets of Holly with many mature trees. In recent years, as Fallow Deer *Dama dama* have fallen from a peak in numbers in the 1970s to a more sustainable managed herd, Holly has regenerated from bushes dwarfed by many years of browsing. Rock Coppice and Burnt Wood are visited

Majestic Yews *Taxus baccata* are common throughout most of the Forest, and some are many hundreds of years old [RW]**. The berries (below left** [PC]**) provide food for birds and the dark foliage is home to the rare Triangle Spider *Hyptiotes paradoxus* (below right** [JB]**).**

by fewer deer than the main woodland block and give a glimpse of a woodscape where groves of hollies thrive under the sheltering oaks, suppressing other plants with their dense shade and persistent prickly leaf litter. Walking through these woods on a bright winter's day you can be dazzled by the stroboscopic effect of sunlight reflecting from the shiny holly leaves.

Birch *Betula* spp. often thrives in the oakwoods. When light levels are high enough its papery seeds germinate if competition is not too fierce. Birch is generally considered to be a weed by foresters because it is quick to invade open areas. Without management its slender shapes would be very common in Wyre, but in the past it was extensively removed to favour oak, and used for making besoms, and wiskets—the brushes formerly used in local carpet manufacturing for cleaning excess fluff or 'flights'. More recently, birch has been cut for firewood and fodder for the animals at the West Midland Safari Park. There are still a few areas of nearly pure birch, which have sprung up following woodland clearance or abandonment of land outside

ancient woodland. Both Silver Birch *Betula pendula* and Downy Birch *B. pubescens* are less common than they could be, a pity because they mature quickly and are valuable for wildlife. Birches die young, often helped on their way by Birch Polypore *Piptoporus betulinus*, and then provide deadwood for hole-nesting birds such as Redstarts *Phoenicurus phoenicurus*. Young birch is an excellent habitat for birds like Willow Warblers *Phylloscopus trochilus* and moths, most notably the Kentish Glory *Endromis versicolora* and the Argent and Sable *Rheumaptera hastata* both now extinct in Wyre. As conifers are removed and new coppice plots are created, birch scrub is likely to increase and more old and senescent trees will survive to benefit wildlife.

Hazel *Corylus avellana* occurs locally throughout the Forest as an understorey shrub, but is uncommon on drier, less fertile ground. Most grows near Dowles Brook on the deeper, richer soils. In Wyre's oak coppice, Hazel is scarce because it is forced to compete with young oaks within the understorey. Hazel coppice

National Vegetation Classification

Ecologists divide plant communities in Britain into various types related to various habitats. The most widely used system is the National Vegetation Classification (NVC) (Rodwell 1991, 1992), based on plant associations. Commissioned by the then Nature Conservancy in 1975 it provides a common standard of classification and description. Using this in Wyre helps to understand the area in national terms and provides a basis to describe the Forest's semi-natural vegetation. The types are titled according to the scientific names of the dominant species, to which the English equivalent is added here.

Woodland
The woodlands of the Forest fit mainly into two NVC stand-types. Most of the oak woodland is classified as **NVC W10**, *Quercus robur-Pteridium aquilinum-Rubus fruticosus*, Common (Pedunculate) Oak-Bracken-Bramble woodland (in Wyre Common Oak is replaced by Sessile Oak *Quercus petraea* or, more correctly, Hybrid Oak *Quercus × rosacea*, which shows more of the characteristics associated with Sessile Oak).

The other main type is **NVC W16**, *Quercus* spp.-*Deschampsia flexuosa*, Oak-Wavy Hair-grass woodland, found typically on the steep valley sides.

In addition, the following types are also found in Wyre's woodlands.

NVC W17 *Quercus petraea-Betula pubescens-Dicranum majus*, Sessile Oak-Downy Birch-Greater Fork-moss woodland, found on the steep sides of the Dowles Brook valley.

NVC W14 *Fagus sylvaticus-Rubus fruticosus*, Beech-Bramble woodland. The modified oak woodland is planted with beech, with examples at New Parks and Earnwood.

NVC W8 *Fraxinus excelisor-Acer campestre-Mercurials perennis*, Ash-Field Maple-Dog's Mercury woodland, a 'lost' woodland type that, for example, persists in the hedgerows at Far Forest.

NVC W4 *Betula pubescens-Molinia caerulea*, Downy Birch-Purple Moor-grass woodland, found on wet flushes within the oak woods.

NVC W7 *Alnus glutinosa-Fraxinus excelsior-Lysimachia nemorum*, Alder-Ash-Creeping Jenny woodlands, found as wet woodlands along the Dowles Brook and at some seepages.

NVC W25 *Pteridium aquilinum-Rubus fruticosus*, Bracken-Bramble underscrub.

Grasslands
NVC MG1 *Arrhenatherum elatius* False Oat-grass grassland, rank grassland especially on roadsides and the Severn's banks.

NVC MG5 *Cynosurus cristatus-Centaurea nigra* Crested Dog's-tail-Black Knapweed grassland, the best species-rich grasslands around the Forest. MG5c is typical.

NVC U1 *Festuca ovina-Agrostis capillaris-Rumex acetosella* Sheep's Fescue-Common Bent-Sheep's Sorrel grassland, a rare acid grassland often with Heather.

NVC U2 *Deschampsia flexuosa* Wavy Hair-grass grassland, on heathland sites like Pound Green Common.

NVC U4 *Festuca ovina-Agrostis capillaris-Galium saxatile* Sheep's Fescue-Brown Bent Grass-Heath Bedstraw grasslands, scattered around the Forest often with MG5.

NVC H8 *Calluna vulgaris-Ulex gallii* Heather-Western Gorse heath, at Pound Green Common.

NVC H9 *Calluna vulgaris-Deschampsia flexuosa* Heather-Wavy Hair-grass heath, at Pound Green Common.

Other
NVC M27 *Filipendula ulmaria-Angelica sylvestris*, Meadowsweet-Angelica mire, the 'Great Bog'.

NVC OV26 *Epilobium hirsutum* Hairy Willowherb, along the Severn

NVC A18 *Ranunculus fluitans* community, in the River Severn

NVC A11 *Potamogeton pectinatus-Myriophyllum spicatum* community, in the River Severn.

Wild Service-tree *Sorbus torminalis*: flowers [JB], berries [PC] and leaf [JB]

is also nibbled by grazing deer and new plants rarely germinate because Grey Squirrels *Sciurus carolinensis* eat the nuts. In the absence of deer fencing, Hazel has to be pollarded rather than coppiced, producing interesting, if unusual-looking shrubs.

Other trees and shrubs found scattered within the W10 stands include Crab Apple *Malus sylvestris*, Wild Cherry *Prunus avium*, Aspen *Populus tremula*, Rowan *Sorbus aucuparia*, Hawthorn *Crataegus monogyna* and occasional Wild Service-tree *Sorbus torminalis*. Wild Cherry, or Gean, is very typical of the Forest but not as common as it might be. Its wood is favoured by timber merchants, so a mature or veteran Cherry is a rare sight. This is a shame as the trees can grow to a considerable size, but there are several old coppiced Cherries which are worth looking for, especially on steeper slopes.

Bird Cherry *Prunus padus* is very rare in Wyre and only seen close to habitation, suggesting it may not be native this far south. This is surprising as it grows in hedgerows and woods just a few miles to the north-west near Titterstone Clee Hill. Similarly Spindle *Euonymus europaeus*, a southern species preferring base-rich soils, has very few locations in the Forest where the soils are too acid, but is scattered through local hedgerows.

In autumn the sunset tints of Wild Service-tree leaves brighten the woodland floor. Wild Service is an ancient woodland indicator, so it is no surprise to find sizeable trees or saplings throughout Wyre. Some large specimens have been spared the axe and can be two

metres in girth. One specimen at Longdon Orchard is large enough to have a Western Hemlock-spruce *Tsuga heterophylla* sapling growing in a fork in its trunk. The white blossoms are popular with insects in spring, and the clusters of tawny berries are eaten by birds, including Mistle Thrushes *Turdus viscivorus*. Although they are edible when ripened or bletted, they can be bitter when unripe and are the origin of the plant's specific name *torminalis* meaning 'twisting', a reference to their effect on human guts.

Another common *Sorbus*, Whitebeam *S. aria*, does not grow well on acidic soils, but there is one large tree (presumably planted) in Worrall's Coppice near Far Forest. Another shrubby species that just manages to reach Wyre from the east is Midland Hawthorn *Crataegus laevigata*; very few are known, but there is one in Burnt Wood and another in Shelf Held Coppice. This species is almost certainly under-recorded and should be found in stream dingles and hedgerows outside the main woodland area.

True Service-tree *Sorbus domestica* or Whitty Pear alias The Old Sorb Tree

In the 1600s there grew in Wyre Forest an unusual tree known to the local people for its ability to ward off the attention of witches. The divided leaves were similar to Ash *Fraxinus excelsior* but each spring it bore clusters of white flowers which in autumn produced a number of small pear-shaped fruit.

The tree eventually became famous, and was visited by many people following a letter from Alderman

Edmund Pitt of Worcester published by the Royal Society in 1678 and transcribed below.

PHILOSOPHICAL TRANSACTIONS.
Volume 12, No. 139 pages 978–979,
for the months of *April*, *May* and *June* 1678.

Extract of a letter from Edmund Pitt, *Alderman* of Worcester, *a very knowing botanist; concerning the* Sorbus Pyriformis.

Last year I found a Rarity, growing wild in a Forest of this County of *Worcester*. It is described by *L'Obelius* under the name of *Sorbus Pyriformis*: and also by *Matheolus*, upon *Dioscorides*. And by *Bauhimus*, under the name of *Sorbus procera*. And they agree, that in *France*, *Germany* and *Italy*, they are commonly found. But neither these, nor any of our own Countrymen, as *Gerard, Parkinson, Johnson, How*, nor those Learned Authors *Merret or Ray*, have taken notice of it being a native of *England*. Nor have any of our *English Writers so much have* mention'd it. Saving, that Mr. *Lyte*, in his Translation of Dodonæus describes it under the name of the Sorb Apple. But saith no more of the *place, but* that it groweth in *Dutch – Land.*

It resembles the Ornus or Quicken tree; only the *Ornus* bears *flowers* and *fruit* at the *end*, this on the sides of the Branch. Next the Sun, the Fruit hath a dark-red blush: and is about the bigness of a small *junketing pear*. In September, so rough, as to be ready to strangle one. But being then gather'd, and kept till October, they eat as well as any *Medlar*. Thus far the letter.

Editor's comment: Whether a Verjuyce made from this Fruit, either ground with Crabs, or Grapes, or if plentiful, alone, would not, being kept for some time, prove one of the best acid astringent sawces, that Nature affords.

Pitt was an apothecary, Mayor of Worcester 1656–57, and a permanent alderman thereafter (Horsman 2000).

Ever since the tree was reported, it has fascinated generations of naturalists (Green 2009). No other specimens could be found, and it was thought to be the only one in Britain.

Nash (1781), states: "Rock: In the eastern part of the parish, about a mile from Mopsons Cross, between that and the Dowles Brook, in the middle of a thick wood belonging to Mr Baldwyn, is a very uncommon tree, which I suppose to be the *Sorbus Sativa Pyriformis*, mentioned by Mr Pitt in the Philosophical Transactions for the year 1678, the bark resembles a pear tree, as does the fruit, except that it is not quite so large as the smallest pear; the leaf and blossom exactly resemble a mountain ash [*Sorbus aucuparia*]; the common people of the neighbourhood, amongst whom this tree had been esteemed a curiosity for upwards of an hundred years, call it not improperly the "quicken pear tree". Not generally known before Pitt's time when he drew attention to it. It was 40 feet high".

Between 1800 and 1820 the Earl of Mountnorris raised two cuttings at Arley Castle and a descendant of one of these trees was planted near Worcester cathedral.

On 24 August 1853, 175 years after Pitt, the Old Sorb Tree was visited by the Worcestershire Naturalists Club. Edwin Lees (1867) later wrote "At our visit it was in a very decrepit state, with lank, bare, and lofty branches, and only exhibited vitality at its very summit. Very little fruit was then produced, and the sorb-tree presented the scraggy and decrepit aspect shown in the annexed woodcut."

Following this visit Lees wrote that hard fruits of the tree were once hung in foresters' houses to give security from witches, and some people carried a piece of Rowan or Witchen in their pockets as a similar talisman. It was thought that the Whitty Pear, and especially its fruit, was even stronger in the way of protection. Apparently many members of the club sought a similar talisman by trying to dislodge fruit from high in the tree!

Illustration of the original True Service-tree *Sorbus domestica* printed in Nash's 1781–1782 *Collections for the History of Worcestershire.*

The club visited again on 25 June 1858 and lunched by the tree, stating that "amidst the festal scene the old sorb tree appeared the withered wreck of centuries". Four years later, in April 1862, the tree was destroyed by a miscreant's fire. Apparently the person concerned was a notorious poacher and burnt the tree as revenge on the magistrate, the Squire of Kinlet, whom he thought had given him too severe a sentence. The Squire owned the land, often visited the tree and took many guests to view it. The poacher was later convicted of setting fire to farm buildings and was transported to Australia, so the annihilator of the revered Sorb Tree spent his remaining days at Botany Bay. Shortly after the fire, remnants of the tree were collected (probably by George Jorden—see below) and turned into cups or chalices. Where these are now is a mystery.

In Lees (1867) *The Botany of Worcestershire*, he writes that "In connection with Bewdley and Wyre Forest, Mr George Jorden merits high commendation as an untired explorer and guide... Having many times guided the Club and its members to the time-honoured though decrepit Sorb-tree *Pyrus domestica*, which he regarded with almost filial love, its wanton destruction by ruffian hands was a source of much grief to him, and he gathered up with decent care the relics that were left of the limbs of the old veteran, some of which he yet retains".

THE SORB-TREE (*Pyrus domestica*) OF WYRE FOREST, WORCESTERSHIRE, before its lower branches were denuded.

From a sketch taken many years ago.

An illustration from *The Botany of Worcestershire*, Lees (1867)

In 1911, 234 years after Pitt and 50 years after the burning, a memorial post with a sign was set up on the site of the tree. It was decided at the gathering to plant a sapling Whitty Pear there that had been raised at Arley Castle by Mr Robert Woodward, when it was large enough (the young trees grow very slowly). Sadly Robert Woodward was killed during the First World War in 1915.

The sign erected read: "At this spot stood for some centuries the only specimen of the Sorb or Whitty Pear Tree *Sorbus domestica* which was burned down by an incendiary in 1862. This post was set up by the Worcestershire Naturalists' Club, 25th July 1911, to mark the site. The Right Rev. The Lord Bishop of Worcester, F.S.A. President. F. T. Spackman, F.G.S., Honorary Secretary."

On 30 March 1916, a large party gathered at the spot and the sapling was planted by Robert Woodward's mother. A history of the tree read by F. Ronald Jeffrey and this was published in the Transactions of the Worcestershire Naturalists' Club later that year.

In 1982 the Wyre Arboretum was started near the 1916 Sorb-tree and several young Sorb trees were planted there between 1993 and 2000.

In 2012, 335 years after Pitt, Hermione Gerry of the Woodward family, in an account of the Arley arboretum and her family, wrote "After my Uncle was killed, in France on 9 May 1915, it was decided to plant a tree in his memory, and what better tree to plant than an offspring, raised by him, of the original Whitty Pear. The place selected to plant this sapling was the site of the original tree, in the Wyre Forest, and so on 30 March 1916 it was planted by my Grandmother, Mrs Robert Woodward (Mary Jane) on that site." (Gerry 2012).

A year later, on the 14 March 2013, 97 years after the planting of the 1916 tree, Hermione Gerry planted a sapling *Sorbus domestica* in the nearby Wyre Forest arboretum. The sapling had been raised from an offspring of the original tree. Readers may wonder why we did not wait until 2016, a century after the 1916 tree was planted, before planting the sapling. There were two reasons. First the sapling, grown in the pot, was quite large and needed planting-out. Secondly, Hermione Gerry had been ill for some time and was receiving chemotherapy for cancer. Without a word being said of this it was apparent she wanted to plant the tree as soon as practically possible. Hence, we planned for 14 March 2013 in the 98th year and it was so. Sadly, Hermione died on 19 July 2013 and we very much hope the tree will grow and thrive as a lasting memorial to a remarkable lady (Green 2013).

Over the years the original tree and its direct descendants have been propagated from seed (with difficulty) or cuttings, or by using suckers. The fruit produces seed erratically, apparently dependent on temperature: it is a tree of warmer climates growing in many parts of Europe. Various Whitty Pear trees have been planted in Worcestershire and elsewhere in England and Wales over a long period of time.

The True Service-tree *Sorbus domestica* in 2009 [PR]; the plaque erected nearby at the time it was planted [HG]; the leaves and pear-shaped fruit in autumn. [HG]

Some are known to be progeny of the original tree; others may have been imported from Europe. For example there were trees at Croome Court and there are trees at Arley Arboretum. One was planted at Worcester Cathedral in the early 1900s by Minor Canon Woodward, a relative of the Arley Castle Woodwards, and this one is mentioned several times in the *Transactions of the Worcestershire Naturalists' Club* as a flourishing tree. Apparently a cricket-loving canon later found that the tree obscured his view of the Worcester County Cricket ground across the River Severn and it was felled. Fortunately two others had been planted in the cathedral grounds.

Five trees are known in Withybed Wood in Wyre and they are thought to be progeny of the original tree, perhaps planted by Wyre Forest botanist George Jorden at an unknown date. However an attempt to age these trees by Wyre Forest Study Group, yet incomplete, suggests they may be too young to be of that origin.

Where did the Wyre tree come from? Was it native or planted? The early naturalists found remnants of buildings and Edwin Lees thought a hermitage existed on the spot, perhaps from pre-Reformation days when the land was in possession of a monastery. Possibly it was a lone tree of a lost British population. Marc Hampton has suggested that the Wyre tree may

have been planted from stock cultivated at South Wales monasteries. He and others quote *The History of Britons* by a Welsh monk Nennius who describes a tree, about 850 years before Pitt, with "pinnate leaves and apple or pear shaped small fruit"—a description akin to Rowan with pear shaped fruits that could only be *Sorbus domestica*. Based partly on linguistic studies Marc Hampton further suggests that it once grew wild in South Wales (Hampton 1996). There is similar evidence of old records from Cornwall.

In 1983 and 1993 Marc Hampton discovered two cliff sites where *Sorbus domestica* was growing on the Glamorgan coast (Hampton & Kay 1995). These are steep cliffs with bands of softer and harder limestone and the trees root into the softer areas. These trees are in an exposed position, stunted, and rarely fruit. They are so similar to Rowan that it was quite difficult to confirm the identification until a few fruits were found. It is highly unlikely that trees would have been planted at this site or derived from trees planted nearby and so they are almost certainly native trees—perhaps a remnant of a previous Welsh population. These trees were shown to be re-growths from the bases of previous bigger trees that had died back. The age of the oldest growing trees was estimated at about 300 years. Continental reports indicate that Sorb trees can live for 1,000 years. Shortly afterwards a few trees were found further upstream on the Severn Estuary (Rich *et al.* 2010). More recently Bennallick & Pearman (2013) reported the discovery of *S. domestica* growing in natural habitat on cliffs in Cornwall, so the historical records may be correct.

Preliminary molecular studies in 2000 at Kew Gardens suggested little difference between trees from across Europe, including Britain. This perhaps suggests European scale movements of orchard grown trees derived from a wild population in the past or that all belong to a once extensive native population. Frances Claxton (1999), who was involved in these studies, produced a preliminary report but nothing further has been published to date. The origins of the Wyre tree remain a mystery but perhaps, in warmer times, there was a native population in the British Isles and maybe we are seeing their descendants: or perhaps *S. domestica* is an ancient introduction (Rich *et al.* 2010).

Plants under the trees

In many places the Forest soils are thin and stony and under the coppiced oaks few plants grow other than tufts of Heather *Calluna vulgaris* or clumps of Bilberry *Vaccinium myrtillus*. This NVC W16 woodland is on the steeper valley slopes or undulating ground and the soils are normally very acid with pH levels around 3.8

to 5. The two main woodland types occur in a mosaic across much of the Forest and are often impossible to separate. They share the same management history but W16 is much more characteristic of the Welsh woodlands and uncommon in lowland England. Bilberry and Heather can be dominant, though not always growing together. Bilberry appears to prefer the deeper clay soils and Heather the shallow, rocky, sandy shales. The 19th century botanist Carleton Rea remarked on the suggestion that the name 'Wyre Forest' was derived from the Bilberry, or rather the old name for it of 'Wyrern', but this seems unlikely given that Bilberry is a common herb in many western woods besides Wyre. In midsummer the magenta splashes of Wyre's other native heather, Bell Heather *Erica cinerea*, brighten dry banks and sunny path sides.

Other plants are often scattered in these dry oak woods, including Common Cow-wheat *Melampyrum pratense* whose flowers are usually creamy-yellow, but in Wyre are often the colour of egg yolk. Goldenrod *Solidago virgaurea*, Hairy Wood-rush *Luzula pilosa*, Wavy Hair-grass *Deschampsia flexuosa*, Wood Sage *Teucrium scorodonia* and Pill Sedge *Carex pilulifera* are characteristic plants of the steeper slopes. Honeysuckle is also common, often growing as low mounds or creeping over the ground rather than as a climber. One very local but special plant is Saw-wort

Bilberry *Vaccinium myrtillus* [PC]

Common Cow-wheat *Melampyrum pratense* [JB]

The boundary between woodland and grassland is an interface or ecotone, a special habitat for many plants and animals. Here Betony *Betonica officinalis* and Bracken *Pteridium aquilinum* scrub grade into species-rich grassland. [JB]

Serratula tinctoria whose slender, thistle-like flowers grow in just three or four places, and Wyre is its main stronghold. These dry woods are also home to the nationally scarce Soft-leaved Sedge *Carex montana* and hawkweeds *Hieracium* spp. including the locally common *Hieracium cinderella* which in Wyre is near its eastern limits in the British Isles. Bitter Vetch *Lathyrus linifolius* and Betony *Betonica officinalis* are both attractive plants of sunshine and dappled shade at woodland edges and in clearings. Woodlands with deep shade favour the growth of Bilberry and the spiky sheaves of Greater Wood-rush *Luzula sylvatica,* but if light levels increase following felling Bramble and Bracken start to appear, and this change in vegetation blurs the boundary between W10 and W16, or even W17 (see box on page 43).

Until recently some of the more acid woodlands, especially those nearest to Bewdley, were clothed in a dense covering of Rhododendron *Rhododendron ponticum*, a legacy of ornamental plantings by the Countess of Portsmouth during the latter part of the 19th century. The cheerful mauve flowers are attractive to bees and to us, but the harm the plant can do to woodland ecosystems by shading and suppressing everything else far outweighs its floral delights. Rhododendron is an invasive plant that has smothered many habitats and in recent years, in places such as Hitterhill Coppice where it was choking a stream valley, it has been reduced considerably to allow native species to recolonise.

On some of the steeper slopes along the Dowles Brook valley and side valleys there are examples of woodland carpeted with mosses and liverworts. This woodland, which flourishes in moister microclimates, is NVC W17 and often occurs with W16 woodland. It is more typical of Wales and north-western Britain than the English midlands although the Wyre Forest sites are not as bryophyte-rich as those found in Wales. In places Bilberry can become a prominent feature of the ground layer but herbs are few.

Beech is probably outside its natural British range in Wyre, but has been widely under-planted beneath mature oaks which act as nursery trees, protecting the growing saplings. Although the beech will eventually shade out the oak, the resulting woods become modified oak woodland. Most Beech trees in Wyre are less than 70 years old, but venerable specimens once included the now defunct Seckley Beech. Norman Hickin visited this in 1969 when it had no fewer than 26 main trunks, plus several smaller ones and a circumference of 11.4 m at a height of 1.5 m from the ground (Hickin 1971).

Modern Beech plantations cast a heavy shade and carpet the woodland with thick leaf litter. Few ground plants can survive in these conditions, but as the trees mature and are thinned, ferns, Heather and Bilberry reappear and this is now happening in places such as Brand Wood, Earnwood and New Parks. There are few sights to match the acid-green of unfurling beech leaves above pools of flowering Bluebells: with luck, a singing Wood Warbler *Phylloscopus sibilatrix* will complete the picture.

In the undulating landscape of Wyre, in the valley bottoms, near the streams and on spring-line seepages, there are very different woodlands. These valley woods are classified as NVC W7 and are dominated by Alder *Alnus glutinosa* which likes its feet wet. These woods are often botanically rich and tend to lie on alluvial deposits with pH levels over 6.0. In the moist earth, which is well seasoned with leaf mould, Lesser Spearwort *Ranunculus flammula*, Wood-sorrel *Oxalis acetosella*, and Opposite-leaved Golden-saxifrage *Chrysosplenium oppositifolium* flourish. Where water flows through these woods, Pendulous Sedge *Carex pendula* forms lush clumps which can crowd out most other species, and more occasionally Wood Club-rush *Scirpus sylvaticus* occurs in profusion. Along Dowles Brook, there is a much more varied ground flora which can include Marsh Valerian *Valeriana dioica* and Remote Sedge *Carex remota*. This wet woodland habitat is becoming increasingly uncommon and is well worth protecting.

Within the drier oak woods occasional damp flushes are betrayed by the dark-green clumps of Tufted Hair-grass *Deschampsia cespitosa*. These wet areas are often small or fragmented and mark out spring seepages near the surface, bringing variety to the more acidic woodland and raising the soil pH to between 5.5 and 6.5. Where they meet streams, these flushes may be rich in plants such as Pendulous Sedge and Remote Sedge. Some of the finest areas of damp woodland are found at Areley Wood near Stourport where Alder forms extensive patches in wet flushes among the oaks. Here a very special plant is Narrow-leaved Bitter-cress *Cardamine impatiens,* an elegant fern-leaved species,

which grows along the damper rides, sometimes with Lesser Centaury *Centaurium pulchellum,* the latter at its only site in Wyre. Both plants are very scarce in Worcestershire (Day 2001), and nationally Narrow-leaved Bitter-cress is classed as near-threatened and declining (Cheffings & Farrell 2005). Elsewhere in Wyre it occurs by a trackside at Eymore Wood.

Sometimes the wet seepages in Wyre's woods are base-rich (pH over 7.0) and more like calcareous fens. These give rise to small pockets of NVC W4 woodland and can support a surprising variety of wild flowers and shrubs. In winter they are pale with the tussocks of Purple Moor-grass *Molinia caerulea* and support shrubs such as Eared Willow *Salix aurita*, Guelder-rose *Viburnum opulus* and even Wild Privet *Ligustrum vulgare*. Choice plants in these calcareous patches include Great Burnet *Sanguisorba officinalis* and Broad-leaved Cottongrass *Eriophorum latifolium*, both of which are very scarce or local in Shropshire and Worcestershire. Marsh Fragrant-orchid *Gymnadenia densiflora* used to be found but has not been seen for many years and may now be lost. In a few sunlit places where mosses and sedges thrive, Bog Pimpernel *Anagallis tenella* grows. In the Midlands this is a rare plant of fens and heaths and usually benefits from grazing to prevent it being overwhelmed by more typical species. In the same places are lower growing plants such as Common Sedge *Carex nigra*, Flea Sedge *C. pulicaris*, Marsh Pennywort *Hydrocotyle vulgaris*, Marsh Valerian, various ferns and *Sphagnum* mosses.

Opposite-leaved Golden-saxifrage *Chrysosplenium oppositifolium* [PC]

Wood-sorrel *Oxalis acetosella* [PC]

Guelder-rose *Vibernum opulus* [PC]

Small-leaved Lime *Tilia cordata* [PC]

Wood Spurge *Euphorbia amygdaloides* [JB]

Marsh Horsetail *Equisetum palustre* and Jointed Rush *Juncus articulatus* are also frequent in the wetter areas, and in places Wood Horsetail *E. sylvaticum* forms stands like tiny fir-trees. Wood Horsetail is scattered in the Forest but often forms dense patches where it occurs. It is quite a common plant in the north-west of Britain but becomes very scarce as you head further east; Wyre lies at the boundary of this distribution. There are larger herbs here too. Hemp-agrimony *Eupatorium cannabinum* whose dusky-pink flowers are so attractive to late-summer butterflies is typical of these flushes and Meadowsweet *Filipendula ulmaria* is often common.

Around the smallholding landscape, especially to the south of the Forest, hedgerows and fields contain a much more varied mix of trees. This may indicate that the former woodlands of Wyre were richer, and not of oak alone, before the demand for oak coppice overtook everything. Even the boundary hedges of the present woodland contain more diversity of tree species, suggesting an original woodland of oak, Ash, Field Maple *Acer campestre* and both Large-leaved Lime *Tilia platyphyllos* and Small-leaved Lime *T. cordata*. This NVC W8 woodland would have been on slightly better soils, so its use as common grazing and clearance for smallholding is perhaps not surprising. There are still relics of this former woodland with scattered old lime pollards in places, for instance Areley Wood, and many old layered Ash or Field Maples along wood boundaries and ancient hedgerows at Far Forest and Bliss Gate. Also, along the Dowles Brook, occasional Small-leaved Lime and Ash with Hazel coppice indicate a richer woodland type.

A rather narrow zone of more diverse W8 woodland with Ash, Field Maple and Lime is found along the valley sides near to the brooks. This merges into the wetter NVC W7 Alder woodland, but in a few locations, especially near the Dowles and Gladder Brooks, it is more evident. Before extensive oak coppicing this woodland type may have been much more common, but is unlikely to have been dominant, especially on the acid soils. Beyond the margins of the present Forest, on farmland where the soils are marginally better, it may have been much more frequent. Most was lost to enclosures, but it persists as a relic habitat in species-rich hedgerows as at Bliss Gate and Far Forest.

There is good diversity of trees and shrubs in W8, with Wych Elm *Ulmus glabra*, Hazel, Dogwood *Cornus sanguinea*, Field Maple, Small-leaved Lime and, very rarely, Large-leaved Lime. The scattering of Large-leaved Lime indicates that it is probably a true native. It is sometimes found as massive old pollards in the stream valleys, notably around Ribbesford and Areley Wood.

As we have seen, most of Wyre's modern woodlands are a product of the oak coppice system. Now that commercial coppicing has ceased, the oakwoods are being allowed to regenerate and diversify as trees are thinned or coppiced for conservation. Tree species that are very scarce today will become more common; these include Birch, Yew, Ash, Field Maple, Crab Apple, Hazel, Aspen, Hawthorn, Wild Cherry and Rowan. The plants of the woodland floor are changing too. As rides are widened and clearings created, some species, much scarcer during the 'Dark Ages' of the 1970s and 80s, are responding well. After recent thinning of oaks and conifer removal in Withybed Wood, Wood Spurge *Euphorbia amygdaloides*, a fine plant of disturbed woodland which nears its national northern limit in Wyre, formed large lime-green patches of flowers in May. These were very attractive to insects including longhorn beetles, hunting wasps and hoverflies. Clearings in other places have also encouraged Wood Spurge and on well-drained acid soils, where bracken and brambles are slow to colonise, Pill Sedge *Carex pilulifera*, Heather and Heath Speedwell *Veronica officinalis* quickly appear along with the violets *Viola* spp. the last a crucial food plant for fritillary butterflies.

Where conifers are removed as part of the PAWS scheme, Foxgloves *Digitalis purpurea* spring up in hundreds or thousands, conjured into bloom by the unexpected light. Growing with them, if Bracken does not first take over, there may be Wood Sage and Heath Groundsel *Senecio sylvaticus*.

The Forest's ferny floor

In his book *The Natural History of an English Forest* Norman Hickin entitles one section 'The Forest's Ferny Floor', but strangely, only describes the more uncommon and localised species of ferns, including Wall-rue *Asplenium ruta-muraria* and Hart's-tongue *A. scolopendrium*. He does however make reference to Hard Fern *Blechnum spicant* as being very typical of Wyre, and its leathery fronds hang on even in dark conifer plantations to this day.

The fern which is unavoidable in Wyre, and is abundant nearly everywhere, is Bracken. It is generally disliked for dominating woodland rides and glades to the exclusion of most woodland flowers. Large bracken glades with their thick mat of fallen dead stems can persist for years, or even centuries. Since the demise of the best Bracken controller, Wild Boar *Sus scrofa*, its chokehold on our woodlands may only be weakened where deer or badgers create tracks, allowing birch saplings to spring up and in time suppress its fronds. The plant certainly seems to be increasing and the late Edwin George, the Forestry Commission Deer Ranger, once remarked that 'fern' (meaning Bracken) had become much more common in the Forest since he was

Scaly Male-fern *Dryopteris affinis* [PC]

Hard Fern *Blechnum spicant* [JB]

Hard Shield-fern *Polystichum aculeatum* [RW]

a lad in the 1930s. This appears to be a national trend, reflecting changes in countryside management. The enrichment of the Forest with atmospheric nitrogen may also fuel its spread. Certainly there are fewer controls on its growth now: once Bracken was cut for animal bedding, and livestock trampled it whilst grazing. Regular coppicing also held it in check. The sterile and rather acid layer of accumulated dead fronds is rather poor in invertebrates, but provides shelter for wintering Woodcock *Scolopax rusticola* and an insulating cover for small mammals.

Our other woodland ferns are not invasive although they often spring up in abundance after clear felling. Wyre is rich in the spectacular Scaly Male-fern *Dryopteris affinis*, whose giant shuttlecocks of fronds can reach 1.5 m; the stem of each frond is clothed in a dense pelt of rusty scales. It sometimes hybridises with the closely related, but less robust, Male-fern *D. filix-mas* which is also very common throughout Wyre in sun or shade. Broad Buckler-fern *D. dilatata* is also well-distributed throughout most of the Forest and can survive even in mature conifer plantations. It is easy to recognise by the dark-centred scales on its leaf stalks. In damper woodland and flushes, often under Alders, Narrow Buckler-fern *D. carthusiana* occasionally appears. As its name suggests its fronds are more narrowly triangular, and a closer look reveals that the scales on its leaf stalks are uniformly pale.

On slopes in shady valleys and dingles Soft Shield-Fern *Polystichum setiferum* unfurls its elegant filigree fronds. Along Dowles Brook, Hard Shield-fern *P. aculeatum* grows on rocky outcrops, but never in quantity. In wetter stream valleys and damp areas lime-green Lady-fern *Athyrium filix-femina* may be abundant and may be accompanied by Lemon-scented Fern *Oreopteris limbosperma*.

One Wyre speciality is Oak Fern *Gymnocarpium dryopteris*, once frequent in the stream valleys, but now surviving at just one location. In common with many native ferns, it suffered greatly at the hands of plant collectors during the Victorian fern craze when the British countryside was systematically plundered to fill a seemingly endless supply of Wardian cases and to adorn conservatories. In 1864 George Jorden reported "a plentiful supply" of Oak Fern in the Forest (Jorden 1864), an interesting choice of words indicating that pteridomania had reached Wyre. Oak Fern appeared to have become extinct here by 1900, presumably collected out, but in 1962 Malcolm Clark and S.W. Green rediscovered a small colony on a steep north-facing slope above Dowles Brook. Thankfully this precarious colony is still there but, despite careful searches, Oak Fern has not been found anywhere else in the Forest. Oak Fern is near the limit of its distribution in the British Isles in Wyre and it occurs on very few sites further to the east and south-east.

Sedges and grasses

Sedges and grasses are subtle plants, often overlooked, but well represented in Wyre and an important part of the Forest flora. There are several interesting or notable species, some of which are scarce in the surrounding countryside.

Every botany student knows 'sedges have edges', a reference to their triangular stems. Some species have precise habitat requirements and a wealth of sedges is a good indicator of a rich mosaic of habitats and often of complex geology. Although rarities like the Fingered Sedge *Carex digitata*, reported by Jorden in 1857 in North Wood Bewdley, have long since gone, there are still some special sedges remaining in Wyre.

Soft-leaved Sedge *C. montana* flowers early and is best seen in late March and early April. Its fresh green fringes of drooping leaves, soft to touch, grow along steep slopes, especially the warmer south-facing ones, on the Shropshire side of Dowles Brook valley and some of its tributaries. In Britain it is a very local plant in more open habitats in south Wales and the south of England, but in Wyre it is a strictly woodland sedge that will flourish under coppice. First recorded by Jorden in 1864 in his *Flora Bellus Locus,* it is frequent, scattered over the Forest with outlying locations in the Golden Valley near Bewdley, and has responded well to canopy thinning in places. It shuns competition, preferring more open and shallow acidic soils where it forms distinctive fragmented rings of growth. The long straw-coloured leaves contrast with the new green shoots in spring. It often grows with Pill Sedge and the two are easily confused. Along the Dowles Brook track near Dry Mill Lane the sedge *C. divulsa* ssp. *divulsa* has persisted for at least 150 years at apparently its only site in the Forest. A plant of woodland margins, very much at home along trackways, this southern species has very few records north of Wyre. The more robust and much rarer subspecies *C. divulsa* ssp. *leersii* grows along the verges of the disused railway near the Great Bog.

In wetter areas with more base-rich soils there are a host of sedges. Remote Sedge is one of the commonest in dense woodland, often found with Star Sedge *C. echinata* which has distinctive star-shaped fruit. Equally common are Carnation Sedge *C. panicea*, with blue-green leaves the colour of garden pinks, and Common Sedge *C. nigra*. A little harder to find, and normally in the wettest areas, is the smaller Flea Sedge whose seeds resemble shiny brown fleas. Although scarce, Tawny Sedge *C. hostiana* grows in one or two places, competing with Purple Moor-grass in the wet seepages. In other wet sites, usually around ponds or along the Severn, are Bottle Sedge *C. rostrata*, Bladder Sedge *C. versicaria* and False Fox-sedge *C. oxtrubae*. Damp rides often bristle with Yellow-sedge: this is a complex group of several similar species, but the Wyre plants are Common Yellow-sedge *C. demissa*. Careful checking may reveal some of its relatives.

In drier, though still quite damp woodland, Wood-sedge *C. sylvatica* can be abundant along paths. More scattered and in wetter spots on Forest paths, Thin-spiked Wood-sedge *C. strigosa*, is very scarce in the

Wood-sedge *Carex sylvatica* is one of the most typical woodland sedges, occurring in many of the damper areas within the Forest. [RW]

main woodlands, but locally common on heavier soils in Eymore and Ribbesford Woods. Spiked Sedge *C. spicata* is thinly distributed, more often on marginal habitats or rough grassland woodland edges. In very acidic dry woodland, Pill Sedge can be common especially after clear-felling, while the rather uncommon but much taller Green-ribbed Sedge *C. binervis* is local on the damper acid soils.

Wyre is an outpost for two special woodland grasses which are more frequent in the north and west of the British Isles. Mountain Melick *Melica nutans* is an attractive and distinctive species which is quite common in Scotland and northern England but very rare south of the Midlands. The first record was in 1834 by Hastings "in Bewdley Forest not far from Dowles Brook" and to this day the greatest concentration of records in Shropshire comes from Wyre (where it is locally notable) close to the county boundary. It is very rare in Worcestershire (Day 2001) and Wyre is the only site mentioned in the County Red Data Book (Fraser *et al.* 1998). Mountain Melick is a subtle and delicate perennial grass whose one-sided spikes strung with flowers like beads on a necklace, needs deliberately seeking out. It grows under light shade in oak woodlands and on the edges of wet flushes or stream sides, but not usually in the rich alluvial soils of the Dowles Brook. It is a grass of shady limestone habitats, so its presence in Wyre's rather acidic woodlands is unusual. April and May are the best months to look for it, on valley slopes above Dowles Brook or lining the banks along the disused railway line. Its distribution seems to follow that of Soft-leaved Sedge, perhaps because they both represent a relic flora that established many thousands of years ago, not long after the start of the post Ice Age re-colonisation.

Another mainly western grass is Wood Fescue *Festuca altissima* which is confined in Wyre to the rocky sides of a stream dingle in Eymore Wood and a ravine in Seckley Wood. Drooping sheaves of dark green leaves surround the tall, graceful panicles of flowers in mid-summer, but this haunter of shady places can be decidedly elusive.

More typical woodland grasses in the oak woods include Creeping Soft-grass *Holcus mollis*, which forms the dominant ground cover in many places, often with Sweet Vernal-grass *Anthoxanthum odoratum*. The distinctive Wood Melick *Melica uniflora*, its individual spikelets held on wiry stems, is common on more base-rich areas, especially along the Dowles valley, wood banks and wood edges. Often found with it is False-brome *Brachypodium sylvaticum*, and occasionally Hairy-brome *Bromopsis ramosa* and Giant Fescue *Schedonorus gigantea* which otherwise find much of the Forest too acid. Wood Meadow-grass *Poa nemoralis* has a similar preference, together with a liking for more shady places.

Slightly damp areas of woodland will support Tufted Hair-grass *Deschampsia cespitosa*. This large grass forms conspicuous dense tussocks of dark green leaves whose serrated margins can inflict cuts.

Mountain Melick *Melica nutans* [PC]

Wood Melick *Melica uniflora* [PC]

Columbine *Aquilegia vulgaris* is scattered throughout the Forest in woodland and occasionally in old grassland and road verges [PC]

Tufted Hair-grass, along with Purple Moor-grass, marks out wet flushes and carr woodlands. In contrast Wavy Hair-grass *D. flexuosa*, which is also common, indicates the driest and most acidic woodland areas, especially on steeper slopes where there is rocky shale. Bent grasses are quite frequent in more open woodland: especially Common Bent *Agrostis capillaris* and Creeping Bent *A. stolonifera*. In wetter habitats Velvet Bent *A. canina* becomes more common, and on Pound Green Common, Brown Bent *A. vinealis* occurs, a species that may be under-recorded in the Forest.

Special flowers of Wyre
Columbine *Aquilegia vulgaris*
Walkers along the disused railway in May and June are often surprised to see patches of purplish-blue among the bracken fronds. The blooms of Columbine or *Aquilegia*, so-called because the curved spurs on the flowers resemble the heads of doves or eagles, are worth looking for throughout the Forest usually on damper clay soils. In many places in the British Isles it is often considered a garden escape, especially when the flowers are pink, white or show double forms. Here though, Columbine behaves as a native plant of the Forest and many of the plants with deep blue flowers are likely to be truly wild. It grows in oak woodland, often in damp spots where its glaucous violet-flushed leaves can look out of place. Sometimes they occur deep into the woodland well away from garden origins, often on old charcoal hearths. Edwin Lees recorded the plant as being abundant in the Wyre Forest in Leighton's *Flora of Shropshire,* and Gissing, in 1855 commented that: "Any botanist who has visited the Wyre Forest will never again doubt the true wildness of Columbine". Columbines however are notoriously fertile escape artists. Nearer Bewdley and cultivated gardens, fence hoppers can easily hybridise with the native plants making the study of columbines in Wyre a botanical challenge.

Wood Crane's-bill *Geranium sylvaticum*
A flash of purple by the roadside at Hawkbatch, glimpsed as you drive past, may be Wood Crane's-bill, a perennial plant which is a northern species in Britain associated with open woodlands and upland hay meadows. In Wyre it was first noted in 1834 by Hastings as "in Bewdley Forest near to Dowles Brook, plentifully". Now it is a scarce plant, scattered around the Forest margins where it produces clusters of violet flowers in May and June. Wood Crane's-bill can be elusive, sulking as leafy clusters in shade for many seasons, then bursting into bloom when overhanging vegetation is cut and sunlight tempts it to flower. In places it grows on road verges, and even in a hedgerow at Bliss Gate, but usually prefers damp soil, typically on a sloping stream gully or the edge of a wet flush. Most records appear to be from the Dowles valley to the Button Oak area, but it avoids grassland in Wyre even near Button Oak where it was once a meadow species, as very few unimproved traditional hay meadows now remain. Although there are escapes from gardens in southern England and Wales, the Wyre plants are among the most southerly native plants in Britain.

Bloody Crane's-bill *Geranium sanguineum*
This is a plant of limestone rocks or calcareous dunes, so the sprawling clumps at the edges of a small field along the Dowles Brook are unexpected to say the least. Here it grows in profusion, its saucer-shaped magenta flowers and ferny foliage spilling out from a hedgerow onto the trackside. It is not clear whether or not this colony derives from a garden escape or is a relic of former native distribution. Certainly this is not a typical location for the plant and the site could be associated with a long-gone dwelling. But there is evidence for its nativeness too. Jorden in 1864 described it as "abundant over an extensive area on the Shropshire side of Dowles Brook over an area of several miles". Norman Hickin reported three sites for the plant (Hickin pers. comm.): the field site and two more along the Dowles Brook valley. It has been lost from the other two due either to collection or shade from conifer plantations, but in 1995 John Bingham found a new site on a steep bank above Dowles Brook. This was a very atypical habitat far from any habitation, strengthening the case for it being a wild native and more in keeping with the original record from Perry in 1841: "on rocks on the Shropshire side of Dowles Brook".

Wood Crane's-bill *Geranium sylvaticum* [JB]

Bloody Crane's-bill *Geranium sanguineum* [JB]

Lily-of-the-valley *Convallaria majalis* is still a common sight in the more acid woodland nearer Bewdley [PC]

Lily-of-the-valley *Convallaria majalis*

In spring when the Forest floor is still winter-brown, Lily-of-the-valley shoots pierce the dead bracken, their leaves unfurling to reveal the spikes of pure white flowers. Although this is a popular garden plant and a common escape or throw-out, in Wyre it is a native, first recorded in 1834 by Hastings as "occurring sparingly in Bewdley Forest". Lily-of-the-valley is scattered in Wyre, and more common in the woodlands near Bewdley in the south-east corner of the Forest, though it grows in several other places, such as Rock Coppice and Shelf Held Coppice, where it forms large patches often near paths. It even has a 'red post' roadside nature reserve location in Ribbesford Woods. It owes some of its abundance in the Bewdley woodlands to the Countess of Portsmouth whose estate included the Hitterhill Coppice area. It is said that the Countess gave the plant some encouragement: how much is uncertain, but we do know that the plant was actively propagated along the woodland carriage rides. In Shropshire it is very scarce, with only a few records at Longdon Wood, which is odd as the woodlands and soils appear to be suitable. Lily-of-the-valley prefers shallow, more acid soils, often growing with Bilberry under oaks. It flowers more profusely in the extra light provided by coppice before the canopy closes over, but although its delicate flowers are often obvious and visited by bees, the red berries are less common.

Wild Daffodil *Narcissus pseudonarcissus*

Daffodils which are garden escapes or gaudy roadside plantings are common around the Forest, but our true native Daffodil survives in many places as a harbinger of spring. The Wild Daffodil, with its twisted cream petals and yolk-yellow trumpet, is a plant of base-rich woods, but often appears in fields probably originally cut out of the woodland centuries ago. Such meadows are now very scarce due to agricultural change but, in a few spots, Wild Daffodils form a yellow tideline around fields, persisting stubbornly at the base of hedges where the plough cannot reach. Far Forest has several of these residual colonies and, in places as far apart as Mad Brook and Eymore Wood, Daffodils still provide an early spring display and memories of past glories. Edwin Lees appears to be the first person to note the wild Wyre Daffodils, in 1841 in his *Botany of Worcestershire* (Lees 1867). Now, with plantings and escapes of cultivars, the wild flowers risk competition from hybridisation, something Lees would not have foreseen.

Chaffweed *Centunculus minimus*

This miniscule plant grows along damp ride-sides and stony tracks in sunny places: it is a poor competitor and prefers bare ground. The plant was first recorded by Beckwith & Serjeantson in 1882, and reported in the *Journal of Botany* as growing in the Shropshire part of Wyre Forest "in the damp drives, on which probably water has stood in the winter". Surprisingly George Jorden missed it in his *Flora Bellus Locus*. Perhaps he can be forgiven as it has one of the smallest flowers of any British plant and barely grows more than a few centimetres high. There were no records for over a century until John Bingham rediscovered the plant in 1991 at Wimperhill Wood, in the same habitat as the 1882 record, and on the Shropshire side of Wyre. More than seven sites are now known. It is rare on the Worcestershire side of the Forest, but that may reflect the challenge of spotting this reclusive annual in low vegetation. Its fondness for wet heathy habitats suggests a very different and more open Wyre landscape before the arrival of commercial forestry. It is listed as near-threatened and declining nationally (Cheffings & Farrell 2005).

Wild Daffodil *Narcissus pseudonarcissus* [JB]

Chaffweed *Centunculus minimus* [JB]

Narrow-leaved Helleborine *Cephalanthera longifolia*

This very local and strikingly beautiful orchid is not a plant that you would expect to find in acidic oak woodland. It prefers more base-rich locations and is usually described as a species of calcareous beech woods, especially in Hampshire. But it does occur in some more acidic sites and has been noted from Wyre Forest since 1834 when Hastings wrote "in the deep retired glades of Bewdley Forest, between Mopson's Cross and the Sorb tree". Edwin Lees added in 1841 that it is found "most abundantly where a recent fall of wood has taken place or on the borders of old rides". This strongly suggests it is a coppice-loving plant, responding to the increased light levels and flowering for a few years before the canopy closes again. But for all its apparent fickleness and delicate appearance, this orchid crops up in surprising places. Amazingly it has appeared on the edge of the Forest in a semi-improved field, where several plants flower well every year among the grasses.

A new site was found in a sheep-grazed pasture in 2014 at St George's Farm and it persists at the edges of a few well-used forest tracks. More typically it occurs under W10 oak woodland along with Bluebell, Wood Anemone and Wood Spurge, often on former charcoal heath sites, where its spires of snowy flowers and bright green leaves can be mistaken at distance for white bluebells. Narrow-leaved Helleborine is listed as vulnerable and declining nationally (Cheffings & Farrell 2005), so it is an important species to protect from illegal uprooting or grazing. Some of the biggest spikes are caged each spring to prevent damage from deer or rabbits. It has not been recorded from the Shropshire side of Wyre Forest and unsurprisingly it is in the county Red Data Book for Worcestershire.

Narrow-leaved Helleborine—special studies

This exquisite member of the orchid family is one of the Wyre Forest's woodland treasures. Its milk-white flowers are not easy to find in dappled sunlight and the vegetative plants are even harder to locate. It is a long-lived perennial pollinated by small solitary bees and, like many orchids, can remain dormant underground. It requires just the right conditions and mycorrhizal fungi to germinate, grow and flower (Plantlife 2010).

In England the Narrow-leaved Helleborine has become extinct in 20 vice-counties and is currently known from only 22 sites in nine vice-counties (Plantlife 2010). It was elected for Plantlife's Back from the Brink rare species conservation programme which started in 1991, and Wyre Forest was chosen as one of three study sites.

When Plantlife visited in 1997, the Forestry Commission (FC) knew of two sites containing 15 plants on their land. After advice from Plantlife, and with Phil Rudlin from FC, Rosemary Winnall volunteered to monitor sites annually, search for unrecorded plants, collect historical data, and work with landowners to conserve these plants. From 1998 helleborines were mapped, numbers of flowers per stem recorded, fruiting documented, and an annual report submitted. Slowly, with help from local botanists and the public, the number of known sites and plants increased; by 2004 there were 10 sites with 114 plants and, by 2014, 21 sites with 244 plants (Winnall 1998–2014) (pictured below growing by the old railway line [RW]). Some sites have only between one and five plants recorded, and others have more. Currently the three with most have up to 96 plants. As the number of monitored sites grew, further help was needed and, in 2006, Paul Reade (now joint recorder for Worcestershire for the Botanical Society of the British Isles) started to help with the fieldwork and his dedicated effort resulted in the discovery of several new sites.

Plantlife has sponsored conservation management work in Wyre and in 2014 Natural England supported an event to train more volunteers to help with the fieldwork. For locating unrecorded plants timing is crucial for finding them in flower before deer or slugs have the chance to browse them. There may be other undiscovered sites in Wyre and, with the current management policy of creating more open glades, searching is worthwhile. This beautiful helleborine is in danger of becoming extinct within the UK. Hopefully it can be protected in Wyre with sensitive land management.

Narrow-leaved Helleborine *Cephalanthera longifolia* once appeared in large numbers after oak was coppiced [RW]

Common Wintergreen *Pyrola minor* [JB]

Violet Helleborine *Epipactis purpurata* [PC]

Green Hellebore *Helleborus viridis* [PC]

Common Wintergreen *Pyrola minor* and Intermediate Wintergreen *P. media*

Common and Intermediate Wintergreen were recorded at a number of locations by George Jorden in the 19th century and later by Carleton Rea in 1905 (Rea 1910). Both species depended on coppice management which declined and ended by the 1940s. Common Wintergreen appears to have been lost during the early 1920s, and Intermediate Wintergreen in 1976 when the hot dry summer brought about its demise at Rock Coppice (Quayle 1976 pers. comm.). In June 2005 Paul Reade discovered over 100 plants of Common Wintergreen by the disused railway line in an area of scrub that had been recently coppiced to help with butterfly conservation. It was close to an area of woodland previously known for this wintergreen, and the best assumption is that the plants came up from buried seed disturbed by the coppicing work, or possibly the seed came from other populations close by. This was a really unexpected discovery and a very welcome return of an important native plant which is very rare in the English Midlands.

Wild roses

Wild roses are common in the Forest and are a promiscuous tribe which hybridise and back-cross freely. In most places Field Rose *Rosa arvensis* and Dog-rose *R. canina* are abundant, the former in damper heavier soils, the latter in hedges and clearings. Although local in other parts of Worcestershire

Sherard's Downy-rose *R. sherardii* is quite common along the old railway line, where its strong pink flowers and glandular leaves smelling of apple often attract attention. For a more detailed understanding of Wyre's roses and their hybrids, *The Flora of Worcestershire* (Maskew 2014) is recommended.

Violet Helleborine *Epipactis purpurata*

Most orchids enjoy the sun, but Violet Helleborine is a plant of dense shade and often grows in unremarkable places under dense conifers or bare disturbed roadside verges. Its tall spikes and purple stems are always a delight to find if Fallow Deer, who are partial to the succulent young stems, have not visited the plant. It is very local and scattered in the Forest but more common to the west, and like a fungus, pops up occasionally in places only to disappear for several seasons. One roadside verge normally provides a few dozen plants in most years. Worcestershire is the Midland stronghold for the plant, but it is commoner in the south-east of Britain.

Green Hellebore *Helleborus viridis*

Something of a mystery plant in Wyre, this apple-green early flowerer occurs naturally in fair numbers at one or two wooded dingles to the north and south of the main Forest, but in the central block only one plant appears to exist. This location is subject to question as it was first recorded in 1910 by Rea as "two or three specimens on the Shropshire side of Dowles Brook".

Norman Hickin reported the plant in his book on Wyre in 1971 but was then told that it had been planted along the brook. Whether it is native or planted here is hard to tell, but no other plants have been found along the Dowles suggesting that it may have been planted. It still survives on the Shropshire side of Dowles, a few flowers appearing in most years.

Plants of the flushes and damp areas

Attractive though the oak woodland is, it would be relatively poor in flowers without the nutrient-enriched wet flushes which occur throughout the Forest. These are very special habitats and stumbling on one of these botanical gems is always exciting as it will invariably contain plants which are now very scarce in the surrounding countryside and often even in Wyre itself.

One flushed area is almost legendary within botanical recording circles: the 'Great Bog' of Wyre. Nearly everything about the Great Bog is misleading except for its rich floristic diversity. The site is in fact not an acid bog, but a base-rich soligenous (surface- and groundwater-fed) flush with high water movement. The pH is between 6.2 and 8.4, usually around 6.5 to 7.0, and there are tufa deposits in the wettest runnels. Neither is it as extensive as the name suggests, perhaps a hectare in total, and consists of runnels from spring line seepages between more acidic dry woodland. It is a mosaic of NVC W4 and W7 (see box, page 43) with some indications of a mire community such as M27 *Filipendula ulmaria-Angelica sylvestris* Meadowsweet-Angelica mire. Vivid descriptions including this one from Lees, enhance the aura of the Great Bog: "Embowered and totally covered in by thick umbrage and shut out from the jarring world by a green curtain of wavy foliage" (Lees 1853).

The name appears to have come from a visit made on 24 August 1853 by the Worcestershire Naturalists' Club (Lees 1853). In the Club's *Transactions* it is referred to as "a great bog" and its botanical riches are described. Edwin Lees, who was present at the meeting, published his book *Pictures of Nature* in 1856 in which he details the visit and names the site "the Great Bog of Wyre": since then the name has stuck. The bog was frequently visited by Worcestershire Naturalists' Club until 1933 after which it fell from favour and its location was lost or forgotten. Norman Hickin, in his book *Forest Refreshed*, remarks that "one of the great changes that have taken place in the Forest during the last 100 years has been the disappearance of the Great Bog … no vestiges remain, nor do any present folk have knowledge of it". In *Natural History of an English Forest* he adds that he had never seen the Fragrant Orchid that flowered on the Great Bog and, more revealingly, "nor for that matter have I ever seen the Great Bog".

Field meeting reports in old Worcestershire Naturalists' Club *Transactions* allow the narrowing down of the Great Bog's location: it was "not far from Park Brook, the railway line was nearby…. works for coal mining are in progress at this spot … on the Worcestershire side of Dowles Brook some distance above it". All these point to one location that is now agreed as its site, south of the disused railway line between Lodge Hill and Park House. It is still the most extensive area of wet flushes within the Forest and botanically very diverse, though some of its past glories have gone: for example, neither Marsh Helleborine *Epipactis palustris*, nor Marsh Fragrant-orchid can now be found. The specimen of the orchid Summer Lady's-tresses *Spiranthes aestivalis*, found by George Jorden in 1854 on the Great Bog, has been determined as a deformed example of Marsh Fragrant-orchid, so Wyre Forest can make no claim for this now nationally extinct plant.

Nevertheless, the Great Bog is still home to many locally scarce plants, and clearance of invading scrub has helped to maintain species such as the Bog

Part of the Great Bog is covered in tussocks of Purple Moor-grass *Molinia caerulea* [JB] and has pools containing a stonewort *Chara* sp., a green alga (below [RW]).

On some of the steeper slopes spring-line seepages provide ideal conditions for plants that require more base-rich habitats, such as cottongrass *Eriophorum* sp. seen here. [RW]

Pimpernel. Throughout the Forest, wet flushes shelter plants such as Marsh Pennywort, whose succulent coin-like leaves form dense mats on the sodden ground. Along damp ride-sides and in ditches and seepages, the tiny pink flowers of Lesser Skullcap *Scutellaria minor* are common: this local species of damp heaths is more frequent in the west and is a county Red Data plant for Worcestershire. Great Burnet is rare in Wyre, more often associated with damp meadows on heavy soils, but here persists in one wet flush where it appears to have been recorded since 1855. Wood Club-rush is another distinctive species that forms dense stands in some wet areas and is an attractive plant with graceful, open, flowering heads.

More typical plants of damp flushes are Square-stemmed St John's-wort *Hypericum tetrapterum*, Marsh Valerian, Common Marsh-bedstraw *Galium palustre*, Water Mint *Mentha aquatica*, Greater Bird's-foot-trefoil *Lotus pedunculatus*, Marsh Arrow-grass *Triglochin palustris*, Lousewort *Pedicularis sylvatica* and Marsh Thistle *Cirsium palustre*. *Juncus* species, in particular Sharp-flowered Rush *J. acutiflorus* and Jointed Rush, form dominant stands in many flushes, often mixed with Hard Rush *J. inflexus*, Soft Rush *J. effusus* and Compact Rush *J. conglomeratus*. Also worth noting is Slender Rush *J. tenuis*, an introduced species from North America whose mucilaginous seeds have been spread by machinery since the 1960s and which is now common everywhere along well-trodden rides and paths. On the damp muddy edges of woodland rides grow a number of small rushes, including Bulbous Rush *J. bulbosus* and Toad Rush *J. bufonius*. These often grow with Bristle Club-rush *Isolepis setacea*, whose lime-green tufts are locally common on disturbed wet soil.

Ferns can be luxuriant in and around damp flushes. The tall shuttlecocks of Lady-fern, Male-fern and Scaly Male-fern are frequent, often with Broad Buckler-fern and, in wetter areas, Narrow Buckler-fern. Along stream-sides and ditches on clay soils, Hard-fern is frequent.

One small willow-swamp woodland near Button Oak has a particularly interesting flora. Water Horsetail *Equisetum fluviatile* and bog-moss *Sphagnum* spp. dominate the vegetation, but amongst these can be found Tubular Water-dropwort *Oenanthe fistulosa*, White Sedge *Carex canescens* and Bogbean *Menyanthes trifoliata* at their only native site in Wyre.

Special flowers of flushes and damp areas
Marsh Violet *Viola palustris*

Although this attractive violet is common in the west of Britain, in Wyre its heart-shaped leaves are absent from the main forest area, and scattered only in the west probably because of the underlying geology of the wet flushes. There is a sprinkling of records for Malpass Wood, Weston Plantation and Coachroad Coppice, some following the Baveney Brook or its tributaries. Marsh Violet is the normal food plant of Small Pearl-bordered Fritillary *Boloria selene* caterpillars, but in Wyre they also feed on Common Dog-violet *V. riviniana*, though they may be faithful to Marsh Violet where it grows.

Marsh Violet *Viola palustris* [JB]

Broad-leaved Cottongrass *Eriophorum latifolium* and Common Cottongrass *E. angustifolium*

Cottongrasses are very scarce in lowland agricultural areas, so records of the two species are locally significant. Broad-leaved Cottongrass is confined in Wyre to a few calcareous wet flushes. The shade of encroaching trees and Purple Moor-grass suppresses flowering and its snow-white tassels appear annually in just one spot. Deer grazing may be all that the cottongrass needs to hold back competition and let in the light. Common Cottongrass, which prefers acidic flushes, is equally rare in the Forest, with perhaps only three sites remaining. It was much more frequent in the most acidic wet flushes including what may have been Wyre's only true acid bog near Burnt Wood, where it grew with two other now locally extinct plants, Round-leaved Sundew *Drosera rotundifolia* and Bog Asphodel *Narthecium ossifragum*. Unfortunately the bog has all but disappeared, its only remaining vestige a small pool within a chalet park. Both species still occur at one special place, where, although the cottongrasses have different pH requirements, Wyre's complex soils allow them to rub roots.

Common Fleabane *Pulicaria dysenterica*

This plant is always a sign of wet woodland or damp grasslands but is surprisingly rather scarce in the Forest, suffering from the drainage of wet sites. This once-common plant is now decreasing in many areas but in Wyre it is still well scattered, more commonly in the west. It is always a welcome sight in late summer, its yellow daisy-like flowers attracting a range of insects. Norman Hickin (1971) remarked that Fletcher's Coppice was the best place to see it, though even here it can be hard to find.

Floating Club-rush *Eleogiton fluitans*

This small grass-like species can form a floating turf on the margins of open pools, or in slow-flowing more acidic water, and may be under-recorded because it is easy to mistake for a grass. It is becoming very scarce in lowland England as shallow pools are drained or dry out and are colonised by more vigorous plants. In Worcestershire the plant is very rare and on the county Red Data list, but it is more common in Shropshire, though still scarce and threatened as it resents enrichment from farming pratices. In upland areas of Britain it has suffered less from intensive farming and is still quite common. Four sites remain in Wyre, three in pools and one in a shallow stream. At one of these it has responded well to clearance of shading plants including Rhododendron. Its future in Wyre will depend on the sensitive management of competing species.

Bog Pimpernel *Anagallis tenella*

In the spongiest and most open wet patches where plants are a few centimetres tall, the delicate pink bells of Bog Pimpernel flowers are a real prize. This minute,

Common Cottongrass *Eriophorum angustifolium* [JB]

Common Fleabane *Pulicaria dysenterica* [PC]

Bog Pimpernel *Anagallis tenella* [JB]

creeping, evergreen perennial is easily swamped by other vegetation and relies on deer grazing or coppicing to keep its habitat open and to protect it from competing species. The pale flowers only emerge in well-lit places above the tiny oval leaves that smell of liquorice when dried. Only a few sites still remain in the woodlands, but this plant could appear on nearly any soligenous (ground-water fed) wet flush and is worth looking out for.

Cross-leaved Heath *Erica tetralix*

A lover of damp acidic places, Cross-leaved Heath is common in the upland wet heath community on Titterstone Clee Hill, a few miles to the west of the Forest. In Wyre, where heathy conditions and open rides seem ideal, it is unaccountably very rare. George Jorden in 1864 recorded it as "plentiful", noting pink and white flowered plants at Hungry Hill. It appears that until the early 1900s Hungry Hill was part of a "heather common" of some extent that contained, amongst other plants, Lesser Butterfly-orchid *Platanthera bifolia*. Perhaps Cross-leaved Heath needs more open habitats in Wyre, such as the old commons or acidic damp grasslands, most of which have been lost. Whatever the reasons for its demise, it survives in just three places. The most obvious of these is Pound Green Common where two small patches occurred for many years: their population has been boosted by heathland restoration using seed from Titterstone Clee Hill. Already, new plants are beginning to appear on cleared ground, but their survival depends on keeping a tide of Bracken and other tall plants at bay.

Tutsan *Hypericum androsaemum*

With its broad leaves, yellow flowers and black berries, Tutsan is an attractive herb (often misidentified as the garden plant Rose of Sharon *H. calycinum*) which seldom grows in large quantities. Tutsan prefers damp woodland and occasionally grows at the edge of wet flushes or damp tracks where the soil is heavier. In Wyre it is a true native species noted as long ago as 1841 by Edwin Lees. It is common in the Forest but often in areas away from the main pathways, in stream valleys and wetter areas. In the UK, it is mainly a south-western species and Wyre is on the edge of its native range. Tutsan does escape from gardens and the situation is further complicated by the arrival in the Forest around the turn of the millennium of a look-alike, Tall Tutsan *H.* × *inodorum,* which is a hybrid between native Tutsan and the garden plant Stinking Tutsan *H. hircinum.*

Dutch Rush *Equisetum hymale* and other horsetails

One of Wyre's rarest plants is so inconspicuous in its damp flush that it needs to be tracked down with great care. The horsetail Dutch Rush was first recorded along several stream sides by Gissing in 1855, but its pencil-thick, unbranched stems, which can reach one metre in length, lurk in just one spot where it is very easy to overlook because the narrow blue-green spikes merge into the background vegetation. John Bingham rediscovered a small colony in 1976, but searching suitable habitat has failed to find it elsewhere. In Wyre it grows under oaks in wet seepages close to streams, where the ground is partly bare or has a modest covering of ferns and mosses. This colony is one of very few in lowland England, though it is still common in parts of northern Britain. Other horsetails of wet flushes include the Shore Horsetail *E.* × *litorale* (a hybrid between the commoner Field *E. arvense* and Water Horsetails) and Wood Horsetail.

Tutsan *Hypericum androsaemum* berries [JB]

Wood Horsetail *Equisetum sylvaticum* [PC]

Lemon-scented Fern *Oreopteris limbosperma*

Lemon-scented Fern crops up throughout the woodland but always in wet areas on poorly drained acidic soils. In Wyre it often follows the course of small streams and rivulets, especially those that have scattered wet flushes. It is easily recognised by its yellow-green fronds and when fresh by the white scales on its unfurling stems. When rubbed between the fingers it has a fresh zesty smell. It needs poorly drained, peaty, acidic soils. In Wyre Lemon-scented Fern was first recorded in 1855 by Gissing and, in common with many of the more localised Forest plants, it is much more widespread in the north and west of the British Isles.

Alien plants in woods

Woodland in Wyre has relatively few alien species besides conifers planted for forestry purposes. Rhododendron has already been mentioned and a vigorous campaign to remove it is underway. Few other plants have established themselves in the woods, although the dense mats of creeping runners and evergreen leaves of the garden escape Lesser Periwinkle *Vinca minor* may become locally dominant as it spreads into the Forest. It is well established in several places, such as by Dowles Brook near Ford Lane Crossing, at the top end of Areley Wood, and on the Betts Nature Reserve.

In a few places Montbretia *Crocosmia × crocosmiiflora* grows by tracksides, and along Dowles Brook Indian Balsam *Impatiens glandulifera* is now locally frequent. Although widespread along the Severn, this tallest of our annual plants came downstream from the Lem Brook. It has begun to invade the Dowles Brook valley where control is now vital to prevent it from swamping small native plants. Clearance of the Lem Brook has progressed well in

Indian Balsam *Impatiens glandulifera* [PC]

recent years. Its smaller and much less invasive relative, Small Balsam *I. parviflora*, has delicate straw-coloured flowers, and grows in Oxbind Coppice and by the Severn in Eymore Wood. A new alien Tall Tutsan has established itself in the Forest and is increasing its range rapidly. It may have been introduced by forestry activity and looks very much like a more robust version of the native Tutsan, but is happy on dry ground and has spread along Forest tracks from its original location in Withybed Wood. It is also common under conifers near Sturt Bank and the black berries which contain the seeds may be spread by pheasants.

A walk along some of the lanes near the Forest margin at Far Forest in early spring will reveal splashes of purple. Bird-in-a-bush *Corydalis solida* is a recent garden escape that has taking a liking to the roadside verges and has spread over the years. It was first recorded in 1910 and, although an alien, was marked in the 1970s by red posts to alert the highways maintenance teams not to cut the verge too early. It is a non-invasive plant which will undoubtedly continue its slow march along the verges and perhaps find its way into the woodland.

Grasslands

Wyre has a wide range of grasslands from improved leys which struggle to muster a handful of grass species with, maybe, White Clover *Trifolium repens*, through semi-improved fields which still support Meadow Buttercup, speedwells *Veronica* spp. and Selfheal *Prunella vulgaris*, to highest quality, nationally important, Biodiversity Action Plan unimproved grassland.

Travelling into Wyre from the south, you notice the fields become smaller and the landscape more intimate. There are flowers here of old countryside, assemblies of species with a long pedigree of historical management. The grasslands in Wyre originate from forest clearance and land taken from the former commons and wood pastures. A combination of poor acid soils and part-time farming meant that agricultural improvements of the 1970s and 80s, using fertiliser and reseeding, had far less impact here than on intensively worked commercial farmland. The traditional smallholdings, with orchards and grazing land, have bequeathed us the now familiar landscape of small fields and hedges.

The Wyre Forest area is therefore comparatively well off for unimproved species-rich or semi-improved grasslands, especially around the smallholdings of the south and west. In England such unimproved grasslands have declined by 98% over the last 50 years and are now amongst the most threatened habitats in Britain (Bullock *et al.* 2011). In Wyre these small pastures, often humpy with the mounds of Yellow Meadow Ants *Lasius flavus*, are botanical jewels, picked out in spring and summer with Meadow Buttercups *Ranunculus acris*, bluebells and orchids. Technically the richest grasslands are classified as NVC MG5 grasslands: in reality they are living tapestries supporting 100 or even 150 species of plants.

Around the Forest are dozens of Nationally Important unimproved grasslands with flowers such as Common Spotted-orchid *Dactylorhiza fuchsii*, Betony *Betonica officinalis* and Rough Hawkbit *Leontodon hispidus*. [RW]

The grassland flora

The best Wyre meadows boast a dazzling directory of wild flowers. Typical species include Cowslip *Primula veris*, Bulbous Buttercup *Ranunculus bulbosus*, Common Knapweed *Centaurea nigra*, Common Spotted-orchid *Dactylorhiza fuchsii* and Heath Spotted-orchid *D. maculata*, Yellow Rattle *Rhinanthus minor*, Greater Bird's-foot-trefoil, Lady's Bedstraw *Galium verum*, Lesser Hawkbit *Leontodon saxatilis*, Devil's-bit Scabious *Succisa pratensis*, Adder's-tongue *Ophioglossum vulgatum* and Pignut *Conopodium majus* (the larval food plant for the Chimney Sweeper moth *Odezia atrata*). Grasses include Quaking Grass *Briza media*, Sweet Vernal-grass, Meadow Foxtail *Alopecurus pratensis*, Common Bent and Heath Grass *Danthonia decumbens*. Unimproved grassland can have Spring Sedge *Carex caryophyllea* in abundance; as the name suggests it flowers early in the year.

In some meadows there are several woodland species including Bluebell, Wood Anemone and Bugle, which indicate grasslands carved or assarted from the original forest. Where scrub grows along the edges of grassland and woodland, this creates an ecotone, or transition zone, from open habitat to closed woodland and is often the richest habitat for birds and insects, supporting species such as the Pearl-bordered Fritillary butterfly *Boloria euphrosyne*.

Damp meadows, if they're not overgrazed, often contain Oval Sedge *C. leporina*, Jointed Rush and flowers such as Meadowsweet, Cuckooflower *Cardamine pratensis*, Sneezewort *Achillea ptarmica*, Ragged-robin *Silene flos-cuculi* and Greater Bird's-foot-trefoil.

In the older meadows there are rarer plants including Dyer's Greenweed *Genista tinctoria*, Common Restharrow *Ononis repens*, Meadow Saffron *Colchicum autumnale*, Common Twayblade *Neottia ovata*, Green-winged Orchid *Anacamptis morio*, Heath Fragrant-orchid *Gymnadenia borealis*, Lady's-mantle *Alchemilla*

agg., Heath Dog-violet *Viola canina* and Pale Sedge. Yellow-wort *Blackstonia perfoliata* used to grow at one site near Furnace Mill, but was lost when conifers were planted. In 2008 it appeared again, this time near Cleobury Mortimer, after 40-year-old conifers were cleared from another former grassland site.

On acid soils there are NVC U1 grasslands (*Festuca ovina-Agrostis capillaris-Rumex acetosella* Sheep's Fescue-Common Bent-Sheep's Sorrel grassland). This is a rare acid grassland often with heather, and frequently associated with MG5. (See box on page 43 for details on NVC classifications.) Some grasslands retain a patch or two of Heather or Bell Heather which, along with Wild Thyme *Thymus serpyllum*, favour the drier soil on anthills. Anthills, known in some places as 'midsummer cushions' or 'tumps', are also home to Tormentil *Potentilla erecta*, Harebell *Campanula rotundifolia*, Heath Speedwell *Veronica*

Sneezewort *Achillea ptarmica* [JB]

Meadow Saffron *Colchicum autumnale* is a rare plant found in a few scattered grasslands in Wyre [JB]

The old pasture grasslands around Wyre can contain hundreds of mounds formed by the Yellow Meadow Ant *Lasius flavus*, as seen here at Lodge Hill. [PC]

officinalis, Heath Bedstraw *Galium saxatile* and Sheep's Sorrel *Rumex acetosella*. Eyebrights *Euphrasia* agg. tend to be more common in acidic grasslands; *E. nemorosa* is the main species, but others may lurk unnoticed.

This rich variety of grassland is valued and some is protected, but threats remain from intensive and inappropriate horse grazing, development pressure for chalet sites, or modernisation of smallholders' cottages.

Special plants of grasslands

Moonwort *Botrychium lunaria*

This small and capricious fern is notoriously hard to find and is rare even in the best grassland sites. There are five known locations in Wyre, but although it is searched for every year, tantalisingly it does not always appear. It is easy to overlook: the lobed frond shielding the sporangia which look like clusters of tiny grapes, may only be a few centimetres tall. Moonwort grows in well-drained more acid soils and species-rich swards. It is much commoner in upland areas of Wales, northern England and Scotland and to the west of Wyre on Titterstone Clee Hill in Shropshire. In Worcestershire it is now very rare indeed and many of its former sites have been lost to ploughing or grassland improvement (Day 2001).

Fragrant Agrimony *Agrimonia procera*

Fragrant Agrimony is not a true meadow plant but in Wyre it thrives best in grassy places near the margins of woodland and grassland. It has hooked fruits like the more common Agrimony *A. eupatoria*, but is a bigger plant with more fragrant glandular leaves. Widely scattered over the Forest, it forms large colonies on the edges of rides or in grasslands, typically along the Dowles Brook.

Lady's-mantles *Alchemilla* spp.

The lady's-mantles, with their soft lobed leaves and sprigs of lime-green flowers, are a complex group of many species, most of which are rare and very localised in grasslands in northern Britain. In Wyre the commonest species is *A. filicaulis* ssp. *vestita* which is the most widespread lady's-mantle in the British lowlands. A second species, Intermediate Lady's-mantle

A. xanthochlora which has a more northern distribution is confined in Wyre to one or two meadows.

Green-winged Orchid *Anacamptis morio*

Green-winged orchids are a flagship species of old traditionally managed meadows in the English Midlands and were once widespread. Their demise mirrors the loss of hay meadows and the increased use of herbicides and fertilisers, though they hang on in some of Worcestershire's unimproved grasslands. The orchid's purple or pink spikes still grace around a dozen of the Wyre grasslands, though they are still in retreat and most places can muster fewer than a dozen flowering plants. With a return to traditional management Green-winged Orchids may return to some of the less damaged grasslands, but this will take time as even a small application of fertiliser takes many years to leach from the soil.

Green-winged Orchid *Anacamptis morio* [JB]

Heather *Calluna vulgaris* is a very characteristic plant of the more acid areas of Wyre. It occurs in abundance in the more open woodlands and rides and at Pound Green Common. [JB]

Heathland

Lowland heath is one of the most threatened habitats in the British Isles and its maintenance is always a challenge. The sole surviving example of an open heathy common in Wyre is Pound Green Common where two heathland types are found: NVC H8 *Calluna vulgaris-Ulex gallii* Heather-Western Gorse heath, and NVC H9 *Calluna vulgaris-Deschampsia fexuosa* Heather-Wavy Hair-grass heath. There are a few other remnants of former heathland sites around the Forest but these are unmanaged and have reverted to coarse grassland. Wyre Common to the west of the Forest was once a heath and is all but lost; the little that remains is covered with scrub and trees. In the woodlands there are many heathy glades but these are not the same as grazed heath. Pound Green is not a fully open heath, but a mosaic of heathland types. Acidic grassland with bracken, scrub and secondary woodland cover large parts of the old common and a small area has always been under trees as wood pasture. Mature oaks survive on the Common's margins.

The Wyre heaths are a glimpse of the once open commons, former medieval hunting chase and forest waste, lost to smallholdings and agricultural improvement under the various 18th century Acts of Common. Scratch the skin of Wyre though, and heath is usually not far beneath. Heather springs up readily in new clearings, though it is usually ousted by Bracken or regenerating saplings. Walk through the woods and you see Heather along the rides and feathering the floor of open oak coppice. Much of the Forest, whilst not managed heathland, is heathy woodland. We can only wonder about the glories of the medieval Hedgewick Common or Bliss Gate Common—could they once have been open heathland complete with purring Nightjars and Red-backed Shrikes? We cannot turn the clock back, but by creating and maintaining large open glades in the Forest, we can recreate a sense of the open heath and provide a habitat for some of the specialist heathland wildlife.

Heathland plants overlap with those of acidic grassland and both habitats include Heather and Bell Heather. Other typical heathland plants include Western Gorse, Slender St John's-wort *Hypericum*

pulchrum, Heath Speedwell, Heath Bedstraw, Tormentil, Mouse-ear-hawkweed *Pilosella officinarum*, Common Centaury *Centaurium erythraea* and the abundant Heath Milkwort *Polygala serpyllifolia*. Heath Rush *Juncus squarrosus* has appeared at Pound Green Common as a result of reseeding using vegetation collected from Titterstone Clee Hill.

A plant worthy of special note is Heath Cudweed *Gnaphalium sylvaticum*. This slender silvery-leaved member of the daisy family is a marginal and often short-lived perennial of acid grassland or heath. It does not tolerate competition from other plants and needs occasional soil disturbance to create bare ground. In Wyre it used to grow along a few forest rides, but is now very rare and threatened with extinction, a decline which shadows a wider national trend (Cheffings & Farrell 2005). It urgently needs management if we are to hold onto it.

Slender St John's-wort *Hypericum pulchrum* [JB]

The River Severn and Dowles Brook

Two main waterways flow through Wyre: the River Severn and its tributary the Dowles Brook. At the end of the last Ice Age around 10,000 years ago, the River Severn took a new course, cutting down through the well-known gorge at Ironbridge to flow south. At the same time it created another much smaller gorge between Seckley in Wyre Forest and Eymore Woods to the east forming the steep-sided valley we see today. This isolated a portion of what eventually became forest on the east side. In the valley, riverine habitat was created between the encroaching trees and the water. The river banks are still fairly wooded, with Osier *Salix viminalis*, willows *Salix* spp., Ash, Alder, Aspen, Field Maple, White Poplar *Populus alba*, Grey Poplar *P. canescens*, and even the occasional native Black-poplar *P. nigra* ssp. *betulifolia*, a scarce tree which also grows along Gladder Brook and Dick Brook. Some of the riverside trees, including willows and Field Maples, are pollards of considerable size and age.

The Severn is a major (354 km long) semi-natural river which enriches the Forest flora with a collection of plants that are only found in any abundance along its banks. The habitat is variable, ruderal and weedy in botanical terms and difficult to assign to NVC communities, but Open Vegetation (OV) types are common, with a rich assemblage of tall herbs and clambering species such as Hedge Bindweed *Calystegia sepium* and Bittersweet *Solanum dulcamara*.

The grassland edges furthest from the river contain NVC MG1, the ranker, but sometimes species-rich, tall vegetation that occurs where there is no grazing. Here there may be ruderal plants such as Redshank *Persicaria maculosa*, Water-pepper *P. hydropiper*, Black Mustard *Brassica nigra*, Winter-cress *Barbarea vulgaris*, Meadowsweet, and Great Willowherb *Epilobium hirsutum*. Three species of yellow-cress are common on the banks: Marsh Yellow-cress *Rorippa palustris*, Great Yellow-cress *R. amphibia* and Creeping Yellow-cress *R. sylvestris*. The white stars of Water Chickweed *Myosoton aquaticum* line the water's edge, and locally there are tall spikes of Common Club-rush *Schoenoplectus lacustris*.

Bristly clumps of introduced Russian Comfrey *Symphytum × uplandicum*, alive with bumble bees, are abundant along the banks, their flowers varying from white to pink and purple. Some have almost sky-blue flowers, a throwback to one of the plant's parents which is Rough Comfrey *Symphytum asperum*. Their other parent is the native Common Comfrey *S. officinale*, also fairly common here. On warm summer days the air is tainted with the mousy smell of Hemlock *Conium maculatum* whose purple-blotched stems signpost its poisonous potential. Growing nearby, especially on rocky ledges near the water's edge, you may see the equally deadly Hemlock Water-dropwort *Oenanthe crocata*, which has grooved stems and a strong smell of celery.

Near the edges of the river a diverse range of emergent plants includes clumps of Reed Canary-grass *Phalaris arundinacea*, Reed Sweet-grass *Glyceria maxima*, and sedges including the uncommon Slender Tufted-sedge *Carex acuta*. Arrowhead *Sagittaria sagittifolia* is occasional, and often overlooked in spite of its distinctive leaf shape. More frequent along the river margin is Flowering-rush *Butomus umbellatus*,

Creeping Yellow-cress *Rorippa sylvestris* is common on the banks of the River Severn. [RW]

with umbels of rosy three-petalled flowers and leaves triangular in section. Botanist George Jorden recorded this plant along the river in 1864. In shallower margins Water-plantain *Alisma plantago-aquatica*, produces a mist of small flowers on branching stems.

One special plant of these riverbanks, especially near seepages, is Green Figwort *Scrophularia umbrosa*, a local species which has one of its national strongholds along the Severn and Teme. Often overlooked, it is bright green with broadly winged stems and succulent leaves rather like those of giant nettles. It grows in small clumps, or as isolated plants, even in cracks in the river walls in the centre of Bewdley, usually though, it relishes dappled shade, preferring some woodland cover. Often it will grow with Water Figwort *S. aquatica*, which has reddish tinges, lobed leaves and more widely spaced racemes of flowers.

On the open banks of the Severn, north and south of Bewdley, the blue saucer-shaped flowers of Meadow Crane's-bill *Geranium pratense* appear in summer. Purple-loosestrife *Lythrum salicaria* is also frequent along the open riverbanks, yet hardly manages to enter the Forest, with just the occasional plant along Dowles Brook. Two stately bellflowers cluster at the wooded edges in a few spots. The attractive blue spikes and rough leaves of Nettle-leaved Bellflower *Campanula trachelium* sprout from riverside pathways in Eymore and Seckley woods, though never in quantity. In a few spots are stands of Giant Bellflower *C. latifolia* taller and more upright, and occasionally with white flowers. The presence of these two bellflowers illustrates the Forest's location, where upland and lowland Britain meet: Giant Bellflower is mostly a northern species, and Nettle-leaved Bellflower is mainly southern. Another attractive plant along the wooded riverside paths at Eymore Wood is Small Teasel *Dipsacus pilosus*, whose round white flower heads are much smaller and more delicate than Wild Teasel *D. fullonum*. Its clusters of fuzzy seed-heads persist in winter and may be spread unwittingly by passing people or dogs.

Other tall herbs along the river include Tansy *Tanacetum vulgare*, with its yellow button heads, and Marsh Woundwort *Stachys palustris*. Where the Severn flows under Victoria Bridge at Eymore Wood, Common Meadow-rue *Thalictrum flavum*, now a local plant in west Worcestershire, may still survive, but one reason for its decline is hard to ignore. Here, indeed all along the Severn in Wyre, are battalions of balsam. The pink pouched flowers of Indian Balsam tower over most other riverside plants and compete with them for light and space. This introduced species with exploding seed heads is our tallest annual plant and generally considered unwelcome, though Honey Bees *Apis mellifera* and bumble bees are attracted to its nectar. For years Dowles Brook held out against its invasion, but by the turn of the Millennium it had penetrated deep into the Forest via the Lem Brook, and sneaked upstream from the Severn to Dry Mill Lane. Control is never easy and the plant may have to be accepted as a modern feature of our riverbanks.

Russian Comfrey *Symphytum × uplandicum* [RW]

Flowering-rush *Butomus umbellatum* [PC]

Tansy *Tanacetum vulgare* [PC]

Less vigorous riverside aliens include Crown Vetch *Securigera varia,* a naturalised species first recorded in the wild in the mid-19th century (Lees 1853). Its coronets of pink and white flowers still appear each summer north of Bewdley at the site where it was recorded by Fraser in 1874, its persistence thanks in part to its deep roots (Preston *et al.* 2002). Soapwort *Saponaria officinalis* is a more frequent riverbank plant with single or double pink flowers. It is an archaeophyte, a plant which has been in the British Isles since 1500, and was originally introduced from continental Europe because when rubbed its leaves provide a greenish soapy hand wash.

In the river itself plant species reflect the varying water conditions. The low-flow riffles are ideal habitat for River Water-crowfoot *Ranunculus fluitans,* with smaller amounts of Common Water-crowfoot *R. aquatilis* in the deeper channels. Several pondweeds occur in the fast-flowing water: Perfoliate *Potamogeton perfoliatus,* Curled *P. crispus* and the finer-leaved Fennel Pondweed *P. pectinatus* are all frequent.

Another submerged species of the faster channels is Spiked Water-milfoil *Myriophyllum spicatum,* a delicate plant with white flowers.

Step away from the Severn, upstream along the shady reaches of Dowles Brook, and the aquatic scene changes. The brook's stony bed supports very little aquatic vegetation but its margins have banks of rich alluvial soils and wet seepages attractive to plants of dappled shade, none more so than Ramsons *Allium ursinum.* This pungent but attractive flower is the essence of the Dowles Brook valley in April and early May, when its masses of starry flowers scent the spring air with garlic. In sunny spots grey and black Ramsons Hoverflies *Portevinia maculata* bask on its broad leaves.

Other characteristic brook-side plants include the majestic Pendulous Sedge whose long drooping flower-tassels are a lure in May for tiny metallic *Micropteryx* moths. The smaller Wood-sedge is also common, along with Lesser Celandine *Ficaria verna,* Greater Stitchwort *Stellaria holostea,* Hedge Woundwort *Stachys sylvatica,* Creeping-Jenny *Lysimachia nummularia,* Red Campion

Silene dioica, Common Valerian *Valeriana officinalis*, Yellow Archangel *Lamiastrum galeobdolon* and Wood Speedwell *Veronica montana*. Many of the more typical woodland herbs are found along the banks of the brook, with dog-violets, Opposite-leaved Golden-saxifrage, Wood Anemone, and, in the wetter areas, Marsh-marigold *Caltha palustris*.

In spring, the pallid spikes of Toothwort *Lathraea squamaria* appear in a few places. This parasite of Hazel and willows lacks chlorophyll and its bone-coloured flowers resemble a jawbone set with teeth. Because of this the plant acquired an unjustified reputation for curing toothache under the Mediaeval Doctrine of Signatures which asserted that divine signs had been planted in nature offering clues as to how humans should use them. Local along Dowles, it is much more common in other stream dingles such as Gladder Brook. The wetter areas along Dowles Brook and its tributaries are favourite habitats for Red Currant *Ribes rubrum*, a native species which may have been encouraged from medieval times for

Pendulous Sedge *Carex pendula* [PC]

Ramsons *Allium ursinum* with leaves smelling strongly of garlic and growing in profusion make a striking feature along the banks of Dowles Brook in spring. [PC] **The larvae of the Ramsons Hoverfly *Portevinia maculata* develop in the bulbs and the male hoverflies can often be found near the plant in May and June, though the female (below** [PC]**) is rarely seen.**

Toothwort *Lathraea squamaria* [JB]

its edible fruits. Dense stands occur especially near to old industrial workings such as dams, mills and blast furnaces. Less common is Gooseberry *R. uva-crispa* which escaped into the wild from cultivation around 1763 (Preston *et al.* 2002) and is now found occasionally along streamsides.

Other habitats

The railway lines through Bewdley and the Wyre Forest opened in the early 1860s. The Severn Valley Line ran north-south close to the Severn and a branch line was constructed running west above Dowles Brook. This Tenbury line ran for over 100 years, closing eventually in 1964. During that time it offered a route for new plants to enter the Forest. Woodlands are generally robust habitats: shady and with a dense ground flora which is well adapted to conditions that prevent many new species from colonising. The railway opened up a linear habitat which was base-rich from imported ballast, very different to the acidic forest soils. In addition there were nutrients from smoke and ash and these conditions allowed new plants to colonise. It is not always possible to say exactly which plants found their way into the Forest this way. There are some good candidates, for example Fly Honeysuckle *Lonicera xylosteum,* which still grows near Dry Mill and may have been introduced from a seed carried by a train or with ballast.

Some plants flourish in the dry well-drained conditions that railways provide. One of these is Long-stalked Crane's-bill *Geranium columbinum* which flourished for a while in the 1970s shortly after the railway closed, but is now scarce as the ballast has become overgrown. It has made use of gravelly areas to spread along the Forest tracks and still crops up occasionally. White Comfrey *Symphytum orientale* grows abundantly on the railway banks in Bewdley and at North Wood, where it is probably a former garden escape. Small Toadflax *Chaenorhinum minus* and Common Toadflax *Linaria vulgaris* are typical species of the old railway line and still occur along tracks and in disturbed areas, often with the woolly spikes of Great Mullein *Verbascum thapsus*, also known as Aaron's Rod. Wild Basil *Clinopodium vulgare* was once very abundant on the old railway but has now declined, as the bare or mossy clinker turns to stable grassland or secondary woodland.

One plant with mysterious origins is Deadly Nightshade *Atropa belladonna* which appeared in 1985 following re-grading work on the railway embankment near Dry Mill Lane. Its livid purple bells and shining berries flourished for a few years and then it vanished.

Much of Wyre outside woodland is farmland, either an intimate network of small fields, hedges, grassland and orchards, or the much larger, more intensively cultivated areas. Orchards provide a habitat for Mistletoe *Viscum album*, not common around the smallholdings but encouraged as a crop along with cherries and damsons *Prunus* spp. Orchards are similar to mini-parklands and provide excellent habitat for invertebrates. Orchards next to houses are used for

lambing or spring grazing, frequently leading to an enriched grassland sward. The best grassland was used for hay, and a few excellent unimproved meadows still survive in private ownership.

Arable land in Wyre is relatively scarce, but more common on the Shropshire side, because soils in most other places are too poor and shallow or subject to seepages. Where they do occur their cultivated margins have a scatter of arable weeds although these are now becoming scarce under the onslaught of herbicides. Occasionally Corn Buttercup *Ranunculus arvensis* and Sharp-leaved Fluellen *Kickxia elatine* attract attention, but the appearance of the rare and local Small-flowered Catchfly *Silene gallica* in an arable field margin in summer 2014 was a real surprise, underlining the possibility of persistent seed-banks.

On the Shropshire side of the Forest, where soils are deeper, cultivation was more widespread and continues to be so. Here large arable fields contrast with the more intimate meadows of Worcestershire Wyre. Unfortunately these more extensive fields are poorer in wildlife, though there remain pockets of more traditional farming around Kingswood and at Baveney Wood. Some other habitat fragments survive along the hedgerows, and one roadside verge is particularly rich with Saw-wort, Betony, violets, Oxeye Daisy *Leucanthemum vulgare*, Cowslip and Bistort *Persicaria bistorta*: the last is scarce in Wyre. Occasionally Wood Crane's-bill occurs on roadside verges but it is becoming much scarcer, as are most wildflowers, due to enrichment from adjacent fields.

Many of the hedgerows are rich in shrubby species and still shelter a woodland flora. These 'woodland

Wild Basil *Clinopodium vulgare* [JB]

ghosts' can contain Small-leaved Lime and Wild Service-tree, remnants of the ancient wildwood. More common hedgerow shrubs are Holly, Hawthorn, Dogwood, Elder *Sambucus nigra*, Hazel and sallows. Holly was cultivated for sale and the variegated form of *Ilex × altaclerensis* is quite common in many hedges where some farmers skilfully grafted this variety onto native hedgerow Hollies.

Bewdley is the main built-up area in Wyre and has its share of interesting plants. In March and April the sandstone quays along the Severn are frosted with the delicate flowers of Rue-leaved Saxifrage *Saxifraga tridactylites*, a local species whose strongholds are often way above our heads. This autumn-germinating annual is a classic plant of old roofs and wall-tops and by May has already withered and dried, showering seeds onto the pavements beneath. The alien Shaggy-soldier *Galinsoga quadriradiata*, a native of South America, has persisted for years by the walls of St Anne's church in Load Street where it is brushed by traffic day and night.

The botanical riches of Wyre Forest do not always leap to the eye. To find them you need patience and good timing, but as the character of the Forest changes as new areas are opened up, there is plenty of interest. When you get to know the hot spots, there's always a chance of discovering plants which are locally scarce or which have very restricted ranges in the English Midlands and beyond. Wyre is a meeting point for many species and marks a division between the upland and lowland flora of the British Isles: a special place for any modern botanist.

Small-flowered Catchfly *Silene gallica* [JB]

Many of Wyre's old orchard trees are festooned with Mistletoe *Viscum album* and occasionally it is to be found in woodland growing on Crab Apple *Malus sylvestris* trees. [RW]

Chapter 5

Mosses and Liverworts

Regional accounts of popular groups such as birds, butterflies and flowering plants are frequently comprehensive, or nearly so. Between them, naturalists find most if not all of the species present; one naturalist will often notice what another overlooks. However, equivalent accounts of organisms that attract few naturalists can only be collations of information gleaned over long periods of time. Accordingly, what is currently known of Wyre's mosses and liverworts is but a collection of records amassed between the 19th and 21st centuries, rather than the result of sustained recording by an army of naturalists. Indeed, the discovery of more than 50 species in Wyre since 2000 strongly suggests that yet more species will come to notice in future.

History of recording mosses and liverworts

The Reverend James Hasselgrave Thompson (1811–1889), vicar of Cradley Heath, whose plants are at Worcester Museum, was the first to collect bryophytes in Wyre. He found Fir Tamarisk-moss *Abietinella abietina* in 1866. John Fraser (1820–1909), a physician at Wolverhampton from 1854, visited Seckley Wood in 1866; his herbarium is at Hull University, with additional plants at Oxford, the National Museum of Wales in Cardiff, and Ulster Museum. James Eustace Bagnall (1830–1918) of Birmingham visited Seckley in 1895, and found numerous interesting species. His herbarium and papers are at Birmingham Reference Library. The Druce Papers at Oxford contain some

of his letters, and the National Museum of Wales in Cardiff has 125 of his bryological gatherings.

John Bishop Duncan (1869–1953) bryologised in Wyre when he lived in Bewdley early in the 20th century, and added numerous species to Wyre's known bryoflora. His discoveries of mosses such as Rufous Beard-moss *Bryoerythrophyllum ferruginascens* (a normally montane species not found in Wyre before or since), Brown Shield-moss *Buxbaumia aphylla*, Short-beaked Wood-moss *Loeskeobryum brevirostre* and Recurved Rock-bristle *Seligeria recurvata*, and the liverworts Prickly Featherwort *Plagiochila spinulosa* and Lyon's Notchwort *Tritomaria quinquedentata* have not been repeated, and remain as challenges to find again. Duncan's 1906 record of Arnell's Apple-moss *Philonotis arnellii* was repeated 20 years later by William Bywater Grove (1848–1938) of Birmingham, but another of Duncan's discoveries—Pendulous Wing-moss *Antitrichia curtipendula*—has much decreased in Britain and is probably extinct in Wyre. However, Fountain Pocket-moss *Fissidens fontanus*, which Duncan (1911) found new to Britain in 1901 on logs submerged in the River Severn at Bewdley, has proved more persistent. Some of Duncan's bryophytes are at Worcester Museum, with many more at the Royal Botanic Garden in Edinburgh, others at the National Museum and Gallery of Wales in Cardiff, and at Oxford. Bagnall, Duncan and others collated and summarised records up to the early 20th century in Amphlett and Rea's *The Botany of Worcestershire*

(1909), although many of their records were not accurately localised.

Members of the British Bryological Society (BBS) spent a day in Wyre in November 1959, and in 1962 S.W. Greene and M.C. Clark published a paper (Greene and Clark 1962) summarising what was known about the Forest's bryoflora. Francis Rose added a few further species in a subsequent paper (Hawksworth & Rose 1969), and the BBS spent a further day in Wyre in 1984 (Burton 1985). Their members also recorded several sites in the Forest during a day in April 2004 (Carrick 2004), and Lorna Fraser and Mark Lawley made numerous excursions into Wyre in the first decade of the 21st century.

Wyre's bryological significance

No-one who wanders through Wyre can fail to notice the Forest's mosses and liverworts. Conspicuous species such as Bank Haircap *Polytrichastrum formosum*, Broom Fork-moss *Dicranum scoparium*, white-mosses *Leucobryum* spp. and others carpet the ground. Others, such as Mouse-tail Moss *Isothecium myosuroides*, bristle-mosses *Orthotrichum* spp., Bruch's Pincushion *Ulota bruchii*, Dilated Scalewort *Frullania dilatata* and Forked Veilwort *Metzgeria furcata*, festoon the trunks and branches of many trees. Unknown in Britain until 1941 Heath Star-moss *Campylopus introflexus*, a native of the southern hemisphere, is now common on heathery slopes and fence-posts.

No-one who walks in Wyre can fail to notice the Forest's mosses and liverworts. They are particularly conspicuous during the winter when there is greater precipitation and more light reaching the ground after leaf fall. [JB]

Some of the Forest's more conspicuous woodland mosses and liverworts

Bank Haircap *Polytrichastrum formosum* [PC]

Broom Fork-moss *Dicranum scoparium* [PC]

Smaller White-moss *Leucobryum juniperoideum* [PC]

Wood Bristle-moss *Orthotrichum affine* [PC]

Bruch's Pincushion *Ulota bruchii* [PC]

Dilated Scalewort *Frullania dilatata* [PC]

Forked Veilwort *Metzgeria furcata* [PC]

Some woodland mosses and liverworts of damp, steep slopes and banks

Whorled Tufa-moss *Eucladium verticillatum* [PC]

Curled Hook-moss *Palustriella commutata* [PC]

Greater Whipwort *Bazzania trilobata* [PC]

Grove Earwort *Scapania nemorea* [PC]

Acid-loving mosses and liverworts of flatter ground within the Forest

Heath Star-moss *Campylopus introflexus* [PC]

Silky Forklet-moss *Dicranella heteromalla* [PC]

Notched Pouchwort *Calypogeia arguta* [PC]

White Earwort *Diplophyllus albicans* [PC]

Wyre has many other species, including less-common mosses and liverworts that are often present in small quantities and take more searching. Some need constant moisture, and may be found particularly on damp slopes in the comparatively humid valleys of Dowles Brook and its numerous tributaries. Such localities are oases in the comparatively dry Midlands, enabling species to survive that are common only further west and north, but rare this far east and south.

Water trickling down steep soil and rocky banks brings nutritious salts and minerals to plants and drains their metabolic wastes, enabling somewhat base-demanding mosses and liverworts to flourish. Furthermore, where streams have eroded small valleys and exposed calcareous rock, lime-loving species such as Top Notchwort *Leiocolea turbinata*, Whorled Tufa-moss *Eucladium verticillatum*, Awl-leaved Screw-moss *Tortula subulata* and Variable Crisp-moss *Trichostomum brachydontium* flourish, contrasting with the acid-loving flora of flatter ground on the Forest's plateau.

The steepness of these slopes has also deterred clear-felling of trees, so shade and humidity have remained continuously present for a very long time. This in turn enables several moisture-demanding species to persist, particularly liverworts such as Greater Whipwort *Bazzania trilobata*, Hairy Threadwort *Blepharostoma trichophyllum*, Autumn Flapwort *Jamesoniella autumnalis*, Palmate Germanderwort *Riccardia palmata* and Grove Earwort *Scapania nemorea*. And do Prickly Featherwort *Plagiochila spinulosa* and Lyon's Notchwort *Tritomaria quinquedentata* (found by Duncan) still occur?

In contrast, flatter ground between these little valleys has been clear-felled in the past, so that moisture-demanding species disappeared with the loss of shade and humidity. Moreover, water seeps more slowly through flatter ground, so holds less dissolved oxygen, making oxidised salts less available to base-demanding plants. This in turn reduces the ability of such species to persist, leaving space for acid-loving species to thrive. Examples include the mosses Heath Star-moss, Silky Forklet-moss *Dicranella heteromalla*, Cypress-leaved Plait-moss *Hypnum cupressiforme*, Mouse-tail Moss and Common Feather-moss *Kindbergia praelonga*, and the liverworts Notched Pouchwort *Calypogeia arguta*, Common Pouchwort *C. fissa*, Two-horned Pincerwort *Cephalozia bicuspidata* and White Earwort *Diplophyllum albicans*.

Wood is also an important substrate for many bryophytes; the consistency and composition of bark and wood influencing which species live on which trees, bushes, and logs. For example, in permanently humid woodland, moist logs which have lost their bark, may develop an interesting bryoflora. Such logs are rare in Wyre, but Lorna Fraser found Palmate Germanderwort on one in 2007, with Dusky Fork-moss *Dicranum fuscescens* on another nearby. Rustwort *Nowellia curvifolia* has become more frequent since the early 20th century.

Many of Wyre's trees however carry a disappointing variety of bryophytes. This is because much of the Forest is composed of oaks of a rather uniform age, and even comparatively mature stands lack the variety of tree species that might enable a

The striking liverwort Rustwort *Nowellia curvifolia* grows on moist logs where it can form conspicuous red mats when not too shaded. [PC]

Shining Hookeria *Hookeria lucens* is a beautiful moss of stream banks [PC]

diverse range of bryophytes to develop on and beneath them. Oak is by far Wyre's most abundant tree; unfortunately for mosses and liverworts its bark is acidic and therefore supports a restricted bryoflora. Trees such as Ash and Sycamore have a less acidic bark, and often support more species, and mature Elders always attract attention from bryologists because their very porous, deeply fissured, bark enables numerous mosses to thrive. But these and other woody species are scarce in Wyre. Epiphytes that have not been found in Wyre, but which might be expected to occur include Spotty Fingers *Frullania fragilifolia*, Dwarf Neckera *Neckera pumila*, Smooth Bristle-moss *Orthotrichum striatum* and Marble Screw-moss *Syntrichia papillosa*.

With prevailing south-westerly winds Wyre lies upwind of the West Midland's industrial conurbation so one might speculate that the Forest escaped the worst effects of atmospheric pollution in the 19th and 20th centuries. But even if so, Wyre's comparatively poor epiflora is more probably attributable to both the lack of variety of tree species and of very old trees. Nevertheless, it is worth bearing in mind that the floras of bark more than two metres above ground are rarely studied, and we know virtually nothing about which species grow in the canopy.

The Forest is also notable for numerous small flushes. Some of these are shaded, but others lie in clearings where bryophytes thrive better. Several bog-moss *Sphagnum* spp. favour these wet places, and may spread into ditches beside forestry tracks. However, Rusty Hook-moss *Scorpidium revolvens* and Straw Spear-moss *Straminergon stramineum* are wetland mosses that Duncan found in the early 20th century and have not been seen since (Duncan 1911). Some of the wet sites that Duncan knew have presumably been drained.

Disturbed ground provides good habitat for rapidly colonising short-lived species. Unshaded ground is particularly attractive for these colonists and the sides of forestry tracks (where wheels and feet compact the ground less) often support an interesting and varied bryoflora. Clay Earth-moss *Archidium alternifolium* and Lindberg's Plait-moss *Calliergonella lindbergii* are reasonably frequent in this habitat, and lime-lovers such as Curly Crisp-moss *Trichostomum crispulum* may occur where base-rich stone has been imported for constructing or repairing tracks. Drummond's Thread-moss *Pohlia drummondii* has been found beside one track, and other bulbiliferous Bryaceae may turn up. Soil overlying the pipe that carries water from Elan to Birmingham is kept free of woody vegetation and supports species such as Oblique-mouthed Beardless-moss *Weissia brachycarpa* var. *obliqua*. The sides of ruts often support small colonists such as Common Frillwort *Fossombronia pusilla* and Acid Frillwort *F. wondraczekii*. Smallest Pottia *Microbryum davallianum* turned up in 2011 on a track in Bell Coppice.

Exposed soil on banks beside streams is another disturbed habitat worth examining for bryophytes

(for example the beautiful moss Shining Hookeria *Hookeria lucens*, or the little liverwort Top Notchwort where damp, calcareous conditions prevail), while rock and stones that are inundated by running water may support aquatic species such as Brown Beard-moss *Didymodon spadiceus*, Fatfoot Pocket-moss *Fissidens crassipes*, Beck Pocket-moss *F. rufulus*, Brook-side Feather-moss *Hygroamblystegium fluviatile*, Fountain Feather-moss *H. tenax*, Long-beaked Water Feather-moss *Platyhypnidium riparioides*, Teesdale Feather-moss *Rhynchostegiella teneriffae* and Water Earwort *Scapania undulata*. Duncan (1911) found Drab Brook-moss *Hygrohypnum ochraceum* in Dowles Brook; does it still occur in Wyre?

Outside the Forest, but within the area covered by this book, the flood zone of the Severn from Arley past Bewdley to Ribbesford provides a specialised habitat for riparian species capable of withstanding periodic inundation by fast-flowing water, abrasion by particles in the water, and long-lasting periods of desiccation. On trees these riparian bryophytes include Many-fruited Leskea *Leskea polycarpa*, River Bristle-moss *Orthotrichum rivulare* and Spruce's Bristle-moss *O. sprucei*, while soil banks may harbour Stanford Screw-moss *Hennediella stanfordensis*. Substrates that remain permanently submerged may support Fountain Pocket-moss.

Other riverine and riparian specialists include Small-bud Bryum *Bryum gemmiferum*, Smaller

Two riparian mosses found on trees in the flood zone of the River Severn

Many-fruited Leskea *Leskea polycarpa* [PC]

River Bristle-moss *Orthotrichum rivulare* [PC]

Lattice-moss *Cinclidotus fontinaloides*, Nicholson's Beard-moss *Didymodon nicholsonii*, Fatfoot Pocket-moss, Petty Pocket-moss *Fissidens pusillus*, River Pocket-moss *F. rivularis*, Brook-side Feather-moss, Willow Feather-moss *Hygroamblystegium varium*, Curve-stalked Feather-moss *Rhynchostegiella curviseta* and Teesdale Feather-moss. Bordered Thyme-moss *Mnium marginatum* grows in shade above the normal flood-zone, and Tozer's Thread-moss *Epipterygium tozeri* also occurs on the banks of the Severn.

The district has many pastures and orchards, few of which have yet been thoroughly examined for mosses and liverworts. Lush, well-fertilised *Lolium* leys do not support diversity because the grass overwhelms smaller plants. The bark of cherry and pear trees is inimical to bryophytes, but old pastures with anthills may reward examination, and the trunks of old apple trees are base-rich and may support a variety of species. Flat-brocade Moss *Platygyrium repens* occurs on old fruit trees in Joan's Hole.

Arable fields that are left fallow in winter may support interesting assemblages of ruderal species. Fallow stubble at Ribbesford in 2009 harboured Hasselquist's Hyssop *Entosthodon fascicularis* and Crisp Beardless-moss *Weissia longifolia* var. *longifolia*. Other species will surely be found when further attention is paid to this habitat.

Other ruderal habitats (gardens and allotments, car parks, mature walls and roofs, churchyards in Bewdley, Ribbesford and elsewhere) have been little recorded compared with the Forest. Numerous species that are characteristic of such places are either grossly under-recorded (for instance, Nicholson's Beard-moss must surely be common on tarmac drives and pavements in Bewdley) or are waiting

to be added to the list of species known from the district. Examples include Sauter's Thread-moss *Bryum sauteri*, Pill Bryum *B. violaceum*, Blunt-leaved Earwort *Diplophyllum obtusifolium*, Smooth Hornwort *Phaeoceros laevis*, Blunt-bud Thread-moss *Pohlia bulbifera*, Yellow Thread-moss *P. lutescens*, and Glaucous Crystalwort *Riccia glauca*.

A brownfield site at Alton, Long Bank was at a rewardingly diverse, intermediate stage of succession in the winter of 2009/10, with the mosses Tufted Thread-moss *Bryum caespiticium*, Pointed Beard-moss *Didymodon acutus*, Serrated Earth-moss *Ephemerum serratum s.l.*, Dense Fringe-moss *Racomitrium ericoides* and Oblique-mouthed Beardless-moss, and the liverwort Acid Frillwort.

Other changes in Wyre's bryoflora are probably attributable to changes in climate or atmospheric pollution, or both. Pendulous Wing-moss *Antitrichia curtipendula* surely became a victim of atmospheric pollution, while the extent to which many epiphytes suffered as a result of industrial pollution and subsequently recovered must remain conjecture because too little bryological recording took place in years gone by. Indeed, many of the bryophytes which have been added to Wyre's list during the late 20th and early 21st centuries had probably lain undiscovered for very many years. The identification of bryophytes has become more accessible since publication of *Mosses and Liverworts of Britain and Ireland, a field guide* (Atherton *et al.* 2010) hopefully attracting more naturalists to the group and more extensive studies of Wyre's bryophytes.

A list of bryophytes whose distributional status in Wyre is ubiquitous, widespread or local is shown in Table 2. A full list of Wyre Forest bryophytes can be found at **www.wyreforest.net**

Flat-brocade Moss *Platygyrium repens* is most often found growing on willows and alders but can occur on a range of other trees. It Is found in Wyre on old fruit trees. [PC]

Table 2 List of mosses and liverworts that are ubiquitous, widespread or local in Wyre

The names of species follow those in *A Check-list and Census Catalogue of British and Irish Bryophytes* (British Bryological Society, 2008)

MOSSES

Species	Status	Species	Status	Species	Status
Amblystegium serpens	Ubiquitous	Hygroamblystegium tenax	Widespread	Heterocladium heteropterum var. flaccidum	Local
Atrichum undulatum	Ubiquitous	Hypnum cupressiforme var. resupinatum	Widespread		
Brachythecium rivulare	Ubiquitous	Orthodontium lineare	Widespread	Heterocladium heteropterum var. heteropterum	Local
Brachythecium rutabulum	Ubiquitous	Oxyrrhynchium hians	Widespread		
Bryum capillare	Ubiquitous	Plagiomnium rostratum	Widespread	Homalia trichomanoides	Local
Bryum dichotomum	Ubiquitous	Plagiothecium denticulatum	Widespread	Hygroamblystegium fluviatile	Local
Bryum rubens	Ubiquitous	Plagiothecium nemorale	Widespread	Hygrohypnum luridum	Local
Calliergonella cuspidata	Ubiquitous	Plagiothecium succulentum	Widespread	Hylocomium splendens	Local
Campylopus introflexus	Ubiquitous	Plagiothecium undulatum	Widespread	Hypnum andoi	Local
Ceratodon purpureus	Ubiquitous	Pleuridium acuminatum	Widespread	Isothecium alopecuroides	Local
Cratoneuron filicinum	Ubiquitous	Pogonatum aloides	Widespread	Leptodictyum riparium	Local
Dicranella heteromalla	Ubiquitous	Pohlia wahlenbergii	Widespread	Leskea polycarpa	Local
Dicranum scoparium	Ubiquitous	Polytrichum juniperinum	Widespread	Leucobryum glaucum	Local
Didymodon insulanus	Ubiquitous	Rhizomnium punctatum	Widespread	Leucobryum juniperoideum	Local
Fissidens bryoides	Ubiquitous	Rhynchostegiella teneriffae	Widespread	Mnium stellare	Local
Fissidens taxifolius	Ubiquitous	Tetraphis pellucida	Widespread	Neckera complanata	Local
Hypnum cupressiforme	Ubiquitous	Thamnobryum alopecurum	Widespread	Neckera crispa	Local
Hypnum jutlandicum	Ubiquitous	Ulota bruchii	Widespread	Orthotrichum diaphanum	Local
Isothecium myosuroides	Ubiquitous	Weissia controversa	Widespread	Orthotrichum stramineum	Local
Kindbergia praelonga	Ubiquitous	Anomodon viticulosus	Local	Oxyrrhynchium pumilum	Local
Mnium hornum	Ubiquitous	Brachytheciastrum velutinum	Local	Palustriella commutata	Local
Orthotrichum affine	Ubiquitous	Brachythecium albicans	Local	Palustriella falcata	Local
Plagiomnium undulatum	Ubiquitous	Bryoerythrophyllum recurvirostrum	Local	Plagiothecium curvifolium	Local
Platyhypnidium riparioides	Ubiquitous	Bryum pseudotriquetrum s.l.	Local	Pleurozium schreberi	Local
Polytrichastrum formosum	Ubiquitous	Bryum ruderale	Local	Pohlia melanodon	Local
Pseudoscleropodium purum	Ubiquitous	Campylium stellatum	Local	Pohlia nutans	Local
Pseudotaxiphyllum elegans	Ubiquitous	Campylopus flexuosus	Local	Polytrichum piliferum	Local
Rhynchostegium confertum	Ubiquitous	Campylopus pyriformis	Local	Racomitrium aciculare	Local
Rhytidiadelphus squarrosus	Ubiquitous	Cinclidotus fontinaloides	Local	Rhynchostegiella tenella	Local
Thuidium tamariscinum	Ubiquitous	Cirriphyllum crassinervium	Local	Rhytidiadelphus loreus	Local
Tortula muralis	Ubiquitous	Cirriphyllum piliferum	Local	Schistidium crassipilum	Local
Archidium alternifolium	Widespread	Dicranella schreberiana	Local	Sciuro-hypnum plumosum	Local
Aulacomnium androgynum	Widespread	Dicranum majus	Local	Scleropodium cespitans	Local
Barbula convoluta	Widespread	Dicranum montanum	Local	Sphagnum angustifolium	Local
Barbula unguiculata	Widespread	Dicranum tauricum	Local	Sphagnum fimbriatum	Local
Bryum argenteum	Widespread	Didymodon luridus	Local	Sphagnum inundatum	Local
Calliergonella lindbergii	Widespread	Didymodon nicholsonii	Local	Sphagnum palustre	Local
Ctenidium molluscum	Widespread	Didymodon spadiceus	Local	Sphagnum subnitens	Local
Dichodontium pellucidum	Widespread	Didymodon tophaceus	Local	Syntrichia latifolia	Local
Dicranella varia	Widespread	Eucladium verticillatum	Local	Syntrichia montana	Local
Dicranoweisia cirrata	Widespread	Fissidens adianthoides	Local	Tortula truncata	Local
Didymodon fallax	Widespread	Fissidens crassipes	Local	Trichodon cylindricus	Local
Didymodon rigidulus	Widespread	Fissidens pusillus	Local	Trichostomum brachydontium	Local
Didymodon sinuosus	Widespread	Fissidens viridulus	Local	Trichostomum crispulum	Local
Eurhynchium striatum	Widespread	Funaria hygrometrica	Local	Trichostomum tenuirostre	Local
Fissidens dubius	Widespread	Grimmia pulvinata	Local	Ulota crispa	Local
Homalothecium sericeum	Widespread	Grimmia trichophylla	Local	Zygodon conoideus	Local
Hookeria lucens	Widespread	Gyroweisia tenuis	Local	Zygodon viridissimus var. viridissimus	Local

LIVERWORTS

Species	Status	Species	Status	Species	Status
Calypogeia arguta	Ubiquitous	Lepidozia reptans	Widespread	Jungermannia pumila	Local
Calypogeia fissa	Ubiquitous	Lophozia ventricosa	Widespread	Leiocolea turbinata	Local
Cephalozia bicuspidata	Ubiquitous	Lunularia cruciata	Widespread	Lejeunea cavifolia	Local
Diplophyllum albicans	Ubiquitous	Plagiochila asplenioides	Widespread	Lejeunea lamacerina	Local
Frullania dilatata	Ubiquitous	Scapania nemorea	Widespread	Marchantia polymorpha	Local
Lophocolea bidentata	Ubiquitous	Scapania undulata	Widespread	Metzgeria conjugata	Local
Lophocolea heterophylla	Ubiquitous	Aneura pinguis	Local	Metzgeria violacea	Local
Metzgeria furcata	Ubiquitous	Calypogeia muelleriana	Local	Nowellia curvifolia	Local
Pellia endiviifolia	Ubiquitous	Cephaloziella divaricata	Local	Radula complanata	Local
Pellia epiphylla	Ubiquitous	Chiloscyphus pallescens	Local	Riccardia chamedryfolia	Local
Plagiochila porelloides	Ubiquitous	Conocephalum salebrosum	Local	Saccogyna viticulosa	Local
Chiloscyphus polyanthos	Widespread	Fossombronia wondraczekii	Local	Scapania irrigua	Local
Conocephalum conicum	Widespread	Frullania tamarisci	Local	Solenostoma gracillimum	Local
Fossombronia pusilla	Widespread	Jungermannia atrovirens	Local	Trichocolea tomentella	Local

Chapter 6

Fungi

For many, the study of fungi is an obscure and difficult area of natural history, and so the species rarely receive the same attention as birds or plants. This is unfortunate, because fungi are vitally important to natural communities. Without them most plants would soon die and whole ecosystems would collapse.

Fungi are not plants, but form a Kingdom of their own. It is impossible to detail all that might occur in a forest such as Wyre, so this book deals with the more familiar larger species. These fall within two main groups, the Ascomycota and Basidiomycota. Ascomycota are the cup fungi, morels and truffles that shoot out their spores. The Basidiomycota are the species that drop their spores, and include the familiar mushrooms and toadstools along with brackets, jelly fungi and puffballs, some of Wyre's more conspicuous fungi.

Fungi are not just rotting agents for wood and vegetation; they also form mycorrhizal associations with higher plants, enabling both to grow. Many have a reputation as pathogenic killers of trees, but most fungi do the opposite: they aid tree growth, and maintain them as they age.

Fungi associated with plants can be either intra-cellular (endomycorrhiza) or extra-cellular (ectomycorrhiza). Their relationship provides the fungi with carbohydrates and the trees use the fungal mycelium's extensive network to improve water and mineral absorption. For example, plants cannot directly utilise phosphorus in the soil, but fungi make it available for them. Many species, especially milkcaps *Lactarius* spp., boletes *Boletus* spp., webcaps *Cortinarius* spp., and brittlegills *Russula* spp., have complex ectomycorrhizal associations with tree roots. These are some of the more familiar species seen in late summer and autumn. Of course the visible signs of a fungus are usually the fruiting bodies: the main bulk of the fungus itself is hidden as a mycelial web below ground or within the trees.

Perhaps 80% of all plants have an associated fungal partner. In Wyre, Heather *Calluna vulgaris* may have special ericoid mycorrhizas that allow it to flourish on acidic, poor soils and provide vital support for seed germination and development.

Just how many fungi occur in Wyre? No-one really knows. Carleton Rea (1861–1946) who lived in Worcester, spent 40 years recording the Forest's fungi in the early part of the 20th century and noted 1,395 species (Rea 1923) Table 3. He considered this number to be about a tenth of the total but of course most of the ones he failed to discover are likely to be small or the more obscure species of rusts, smuts, mildews and the like. Rea was an eminent mycologist in his day, a founder member of the British Mycological Society and first editor of the Society's transactions. In 1922 he wrote and published the standard reference work on fungi, *British Basidiomycetae, a Handbook to the Larger British Fungi*.

John Bingham's growing list has over 700 species, including additions to Rea's impressive total. Most experts suggest the fungal flora outnumbers the plant flora by a factor of at least seven: at a scientific guess there are about 14,000 species of fungi in Britain. In

Table 3 Notable Wyre Forest species discussed by Carleton Rea on 15 February 1923 (Rea 1923)

Species name then	Species name now	Location
Glischroderma cinctum	Same	Regarded as an error
Lepiota pratensis	*Lepiota oreadiformis*	On many of the commons throughout the Forest
Lepiota citriophylla	*Lepiota xanthophylla*	Wyre Forest
Cortinarius epipoleus	*Cortinarius emunctus*	Wyre Forest
Cortinarius argutus	Same	Wyre Forest
Cortinarius cyanites	Same	Coachroad Coppice
Cortinarius queletii	*Cortinarius uliginosus*	Coachroad Coppice
Cortinarius psammocephalus	Same	On every old charcoal heap
Cantharellus carbonarius	*Faerberia carbonaria*	On every old charcoal heap
Astrosporina fulvella	*Inocybe fulvella*	Coachroad Coppice
Flammula rubicunda	*Cortinarius rubicundulus*	Throughout the Forest in Worcs and Shropshire
Boletus nigrescens	*Leccinum crocipodium*	Near The Great Bog
Clavaria greletii	Same	On an old charcoal heap at Breakneck Bank
Galactinia olivacea	*Peziza badioconfusa*	Weston Plantation
Pustularia rosea	*Tarzetta rosea*	Near the pools in the Golden Valley

one square kilometre of fairly typical woodland in the Forest you could expect to find perhaps 300 species of vascular plants, which might equate to around 2,000 species of fungi. When grassland, heathland, farmland and river habitats are added the number of plants in the whole Forest could exceed 600, which suggests there are over 4,000 fungi and possibly more. The latest list, including the smaller rusts and smuts, now stands at a very respectable total of 2,050 species, bringing us halfway to the potential total.

Some fungi appear to fruit every year unless weather conditions are really unsuitable. Others are more irregular, missing a year or two until the right conditions occur. Some are even more erratic. There appears to be a large number of fungi that fruit only when the weather is ideal, once in perhaps ten or 20 years (or even longer). In a good fruiting season the number of species and their sheer abundance is quite overwhelming. The importance of Wyre has been assessed in the publication *Important Fungus Areas* and is listed as a Criteria A and B site with 500 species recorded recently (Plantlife 2003).

Most people know what fungi look like even if they cannot identify them to species level. A summary of some of the larger groups follows, but be aware that this is the tip of the iceberg. Here we don't distinguish between 'mushrooms' and 'toadstools' as the terms have no real relevance; mushrooms are sometimes thought of as the edible species and toadstools as the poisonous ones, but this is misleading. We are mainly concerned with the Larger Fungi, though many of the smaller species of smuts, rusts and moulds are very noticeable. For example, the underside of Ramsons *Allium ursinum* leaves are often covered by orange blisters caused by the rust *Puccinia sessilis*, and *Triphragmidium ulmariae* commonly appears as an orange rust on the distorted stems of Meadowsweet *Filipendula ulmaria*. But here we shall confine our foray of Wyre fungi to the more typical and obvious species.

Scarletina Bolete *Boletus luridiformis* **is common in oak woodland and has striking orange pores that turn dark blue when bruised** [JB]

Woodland fungi
Cup fungi, morels, truffles

Many of the cup fungi are quite small and a hand lens helps. They are not hard to find and despite their small size they are wonderfully varied, typically cup-shaped and often colourful. They are important decomposers breaking down plant and animal organic matter, and appear on all manner of substrates ranging from living and dead wood to dead animals and dung. The late Malcolm Clark recorded many small species in Wyre, but there are many more to be discovered.

Some of this group are large, for example the brilliant Orange Peel Fungus *Aleuria aurantia*, commonly found on bare ground along the Forest rides. On calm days a cloud of its white spores can be released by gently blowing across the cup-shaped fruiting body. A rather uncommon species which can be locally frequent in Wyre, is Bog Beacon *Mitrula paludosa*, an aquatic species found in shallow ditches where it grows on submerged oak leaves. In spring its golden heads on pale stalks emerge luminously from the dank water, a striking sight in the gloom of the Forest floor. This unusual species plays a major role in the decomposition of leaf litter in very damp habitats.

Morels, with their crumpled brain-like 'caps' are some of the best-known spring fungi, but they are very scarce here; Carleton Rea commented that no morels have ever been recorded in Wyre Forest (Rea 1929) and in 30 years of searching John Bingham has only ever seen Common Morel *Morchella esculenta* once, on the old railway line. The acidic soils are not really suitable for them, but they relish disturbed habitats and may be overlooked.

Bog Beacon *Mitrula paludosa* [JB]

One fungus worth searching for is Anemone Cup *Dumontinia tuberosa* which occurs in spring on Wood Anemone *Anemone nemorosa*. It is parasitic, attacking the roots and weakening the whole plant. The fungus has a goblet-shaped brown cup on a long black stalk, often hidden amongst the Wood Anemone leaves. It arises from the underground seed-like sclerotia on old tubers. Although widely distributed nationally, it is scarce and even in Wyre appears to be very localised despite the abundance of its host. Anemones that look anaemic, or turn brown early in the spring are worth a closer look.

Many of the smaller cup fungi are abundant in the Forest and exquisite to observe under a low-power microscope or hand lens. One of the more conspicuous and striking species, Green Elfcup *Chlorociboria aeruginascens*, stains rotten oak wood a vivid blue-green, but its turquoise fruiting bodies are less often seen.

Truffles are almost unheard of in Wyre. The soil is too acid and without a truffle pig (or dog) they are almost impossible to find.

Orange Peel Fungus *Aleuria aurantia*, commonly found along the Forest tracks, where it looks very like discarded orange peel. [JB]

The striking Green Elfcup *Chlorociboria aeruginascens*, stains oak wood a vivid turquoise green but its turquoise fruiting bodies (below) are less often seen. The fungus used to be introduced into oak to produce marquetry veneer used in decoratively inlaid woodwork known as Tunbridge Ware in the 18th and 19th centuries. [Both RW]

A selection of other cup fungi found in Wyre

Scarlet Elfcup *Sarcoscypha austriaca* [JB]

Felt Saddle *Helvella macropus* [JB]

Eyelash Fungus *Scutellinia scutellata* [JB]

Stinkhorns, earthstars, puffballs, false truffles

This is a rather odd group of fungi that doesn't fit into the major groups. Gasteroid fungi produce their spores inside their basidiocarps (fruit bodies) rather than on an outer surface. They include puffballs, earthstars, bird's nest fungi, stinkhorns, and false truffles.

The Stinkhorn *Phallus impudicus* is one species that is often smelled before it is seen. Its distinctive mass of spores is contained in a putrid greenish mass (the gleba) on top of the stalk, or receptaculum. The foul stench from the gleba attracts numerous flies which disperse the spores on their feet. The fruiting bodies emerge from 'eggs' just below ground and as they appear on the surface, have been gathered and sold as truffles to unsuspecting people. The Stinkhorn is common in Wyre, especially in conifer woods, and can turn up in gardens where it is not always welcome. The smaller Dog Stinkhorn *Mutinus caninus* is much scarcer and rarely seen in Wyre, preferring more base-rich soils.

Earthstars *Geastrum* spp. are usually unexpected and always pleasing to find. They prefer more calcareous soil and so are uncommon in the Wyre area where very few have been recorded. The only regular records are of Collared Earthstar *G. triplex* which is most likely to turn up along hedgerows or railway embankments: it has never been seen within the typical oak woodland. Bewdley botanist George

Jorden preserved some specimens in his herbarium dating back to the 1840s and these still survive in his collections at Worcester Museum.

The most obvious gasteroid fungi are the puffballs. The Common Puffball *Lycoperdon perlatum* is typical and grows in large troops along the grassy edges of tracks and rides. On more acid ground, often where Heather grows, Dusky Puffball *L. nigrescens* is the more common species. In contrast the less often seen Spiny Puffball *L. echinatum* prefers a more base-rich soil: it occurs in valleys and hedgerows. Stump Puffball *L. pyriforme* is unusual in growing on decaying wood. Outside woodland on short grasslands, four other species occur; the smaller Brown Puffball *Bovista nigrescens*, the Grey Puffball *B. plumbea* and the much larger Mosaic Puffballs, *Lycoperdon utriforme* and *L. excipuliforme*, often persisting as loose empty cases.

There are two unusual false truffles (not related to truffles at all) but they are not worth eating. The largest, which appears just above ground, is *Choiromyces meandriformis*, a large white fungus with an odd, strongly aromatic smell. The Yellow False Truffle *Rhizopogon luteolus* is sometimes found under Scots Pine *Pinus sylvestris*. Normally just visible above the ground amongst the pine needles, it looks like a yellow potato over which the tawny mycelial threads have spread and entered the soil.

The putrid smell of the Stinkhorn *Phallus impudicus* is likened to that of rotting meat. This attracts flies to feed. The fungal spores are dispersed on the flies' bodies and through their droppings because they pass through their gut unharmed. [RW]

Collared Earthstar *Geastrum triplex* [JB]

Yellow False Truffle *Rhizopogon luteolus* [JB]

Four distinctive puffballs found in Wyre

Common Puffball *Lycoperdon perlatum* [PC]

Stump Puffball *Lycoperdon pyriforme* [PC]

Spiny Puffball *Lycoperdon echinatum* [JB]

Mosaic Puffball *Lycoperdon utriforme* [JB]

Fungi with gills

The vast majority of fungi have the typical toadstool and mushroom form with umbrella-like cap and gills beneath. Many different species occur all over the Forest in a good year. Perhaps Fly Agaric *Amanita muscaria* is the most recognisable because its white-spotted red cap is illustrated in many children's books. This unmistakable fungus normally grows in association with birch trees. Its relative, the Deathcap *A. phalloides*, an olive-capped species with a large stem-ring and volva bag, is less obviously recognisable and is sometimes mistaken for an edible mushroom. It is rare here, occurring in stream valleys and hedgerows, and as the common name suggests, it is deadly poisonous.

In total 23 species of *Amanita* occur within the Forest. The abundant False Deathcap *A. citrina*, with its yellowish cap also has a variety with a pure white cap *A. citrina* var. *alba* which is not uncommon: both varieties have a distinctive smell of raw potatoes and though not poisonous, are best avoided. The Blusher *A. rubescens* occurs in both deciduous and conifer woods, and the Grey Spotted Amanita *A. spissa* is more confined to oak and birch woods. Both fruit over a long period and can sometimes be found as early as July. Several smaller *Amanitas* are common, especially in association with birches, such as Tawny Grisette *A. fulva* and Grisette *A. vaginata*. They lack the ring on the stem shown by the larger *Amanita*

species but have the typical swollen volva bag at the base of the stem.

Even larger than many *Amanitas* are the parasols. The one most commonly found in woodland away from grassland is the Shaggy Parasol *Chlorophyllum rhacodes*. This is rare in ancient broadleaved woodland where it prefers disturbed ground such as secondary woodland or where conifers have been planted. It also grows on abandoned Southern Wood Ants' nests, especially where the vegetation has started to rot down. The commonest and largest species along grassy woodland rides is the Parasol *Macrolepiota procera* but this is more at home in heathy grasslands. There are many smaller *Lepiota* species, many of which prefer more enriched soils and grow by roadsides or streams. Stinking Dapperling *L. cristata* is a typical example and smells strongly of new polythene.

Funnel caps *Clitocybe* spp. comprise many small white- or cream-coloured species, often with distinctive smells. The gills typically run down the stem and most species are saprotrophic, occurring in leaf litter. Twenty-five species are recorded from the Forest, and some are very distinctive. One of the commonest is Clouded Funnel *C. nebularis,* a large and robust fungus which forms 'fairy rings' in woodland, often late in the season. The strong-smelling Aniseed Funnel *C. odora* wafts the smell of aniseed on the wind. Its brightly coloured greenish-blue cap is very distinctive. The Club Foot

False Deathcap *Amantita citrina* **var.** *alba* [JB]

Shaggy Parasol *Chlorophyllum rhacodes* [JB]

Clouded Funnel *Clitocybe nebularis* [PC]

Fly Agaric *Amanita muscaria*, one of our poisonous fungi, is commonly found in the autumn near birch trees [JB]

Butter Cap *Rhodocollybia butyracea* [JB]

Amethyst Deceiver *Laccaria amethystina* [JB]

Deceiving Knight *Tricholoma sejunctum* [JB]

Rosy Bonnet *Mycena rosea* [JB]

Ampulloclitocybe clavipes is quite a large species with a swollen base to the stem, hence the name. It can be found in both conifer and broadleaved woods.

Toughshanks are rather similar to funnel caps and can be very common and at times very variable in form, but they always have tough fibrous stems. The Butter Cap *Rhodocollybia butyracea* is greasy to touch and found in all kinds of woodland. Its several forms make it hard to identify, and it is often confused with the similar Russet Toughshank *Gymnopus dryophilus*. In oak woodland Wood Woollyfoot *G. peronatus* can be common. It is often yellowish with a pale pink cap and a hairy base to the stem. Similar to funnel caps are two very common and colourful fungi: the peach-coloured Deceiver *Laccaria laccata*, and the rich purple Amethyst Deceiver *L. amethystina*. Both are very variable in form and size and often confuse the inexperienced forayer.

The knights *Tricholoma* spp. make up a genus of ectomycorrhizal species which are quite large and robust. The commonest in Wyre is Birch Knight *Tricholoma fulvum,* which only grows with its host tree. Some knights have strong smells such as Soapy Knight *T. saponaceum* which smells like carbolic soap, and the yellow Sulphur Knight *T. sulphureum* which smells of tar gas. The Deceiving Knight *T. sejunctum,* is a yellowish-green species which is usually found in base-rich woodland and is local in Wyre.

Bonnet caps *Mycena* spp. are a large group of small saprotrophic fungi with conical caps and fragile stems. Most grow on dead wood or stumps, sometimes in dense clusters, and some in leaf litter. Many have white or red 'milk' in the stem and some have distinctive smells, such as that of bleach. There are over 90 species in Britain with 58 recorded from Wyre. Identification can be difficult especially of the more nondescript species. Rosy Bonnet *M. rosea* is a common species in leaf litter, having a pink cap. The Milking Bonnet *M. galopus,* another common species, yields a white milk in the stem when broken. Clumps on stumps are often Common Bonnet *M. galericulata* (especially on oak), Clustered Bonnet *M. inclinata* or Grooved Bonnet *M. polygramma.*

Inkcaps are also saprotrophic fungi, and the familiar Shaggy Inkcap *Coprinus comatus* is a frequent adornment to grassy woodland rides. When fresh it looks like a small white busby, but soon auto-digests into a dripping black mass. Old rotting stumps and hidden tree roots sometimes support hundreds of fruiting bodies of the tiny Fairy Inkcap, *Coprinellus disseminatu*s and also the larger Glistening Inkcap *C. micaceus*. In contrast the large and robust Common Inkcap *Coprinopsis atramentaria* grows on stumps and woody debris. Although it can be edible, eating this fungus along with alcohol can bring on sweating, palpitations and nausea.

Few fungi deserve their bad reputations, but the Honey Fungus *Armillaria mellea* is rightly dreaded by foresters and gardeners because it is a killer of trees and will even attack garden roses. The *Armillaria*

Glistening Inkcap *Coprinellus micaceus* grows on wood and when young the caps have veil fragments that glisten like mica grains [JB]

group is a species complex and not all are dangerous. The two most aggressive pathogens of trees are Honey Fungus on broadleaves, and Dark Honey Fungus *A. ostoyae* which prefers conifers and is quite common in Wyre. Even if the fruiting bodies are absent, look for the broad flat rhizomorphs which run under the bark of trees and give *Armillaria* the alternative name Bootlace Fungus. Similar to honey fungi, and very common on stumps, is the poisonous Sulphur Tuft *Hypholoma fasciculare*. Its gills are yellow but the blackish spores make the underside of the cap look greenish.

Within the woodland, some families are especially common. Milkcaps *Lactarius* spp. are easy to identify because they yield a milky fluid when the cap or gills are damaged. They are ectomycorrhizal on many trees and shrubs, so knowing the host plant will help to identify the species. They are a large group of 75 British species, 50 of them recorded in Wyre.

A common species under Hazel *Corylus avellana* is Fiery Milkcap *L. pyrogalus*. This has a buff-brown cap and stem with milk that is very hot on the tongue. (Taste is a useful way to help identify many species, but don't eat or swallow the fungus.) As its name suggests the Oak Milkcap *L. quietus* is commonly found under oaks, a pinkish-brown fungus with a

Fiery Milkcap *Lactarius pyrogalus* [PC]

Yellowdrop Milkcap *Lactarius chrysorrheus* [PC]

zoned cap and an oily smell said to be like bedbugs. Another oak woodland species is Yellowdrop Milkcap *L. chrysorrheus* which has a pinkish-red cap with concentric zoning and whose white milk turns yellow in a few seconds when exposed to the air. The large off-white Pepper Milkcap *L. piperatus* is found under oaks, especially on the steeper banks along Dowles Brook valley. Its milk is hot and peppery, but it has several look-alikes, for example Grey Milkcap *L. vellereus, L. glaucescens*, and even the Milk White Brittlegill *Russula delica*.

Some of the most obvious fungi are the Brittlegills *Russula* spp, a distinctive and colourful genus, all with rather brittle caps and crumbly stems. They have mycorrhizal associations with trees and shrubs and some are confined to a single host species. In total 145 species are recorded from Britain, 63 of them from Wyre.

The commonest species include Blackening Brittlegill *R. nigricans,* Ochre Brittlegill *R. ochroleuca,* Purple Brittlegill *R. atropurpurea,* Geranium Brittlegill *R. fellea* and Stinking Brittlegill *R. foetens.* Blackening Brittlegill occurs in mixed woodland and is a robust species which can persist from early summer to late winter. In fresh specimens the flesh turns from white through reddish-pink to a darker brownish-black. This fungus is occasionally parasitised by piggybacks *Asterophora* spp. (see Fungi parasitic on other fungi box). Ochre Brittlegill is yellow and abundant in most years in broadleaved and in coniferous woodland where specimens can take on a brownish or greenish tint.

If any species characterises the Wyre Forest, then the Charcoal Burner *R. cyanoxantha,* is a strong candidate. This is a common fungus, especially under oak, and its cap can be purplish, olive, green or grey or a combination of all these. It is reputed to derive its name from the complexion of a charcoal burner's face, a rare sight in modern Wyre. A totally green form (f. *peltereaui*) is also common here. Bright red brittlegills are fairly widespread, but beware many look-alike species. Under conifers the Sickener *R. emetica* is fairly common and as both its common and scientific names suggest, it has a nasty effect if eaten: the flesh is very hot to the taste. Under Beech the Beechwood Sickener *R. nobilis* is the most frequent red species with a coconut smell and hot taste. In oak woodland the larger Scarlet Brittlegill *R. pseudointegra* is common. The cap colours of brittlegills fade with rain, perhaps none more so than Slender Brittlegill *R. gracillima,* a small species found under birch in damp habitats. When fresh the cap is bright red but soon washes out to pale pink then white. Green fungi are scarce but Greencracked Brittlegill *R. virescens,* a species of broadleaved woodland not uncommon in the Forest, is an amazing sea-green colour. Two uncommon species of note are Velvet Brittlegill *R. violeipes*, with a yellow cap and purple-flushed stem, and Gilded Brittlegill *R. aurea,* with a vivid bright orange-red cap.

Three common woodland brittlegills

Blackening Brittlegill *Russula nigricans* [JB]

Ochre Brittlegill *Russula ochroleuca* [JB]

Charcoal Burner *Russula cyanoxantha* [JB]

Fungi parasitic on other fungi

Fungi parasitic on fungi are unusual: *Squamanita* spp. and *Asterophora* spp. are two groups considered to be obligate parasites. In 2004 John Bingham had the good fortune to discover an exceptionally rare species in the Forest, the Powdercap Strangler *S. paradoxa* (pictured left [JB]). It was growing on a grassy forest ride on the Shropshire side and its host was Earthy Powdercap *Cystoderma amianthinum*. The *Squamanita* takes over the host and replaces the cap and upper stem with its own fruiting body. The result is two fungi in one, as the orange stem of the Earthy Powdercap remains, topped by the Powdercap Strangler's grey cap. This situation makes the *Squamanita* a gall-causer. The exact nature of this parasitising fungus was not fully discovered until 1994 (Redhead 1994) following a review of the genus.

Whilst *Squamanita* is clearly rare, Piggybacks *Asterophora* spp. are much more common and can be found in most years growing on the decaying fruitbodies of brittlegills, often on the underside and typically on Blackening Brittlegill. There are two piggybacks, the Powder Piggyback *A. lycoperdioides* (top right [JB]) and Silky Piggyback *A. parasitica* (bottom right [JB]). Powder Piggyback appears to be the more common consisting of small button-like fruit bodies covered with a brown powder (the spores or chlamydospores in this primitive fungus). As they often occur on the underside of the fruit bodies they may not be obvious unless the fungus is turned over. The Silky Piggyback looks more like a small capped fungus with a silky cap. Both tend to grow in small clusters.

Violet Webcap *Cortinarius violaceus* is a large and handsome species whose violet hues soon fade to brown [JB]

Webcaps *Cortinarius* spp. make up a large genus of ancient woodland indicator species that can defy identification by all but the keenest mycologists. Wyre has some important species which is not surprising given the webcaps' affinity for old forest. There are over 300 species in Britain, and perhaps 200 could occur in Wyre, though to date only 83 species have been positively identified. Some are large and colourful, others much more nondescript, but all have a cortina, or cobweb-like ring, that joins the cap to the stem in early growth.

Wyre is home to an exceptional population of the impressive Violet Webcap *C. violaceus,* a European Red Data Book species rare in Britain. There are many locations in the Forest for this striking species and in good fruiting years dozens, if not hundreds, of robust specimens appear under oak and birch. It shows a distinct preference for birch woodland and the best site in Wyre is a wooded area cultivated during the Second World War. Another strong population grows on ground disturbed by forest road construction which suggests that it may welcome an element of disturbance. Wherever it grows, its unpredictable fruiting and spectacular appearance makes it an exciting find.

Another rare and very distinctive species of the oak woods is *C. humicola,* a dark yellow fungus with a shaggy stem and cap resembling a scalycap *Pholiota* sp. It has only been recorded ten times in the British Isles and is on the Red Data List as Endangered: in Wyre it grows on a steep wooded slope. Colourful species include the very striking Bloodred Webcap *C. sanguineus,* a smaller species which is found in both broadleaved and coniferous woodland. Although no *Cortinarius* is really common, Yellow Webcap *C. delibutus* is one of the more frequent species, often found under birch or oak in drier woodland. On oak banks, especially above Dowles Brook, Purple

Cortinarius humicola [JB]

Stocking Webcap *C. mucifluoides* and the similar Wrinkled Webcap *C. elatior* are often found: both have a wrinkled, sticky cap and white stem, with traces of a violet cortina.

Similar to webcaps are fibrecaps *Inocybe* spp. They are generally smaller and often have pointed caps with fibrous scales. Most are difficult to identify and the spores need to be checked under a microscope for certain identification. *I. geophylla* is a widespread and beautiful white species as is the lilac *I. lilacina*, both with a strong earthy smell. Forty-eight Fibrecaps have been identified in the Forest, but many more are likely to occur.

The striking Bloodred Webcap *Cortinarius sanguineus* is found in both broadleaved and coniferous woodland, and can produce a bright red dye. [PC]

Boletes—fungi with sponge-like pores

The boletes are often conspicuous fungi identified by the sponge-like underside to their caps. They are constantly being renamed, although the genera *Boletus*, *Leccinum* and *Suillus* appear to be stable for now and contain some of the larger and more obvious species. They grow on the roots of trees and of the 73 species known from Britain, 29 have been seen in Wyre.

Oak has its fair share of these and Scarletina Bolete *Boletus luridiformis* is one of the commonest, with a brown cap and bright orange-red pore surface. When cut or damaged the flesh turns dramatically and rapidly from yellow to inky blue. The recent division of the smaller boletes into new species makes it difficult to know which are the most common. At one time Red Cracking Bolete *Xerocomellus chrysenteron* would have been regarded as the commonest in Wyre, and it may still be. It is, however, now split into several species, including *X. cisalpinus* and *X. declivitatum*, making it much harder to identify in the field. Similar to it is Suede Bolete *Xerocomus subtomentosus* another common species which lacks the red cracking on the cap.

Birches are host to a number of *Leccinum* species of which Brown Birch Bolete *L. scabrum* is particularly common. The tall Orange Birch Bolete *L. versipelle* is also widespread but it fruits much less frequently, needing a 'good fungus year' to show well. The most well-known bolete is the Cep, 'Porcini' or Penny Bun *Boletus edulis.* It is quite common across the Forest, but not as abundant as might be expected because birch woodland is localised.

Somewhat less common except in good fruiting seasons, and more a specialist of oak woodland, is the robust Orange Oak Bolete *L. aurantiacum.* Saffron Bolete *L. crocipodium* is a southern species that occurs as far north as Wyre and although uncommon it does fruit well in some years when the large fruiting bodies, with their striking yellow caps, are very distinctive. The Forest's rarest *Leccinum* is *L. holopus*, aptly named the Ghost Bolete from the pale colours of its cap. It is found occasionally, associated with birches in damp moorland-like areas, often with *Sphagnum* moss. John Bingham has only seen it once in Wyre in 30 years.

Under Larch the slimy yellow Larch Bolete *Suillus grevillei* is normally abundant: some caps are orange/brown and are var. *clintonianus.* Under Scots Pine Slippery Jack *S. luteus* appears, another viscid fungus with a darker chestnut cap and a ring on its stem. Bay Bolete *B. badius* is common and can become frequent in good years. The pores and flesh turn blue-green when damaged.

Bay Bolete *Boletus badius* [JB]

Fungi associated with conifers

Generally, converting conifer plantation back to native broadleaved woodland is a welcome policy, but it affects the fungi which are totally dependent on conifers. These include several orange-capped *Lactarius* species such as False Saffron Milkcap *L. deterrimus* (pictured below left [JB]) which grows under spruce, Saffron Milkcap *L. deliciosus* found under Scots Pine, and the rarer *L. quieticolor*. *Russula* species under pine include Bloody Brittlegill *R. sanguinaria* and Primrose Brittlegill *R. sardonia* (below centre [PC]), with several boletes like Slippery Jack. The Earpick Fungus *Auriscalpium vulgare* (below right [JB]) grows on old pine cones. The rare Larch Spike *Gomphidius maculatus* grows in association with the Larch Bolete. It is not just the fungi themselves that are significant, but the biomass of their fruitbodies. Many large, fleshy bolete species associated with conifers produce fruitbodies in autumn to early winter, after most broadleaved woodland fungi, and therefore extend the food supply for many species of invertebrates.

Common and not so common woodland boletes of Wyre

Red Cracking Bolete *Xerocomellus chrysenteron* [JB]

Cep or Penny Bun *Boletus edulis* [JB]

Saffron Bolete *Leccinum crocipodium* [JB]

Larch Bolete *Suillus grevillei* [PC]

Chanterelles, hedgehogs, jellies, corals, clubs

Regarded by many as the best edible fungus the egg-yellow Chanterelle *Cantharellus cibarius* is found under oak on many of the Forest's steeper banks. It is rarely common in Wyre but a closely related species Trumpet Chanterelle or Yellowlegs *C. tubaeformis* can be abundant in some years, often growing amongst Bilberry. Often found with these species is the Horn of Plenty *Craterellus cornucopioides*, a funnel-shaped fungus with dark grey and black-brown colour. Despite its other name Trumpet of Death this is an edible fungus and used more as a flavouring than as a main dish; they persist well into the winter months.

Tooth fungi are a small group of fungi with fragile tooth-like projections instead of the typical gills or pores on the underside of the cap. They include the Wood Hedgehog *Hydnum repandum* with a creamy white cap, often found growing with brittlegills, and the less common Terracotta Hedgehog *H. rufescens* which has a more orange cap. Both can be found in conifer or deciduous woodland but beech seems to be the more favoured tree in Wyre. Another unusual tooth fungus that grows on conifer stumps is the Toothed Jelly Fungus *Pseudohydnum gelatinosum*, similar to the Wood Hedgehog but a member of the Auriculariales order of fungi. Some English

woodlands have other toothed or stipitate fungi, many that are typically common in Scotland's pine forests, and appear to have come with the introduction of conifer or Sweet Chestnut *Castanea sativa* trees. Wyre however, as yet, does not appear to have any of these species but they may appear in time. We also lack the tiered tooth fungi that favour old beech trees.

Clavarioid fungi form a distinctive but varied group unlike most other species of fungi. Typically they are spindle-shaped, often branched like deer antlers and sometimes coral-like. Some jelly fungi such as Yellow Stagshorn *Calocera viscosa* can look similar but are very gelatinous. Most clavarioid fungi are saprotrophic growing in grassland often with moss or in woodlands on leaf litter of both deciduous and coniferous trees. A few grow on wood or on decaying plant matter. Crested Coral *Clavulina coralloides*, is perhaps the commonest species, it varies in form but has typically branched forms with numerous small spikes, like a tree with small spiky side branches. It is found in both broadleaved and conifer woodlands, often abundant. Grey Coral *C. cinerea* is also common, grey-brown in colour or even with a violet-purple tone which is caused by an ascomycete fungus, *Helminthosphaeria clavariorum*. Grey Coral is more robust than Crested Coral but although branched it is far less spiky in

Wood Hedgehog *Hydnum repandum* [JB]

Toothed Jelly Fungus *Pseudohydnum gelatinosum* [JB]

Crested Coral *Clavulina coralloides* [JB]

appearance. Wrinkled Club *C. rugosa* is typically less branched and a dull white in colour, quite common in Wyre's woodlands especially with conifers. Giant Club *Clavaridelphus pistillaris* is a rather special fungus for Wyre being quite scarce nationally. It has been found a few times in recent years in various parts of the Forest. Most sites are under oak woodland with a weak scattering of bracken with Bilberry often present. The fungus is pale brown and looks like a stout club about 12–15 cm tall and quite broad at the top but often partly eaten by slugs. The thin Pipe Club *Macrotyphula fistulosa* var. *fistulosa* grows on small dead branches on the ground in broadleaved woodland. In some years it can be quite common and occasionally found in more open woodlands. Slender Club *M. juncea* is less common but often found in damper woodlands growing on wet leaf litter. Both are found along Forest stream valleys and ash or sallow are often the preferred trees they grow under.

Small clubs can be found on the leaf litter but a hands and knees search is needed and a magnifier useful to appreciate these small fungi. Straw Club *Clavaria straminea* is found growing most often on bare wet soil under bramble in woodland. Dark Club *C. greletii* is our rarest club species in Wyre with a conservation status of Endangered, first recorded by Carleton Rea (his daughter Violet collected it) on an old charcoal burn hearth site in 1922. It had never been seen for years in the Forest when it was found 83 years later by Rosemary Winnall on a Wyre Forest Study Group meeting (see also box on page 113). Redleg Club *Typhula erythropus* is a tiny thread-like fungus about 25 mm long with a white head. It is attached to a tiny blackish sclerotium (a small seed-like structure) hidden in the leaf litter which it grows from. At times this fungus is very common, especially along the Dowles Brook valley where ash can be found. *T. phacorrhiza* is another thread-like fungus but often longer up to 10 cm and occurring *en masse* in deep leaf litter in damp woodland. On bracken stems the tiny white Bracken Club *T. quisquiliaris* is often seen. It needs old stems, often those that are damp and hidden from view.

Larger coral fungi appear to be rare in Wyre but eight species have been noted. The pale buff to cream coloured Upright Coral *Ramaria stricta* grows typically in broadleaved woodland and has occurred under oak. The only other *Ramaria* species seen in the Forest recently are *R. formosa* and *R. abietina*, both are uncommon. *R. formosa* favours beech woodland but to date does not appear to like the planted beech in Wyre Forest. *R. abietina* has appeared under conifers as well as occasionally under broadleaved trees.

Horn of Plenty *Craterellus cornucopioides* [JB]

Trumpet Chanterelle *Cantharellus tubaeformis* [JB]   Yellow Stagshorn *Calocera viscosa* [JB]

Pipe Club *Macrotyphula fistulosa* var. *fistulosa* [PC]

Chicken of the Woods *Laetiporus sulphureus* [RW]

Fungi growing on trees

The history of coppice management has limited the number of old mature trees in the Forest and so has considerably reduced the habitat for arboreal fungi. The only common arboreal species in Wyre is Birch Polypore *Piptoporus betulinus* which, when given the chance, can be abundant on old and young birches. The traditional orchard fruit trees provide some old timber, but are more localised than mature oaks, Ash or Beech. Old cherry trees often support the large yellow-orange brackets of Chicken of the Woods *Laetiporus sulphureus,* a serious pest that eventually causes brown cubical rot of the heartwood, but in doing so provides habitat for hole-nesting birds and

other species. Occasionally it is found on mature oaks and even on Yew. Also fairly common on fruit and Ash trees is Shaggy Bracket *Inonotus hispidus*. This causes white-rot, giving the wood a spongy appearance as it decays. It is one of the few species to attack Wild Service-tree *Sorbus torminalis* and has been seen on several trees in Wyre.

On more mature oaks, and occasionally old coppice stools, Southern Bracket *Ganoderma australe* can be found. It is quite scarce in the Forest and is more likely to be seen in the surrounding landscape, as are Oak Bracket *Inonotus dryadeus* and Beefsteak Fungus *Fistulina hepatica*. In woodland, desiccated oak stumps, perhaps 30 or more years old, are home to Oak Mazegill *Daedalea quercina,* a woody bracket with a labyrinthine underside: it will also appear on oak gateposts if there are no stumps around. Cinnamon Porecrust *Phellinus ferrus* and Rusty Porecrust *P. ferruginosus* grow high in mature oaks, often unnoticed until branches fall from the canopy. On recently fallen trunks and live branches of oak, eruptions of Black Bulgar *Bulgaria inquinans* can occur, covering the trunks and branches with hundreds of waxy buttons about 2 cm across, looking more like liquorice allsorts than fungi.

Small stumps are normally overrun with Candlesnuff Fungus *Xylaria hypoxylon* and, more rarely, the larger and fatter Dead Moll's Fingers *X. longipes* or Dead Man's Fingers *X. polymorpha*. A common species of conifer stumps is the viscid, rubbery Yellow Stagshorn. On smaller branches other colourful jelly fungi include the Yellow Brain *Tremella mesenterica*, Witches Butter *Exidia glandulosa* and White Brain *E. thuretiana*. Smaller branches are normally overrun by resupinate fungi, such as Bleeding Broadleaf Crust *Stereum rugosum* which is very common on dead oak branches, Hairy Oak Crust *S. hirsutum*, Hairy Bracket *Trametes hirsuta* and Turkeytail *T. versicolor*.

Oak Mazegill *Daedalea quercina* is a woody bracket found on old desiccated oak stumps and even gateposts. [JB]

A selection of other fungi found on trees and timber within Wyre

Oyster Mushroom *Pleurotus ostreatus* [JB]

Porcelain Fungus *Oudemansiella mucida* [JB]

Dryad's Saddle *Polyporus squamosus* [JB]

Turkeytail *Trametes versicolor* [JB]

Jelly Rot *Phlebia tremellosa* [JB]

Grassland fungi

Probably the best-known fungi of grasslands are the Field Mushroom *Agaricus campestris* and Horse Mushroom *A. arvensis*. Both can be numerous in unimproved or semi-improved fields but, regrettably, these are no longer common. In good years Parasols *Macrolepiota* spp. are abundant in grassland and along forest rides. The commonest is the Parasol Mushroom, but in woodland glades the similar *M. konradii*, can be more frequent; in more open grassland Slender Parasol *M. mastoidea* is the most commonly found species.

Waxcaps *Hygrocybe* spp. are brightly coloured smallish fungi tending to appear in late autumn. They are well studied and recognised as very important indicators of ancient turf and biological richness linked to unimproved grassland that has not been chemically fertilised or re-seeded (Boertmann 2000). One, *Hygrophorus reae* was named after Carleton Rea who, in 1923, produced what may have been the first list of fungi for Wyre. This species has since been reassigned to be a form of *Hygrocybe mucronella*.

Work in Denmark has provided a guide to the significant waxcap species, and the numbers which indicate whether a given site is ancient grassland. The work has led to a system of recording fungal richness using the CHEG score system proposed by Rald (Rald 1985). This represents the groups Clavariaceae, *Hygrocybe*, *Entoloma* and Geoglossaceae, all of which include strong ancient grassland indicator species.

Table 4 Waxcap species found recently around Wyre		
Species name	**Common name**	**Occurrence**
Hygrocybe acutoconica	Persistent Waxcap	Occasional
Hygrocybe aurantiosplendens	Orange Waxcap	Rare
Hygrocybe calyptriformis	Pink Waxcap	Rare
Hygrocybe cantharellus	Goblet Waxcap	Occasional
Hygrocybe ceracea	Butter Waxcap	Common
Hygrocybe chlorophana	Golden Waxcap	Frequent
Hygrocybe citrina		Occasional
Hygrocybe citrinovirens	Citrine Waxcap	Rare
Hygrocybe coccinea	Scarlet Waxcap	Common
Hygrocybe colemanniana	Toasted Waxcap	Rare
Hygrocybe conica	Blackening Waxcap	Frequent
Hygrocybe flavipes	Yellow Foot Waxcap	Occasional
Hygrocybe fornicata	Earthy Waxcap	Rare
Hygrocybe glutinipes	Glutinous Waxcap	Occasional
Hygrocybe ingrata		Rare
Hygrocybe insipida	Spangle Waxcap	Common
Hygrocybe intermedia	Fibrous Waxcap	Occasional
Hygrocybe irrigata	Slimy Waxcap	Occasional
Hygrocybe lacmus	Grey Waxcap	Rare
Hygrocybe laeta	Heath Waxcap	Occasional
Hygrocybe miniata	Vermilion Waxcap	Occasional
Hygrocybe mucronella	Bitter Waxcap	Occasional
Hygrocybe nitrata	Nitrous Waxcap	Rare
Hygrocybe ovina	Blushing Waxcap	Rare
Hygrocybe pratensis	Meadow Waxcap	Frequent
Hygrocybe psittacina	Parrot Waxcap	Frequent
Hygrocybe punicea	Crimson Waxcap	Common
Hygrocybe quieta	Oily Waxcap	Occasional
Hygrocybe reidii	Honey Waxcap	Common
Hygrocybe russocoriacea	Cedarwood Waxcap	Occasional
Hygrocybe virginea	Snowy Waxcap	Frequent

The Parasol Mushroom *Macrolepiota procera* is a large fungus and abundant along forest rides. It is good to eat when young. [PC]

Waxcaps add colour to the meadows and grasslands within Wyre

Butter Waxcap *Hygrocybe ceracea* [JB]

Pink Waxcap *Hygrocybe calyptriformis* [RW]

Honey Waxcap *Hygrocybe reidii* [JB]

Persistent Waxcap *Hygrocybe acutoconica* [JB]

Blackening Waxcap *Hygrocybe conica* [JB]

Crimson Waxcap *Hygrocybe punicea* [JB]

Scarlet Waxcap *Hygrocybe coccinea* [JB]

Parrot Waxcap *Hygrocybe psittacina* [JB]

Snowy Waxcap *Hygrocybe virginea* [JB]

Snowy Waxcaps *Hygrocybe virginea* can be abundant in grassland. [JB]

The system has been further refined, and various methods can be used, but they all basically score a site based on the indicator fungi that are found there.

These results lead to the recommendation that 4–8 waxcap species make a site locally important, 9–16 regionally important, and 17–21 nationally important (Vesterholt *et al.* 1999).

Using this ranking Wyre is of national importance with 28 species of waxcaps recorded to date including several sites with between nine and 16 species.

A site at Bliss Gate, well studied by Rosemary Winnall, has a total of 23 waxcaps and is therefore of national importance. Recent work has shown that one species, Parrot Waxcap *Hygrocybe psittacina*, is part of a species complex, and a specimen from Bliss Gate has been used as the type specimen for a new species called *Gliophorus reginae* (Ainsworth 2013). This was probably originally described as *Hygrophorus sciophanoides* by Carleton Rea in 1922, based on a painting of an English specimen he found in 1909 in Derbyshire. Unfortunately no type specimen was kept (Rea 1923).

Over the Forest there are numerous small unimproved grasslands and those that are sensitively grazed have a rich waxcap community with associated Fairy Clubs (Bingham 2014a). Typical Clavariaceae species include Meadow Coral *Clavulinopsis corniculata*, a common species on short grazed acidic turf over most of the Forest, and Golden Spindles *C. fusiformis*, more local, but often present in large clusters in grasslands. Yellow Club *C. helvola* is very common on grassland that has not been fertilised or disturbed. The similar looking *Clavaria* species include White Spindles *C. fragilis*, and Smoky Spindles *C. fumosa*, both more restricted but quite frequent in good grassland. Finally Dark Club is worthy of special mention as a particularly rare species recorded from charcoal burn sites (see box opposite).

Pinkgills *Entoloma* spp. have not been studied so well. They are more difficult to identify but Wyre supports a good range. The pink spores are obvious on the gills. The most conspicuous species in grassland or rides is Star Pinkgill *E. conferendum*, a large pinkish-brown species. More colourful species, often in shades of navy or black, are Indigo Pinkgill *E. chalybaeum* and Blue Edge Pinkgill *E. serrulatum*.

The Caterpillar Club *Cordyceps gracilis*, is an entomogenous species which attacks the underground larvae of swift moths in the family Hepialidae. It is visible in spring as a small white stem a few centimetres high, surmounted by a yellow 'drum-stick' which produces the spores. Old grasslands appear to be the best places to look for this unusual species.

Finally, the Earthtongues *Geoglossum* spp. are more scattered and seem to prefer acidic soils and a mossy sward. The black solitary spindles are easy to pick out but precise identification requires microscopic examination of the spores and setae.

Whilst this summary of the fungi of Wyre has included many significant species, many more have been omitted. Clearly Wyre is a nationally important site for fungi with many species yet to be discovered, and we are only just beginning to understand their vital roles in maintaining our woodland ecosystem.

Gliophorus reginae, a newly described species [JB]

A selection of other grassland fungi found in Wyre

Indigo Pinkgill *Entoloma chalybaeum* [RW]

Petticoat Mottlegill *Panaeolus papilionaceus* [JB]

Golden Spindles *Clavulinopsis fusiformis* [JB]

An earthtongue *Geoglossum glutinosum* [RW]

Old charcoal hearths—a special habitat

When coppicing for charcoal was the main industry in the Forest, numerous hearths were created by charcoal burning. The burning sterilised the ground and also altered the chemistry of the soil, making it more base-rich than the acidic surroundings. This did not escape Carleton Rea who took great interest in the fungi associated with the charcoal hearths, recognising them as an unusual and special habitat (Rea 1929). Although burning oak for charcoal is long gone, to a lesser extent burning brash, as part of conservation work, provides similar conditions.

Rea's list was quite extensive and included many species now absent from modern inferior burn sites. He recorded *Cantharellus carbonarius* (= *Faerberia carbonaria*) now occasional in England on old bonfire sites, *Cortinarius psammocephalus*, *Flammula carbonaria* (= *Pholiota highlandensis*) still quite common in Wyre and *Polyporus perennis* (= *Coltricia perennis*) a fungus of heaths and old fire sites. His record of *Glischroderma cinctum* is now considered a mistake, but the rare club fungus he recorded from charcoal hearths, Dark Club *Clavaria greletii* (pictured right [RW]), is still to be found occasionally on bare acidic ground. Other species noted by Rea which turn up now and then include *Helvella sulcata*, *Tephrocybe atrata*, *T. ambusta*, *Loreleia postii* and *Rickenella fibula*.

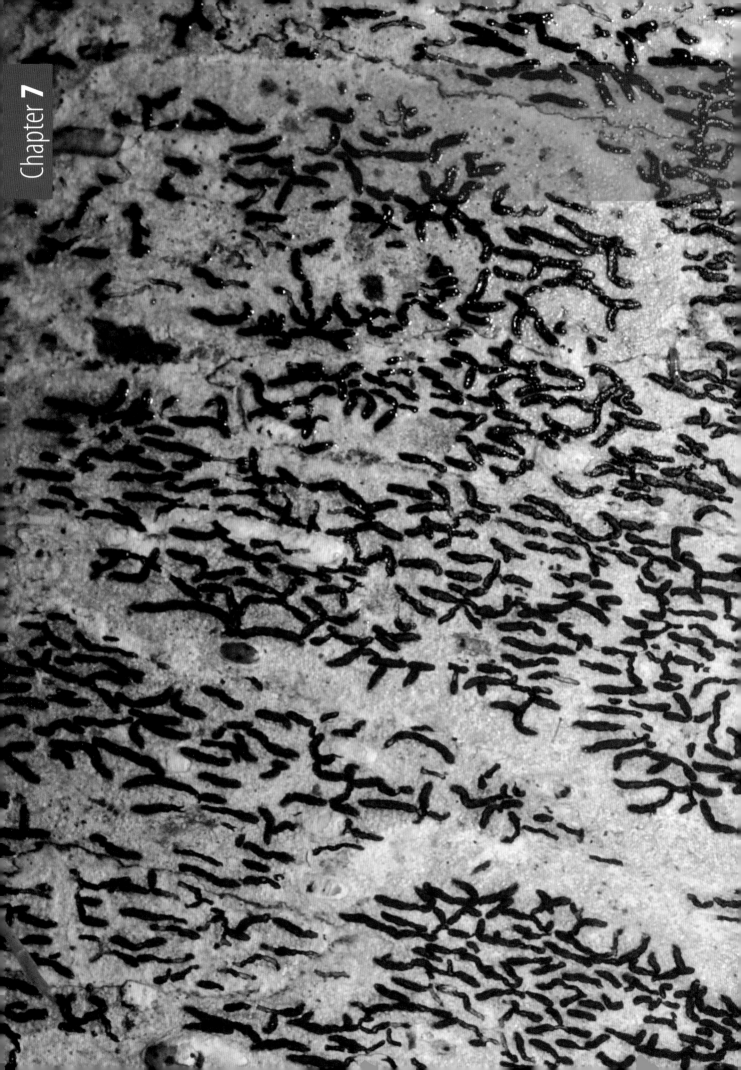

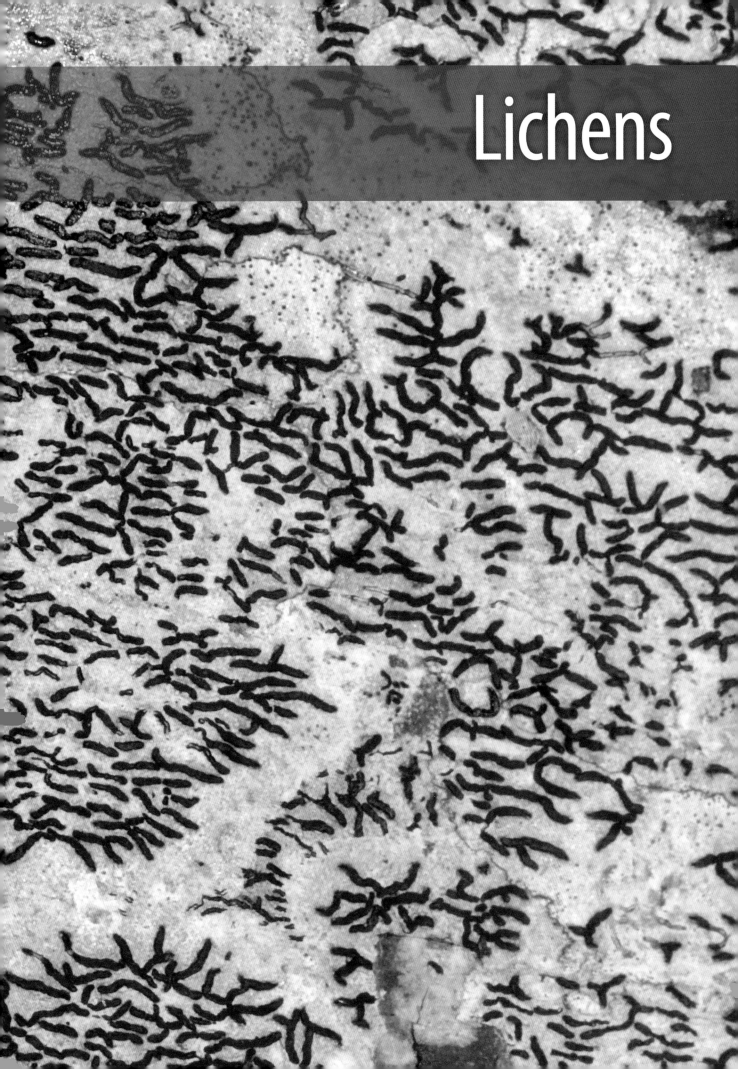

Chapter 7

Lichens

Lichens are present throughout Wyre, although most people have no idea they are there; their beauty and diversity often go unnoticed. If you pause for a moment, crouch down beside a sunny heathery bank and peer between the foliage, a miniature lichen world may be revealed. You might see tiny pixie cups standing erect like drinking vessels, minute pink-capped fruiting bodies growing out of the soil like miniature mushrooms, and small grey antlers reaching for the sky.

Lichens have been used down the ages in medicine, dyeing, the manufacture of perfume, suncream, antibiotics, for making fishing flies and wreaths, also in taxidermy and the construction of model railways (Gilbert 2000). They are collected each spring by Long-tailed Tits *Aegithalos caudatus*, Hawfinches *Coccothraustes coccothraustes* and Goldfinches *Carduelis carduelis* for constructing their nests, and they provide refuge and food for a large range of small invertebrates. Some lacewing larvae attach small pieces of lichen to their backs for camouflage; caterpillars of the Beautiful Hook-tip *Laspeyria flexula*, Marbled Beauty *Bryophila domestica* and all footman moth larvae feed on lichens; Merveille du Jour *Griposia aprilina* and Oak Beauty *Biston strataria* moths often rest up by day on lichen, assured of a good disguise.

One of the best times to look for lichens growing on trees is in winter, when twigs from the canopy have been snapped off by the wind and fallen to the ground. A close view may reveal a host of different species with a range of textures and colours—greys, pinks, browns, yellows, greens and blacks. The base of better-lit trunks may reveal other species huddled amongst the mosses. In some places close examination of the smooth bark of Ash *Fraxinus excelsior*, Hazel *Corylus*

Pixie cups *Cladonia fimbriata* [PC]

avellana, even a fence post or wooden seat, may show a range of spots, dashes, lines and squiggles. A hand lens will reveal the detail of these individual crustose lichens, each species having its distinguishing features. They often grow closely together but separately defined, like counties on a map. Outcrops of rock, walls and gravestones will all have their own lichens depending on the type of rock, and the aspect, light, and moisture present. Rocks and pebbles submerged in the clear-water streams can reveal another world of aquatic lichens but, although relatively clean, the waters of Wyre are too rich in nutrients and lichens tend to be outcompeted by a fine growth of algae and aquatic mosses.

Lichens are a symbiotic relationship between a fungus and an alga and/or a cyanobacterium (blue-green alga). The alga manufactures food on which

Crust-forming lichens growing on the bridge over the old railway line at Lodge Hill in the heart of the Forest. [BK]

The Merveille du Jour moth *Griposia aprilina* is hard to spot when resting on lichen *Parmelia sulcata* [RW]

Evernia prunastri and other lichens growing on the trunk of an Ash, Cox's Coppice, Eyemore Wood [RW]

the fungus feeds, and the fungus provides a stable substrate in which the alga flourishes (Orange 1994). Algae require sunlight for photosynthesis, so lichens grow best in the light, although some species will cope with lower light levels. They also need some moisture, although many can withstand long periods of drought. They do not always have to be exposed to rain as some can absorb moisture from dew, or even from water vapour. Many are particularly sensitive to air pollution and will only grow where the air is clean: lichen diversity declines as sulphur dioxide levels increase (Gilbert 2000). Lichens are to ecologists what canaries are to coal miners; the species present providing clues to the quality of the air and atmospheric conditions.

As with ancient meadows, with their rich assemblages of flowering plants and insects, it is ecological continuity that is key to a rich lichen community. For woodland lichens the nature and age of the bark, degree of illumination or shade and the quality of the air are all important features. Although Wyre is an ancient semi-natural woodland it does not have a rich variety of lichens. There are several reasons for this. Firstly, different tree species exhibit varying degrees of bark acidity, attracting different lichen communities: the richest are found on the less acidic or neutral bark. The two commonest tree types in Wyre are oaks *Quercus* spp. and birches *Betula* spp. and these, with Alder *Alnus glutinosa*, cherries *Prunus* spp. and pines *Pinus* spp., are in the group with the most acidic bark, supporting the fewest lichen species (Nimis *et al.* 2000). Less frequent in Wyre are Sycamore *Acer pseudoplatanus* and limes *Tilia* spp. which usually have a moderately acid bark, and willows *Salix* spp., poplars *Populus* spp., apples *Malus* spp., Ash and elms *Ulmus* spp. which have a more or less neutral bark favouring the richest lichen communities. However, acidification of bark caused by atmospheric sulphur dioxide pollution can dramatically change the balance toward those lichen species more normally associated with acid-barked trees.

Secondly, the Forest has been coppiced for many generations, and since 1926 the Forestry Commission and some other owners have cleared and replanted large areas, many with conifers. As a result there are very few veteran trees and little continuity of woodland structure. Francis Rose realised the importance of continuity for good lichen communities to develop, and pointed out that coppice woodland may be good for flowers, insects, birds and dormice, but was third-rate for lichens (Gilbert 2000). By its nature the coppice regrowth is densely shaded and only a few years old at most so there is insufficient time for rich lichen communities to develop. The trunks of any standard trees left within the coppice are densely shaded for much of the year, and only periodically exposed after coppicing. Rose found that coppice woodland only supported 15–20 species of epiphytic lichens per 1 km^2 compared to 100 species per 1 km^2 in woodland that had no history of coppicing (Gilbert 2000).

Thirdly, air pollution has had a huge effect on lichen growth in Wyre. The heavy sulphurous pollution from the furnaces and major industries that developed across the Black Country to the east and Wolverhampton to the north reached Wyre on northerly and easterly winds, leaving a long-term legacy affecting lichen numbers and species. Air pollution from South Wales, carried on the prevailing south-westerlies, added to this. The steam trains that ran for a hundred years from 1863 through the Forest alongside Dowles Brook billowed out sulphur dioxide. Nowadays the restored Severn Valley Railway, which reopened from Bewdley in 1974, continues to run steam trains through the eastern side of the Forest.

The Botany of Worcestershire (Amphlett & Rae 1909) describes several lichen species recorded by the Reverend Joseph Hesselgrave Thompson in Wyre, namely from Eyemore Wood, Hawksbatch [sic] and the Seckley Ravine. Thompson (1811–1889) was a curate in Worcester for ten years before moving to become the incumbent in Cradley in 1856 (Middleton 2009). He stayed there for the rest of his life, during which he was very interested in natural history, belonging to various local societies. He made his name as a botanist, making trips abroad as well as visiting local counties. He must have been eager to journey further afield as at that time the Black Country was heavily polluted with the outpourings from mines, furnaces and factories. Edwin Lees documented this desolate landscape in 1867 (Amphlett & Rae 1909) when he wrote: "Even the lichens Mr Thompson tells me will not grow upon the trees at Cradley and their bark brings a lower price in consequence nor has he ever been able to detect even an *Opegrapha*." [sic]

Thompson visited the Wyre Forest on a number of occasions and recorded the ancient woodland species *Thelotrema lepadinum* from Seckley Wood. It is this species that Hawksworth and Rose found later in Seckley Ravine in 1968, growing on Ash bark. They commented that this deep ravine, with its mature trees, had probably been sheltered from the worst of the air pollution and this resulted in more lichens being found here than in other parts of Wyre

Thelotrema lepadinum, an ancient woodland species [BK]

(Hawksworth & Rose 1969). They examined six sites within Wyre and were surprised by how few species they found compared to other English woodlands of a similar nature. Hawksworth and Rose recorded 28 corticolous (growing on bark) and lignicolous (growing on wood stripped of bark) species at Seckley Ravine, the more interesting included *Thelotrema lepadinum*, *Arthonia spadicea*, *Graphis elegans* and *Pertusaria leioplaca* (Hawksworth & Rose 1969). In a more intensive study of the ravine in 1993/4 Trevor Duke increased the list of corticolous lichens to 42. Interesting additional species included *Enterographa crassa*, *Jamesiella anastamosans*, *Cresponea premnae*, *Micaria prasina*, *Phaeographis dendritica*, and *Schismatomma decolorans* (Duke 2015).

D.C. Lindsay wrote a short article about lichens he recorded during a British Bryological Society field meeting to Park Brook in September 1985. He recorded several species not in the Hawksworth and Rose list, including *Caloplaca citrina*, *Chrysothrix candelaris*, *Cladonia digitata* and *C. polydactyla*. He also noted *Platismatia glauca* forming a distinctive community with *Hypogymnia physodes*.

Joy Ricketts made a great difference to our appreciation of Wyre's lichens when she started recording there in the late 1990s (Ricketts 2000; 2001). In 2005 she compiled a list of lichens for Greater Worcestershire from records on the British Lichen Society database (from 1970) and mentioned a few species of note from the Forest, namely: *Parmeliopsis hyperopta*, *Graphis elegans*, *Lepraria membranaceum*, *Dibaeis baeomyces* and *Anisomeridium polypore*. Between 2003 and 2008 she made many visits to the woodland, orchards, hedgerows, heathland and streamsides around Wyre, adding significantly to the list of lichens year by year. Although the Forest was not her favourite location for lichens, her enthusiasm and diligence encouraged many others to appreciate what was present, and to understand a little better the place of lichens within Wyre's ecosystems. She introduced us to circles of *Porpidia macrocarpa* on local stones, the delightful *Opegrapha atra* on Hazel bark, encouraged us to taste *Pertusaria amara*, to get excited about clinker as a substrate

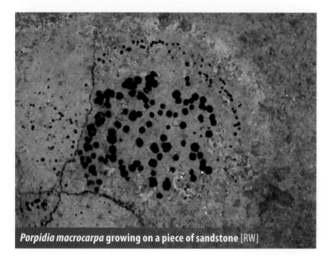

Porpidia macrocarpa **growing on a piece of sandstone** [RW]

for *Peltigera lactucifolia* along the railway line, and to systematically check tiny fissures in bark so that we didn't miss one of her lichen treasures. Joy's indefatigable hard work (before ill health restricted her mobility) substantially increased the number of lichen species for greater Wyre.

Joy Ricketts noted that although Rose and Hawksworth were disappointed by the paucity of lichens here in 1968, the Clean Air Acts (1956 to 1964) resulted in less sulphur dioxide in the air and gradual improvements to the lichen flora (Ricketts 2001). However, there is a substantial lag between improved air and the return of sensitive species (imagine leaving an arable field and just waiting for the rich flora to return). Acidified and polluted bark may take years to return to its original condition, if indeed it ever becomes fully palatable to the most demanding lichen species. Some species are more active colonisers and have increased in Wyre and across the country in recent decades, following the reduced sulphur dioxide emissions. Many of these are the more acid-tolerant species, including *Evernia prunastri*, *Flavoparmelia caperata*, *Punctelia subrudecta*, *Physcia aipolia*, *Ramalina farinacea*, *Usnea subfloridana* and *Xanthoria polycarpa*.

In recent times moth recorders in Wyre have certainly noticed an increase in footman moths that feed on lichens. In 2000 Tony Simpson (Harper & Simpson 2000) noted only five species being present: Four-dotted Footman *Cybosia mesomella*, Scarce Footman *Eilema complana*, Buff Footman *E. depressa*, Dingy Footman *E. griseola* and Common Footman *E. lurideola*. In 2008 Dave Grundy reported that the first three were all rapidly expanding their range, and three new species had been recorded: Rosy Footman *Miltochrista miniata*, Red-necked Footman *Atolmis rubricollis* and Orange Footman *Eilema sororcula*.

Nowadays the major pollutants are nitrogen compounds from road traffic and intensive farming (Natural History Museum online). Not all lichens are affected adversely and Physcian and Xanthorian communities flourish in these eutrophic conditions. This is noticeable in the increase of bright yellow patches of lichen near farms particularly on the bark of Elder *Sambucus nigra*, and along busy roadsides: the roundabouts at each end of the Bewdley bypass have conspicuous yellow lichen growth, especially on the south-western 'weather' sides.

A chance to look at canopy lichens was provided when an oak tree was cut from Cleobury Coppice in 2012 to check for invertebrates (Winnall *et al.* 2012). It was noticeable that the twigs at the very top of the tree were covered in a lot of lichens, which is not surprising as the light is much greater in the tree canopy. Joy Ricketts kindly identified the lichens on a few small twigs sent to her. Fifteen corticolous and lignicolous species were present, a good number from such a small sample. It is a pity that the Forest canopy remains out of reach for most lichenologists, but gives hope for future additions to the Wyre Forest lichen list.

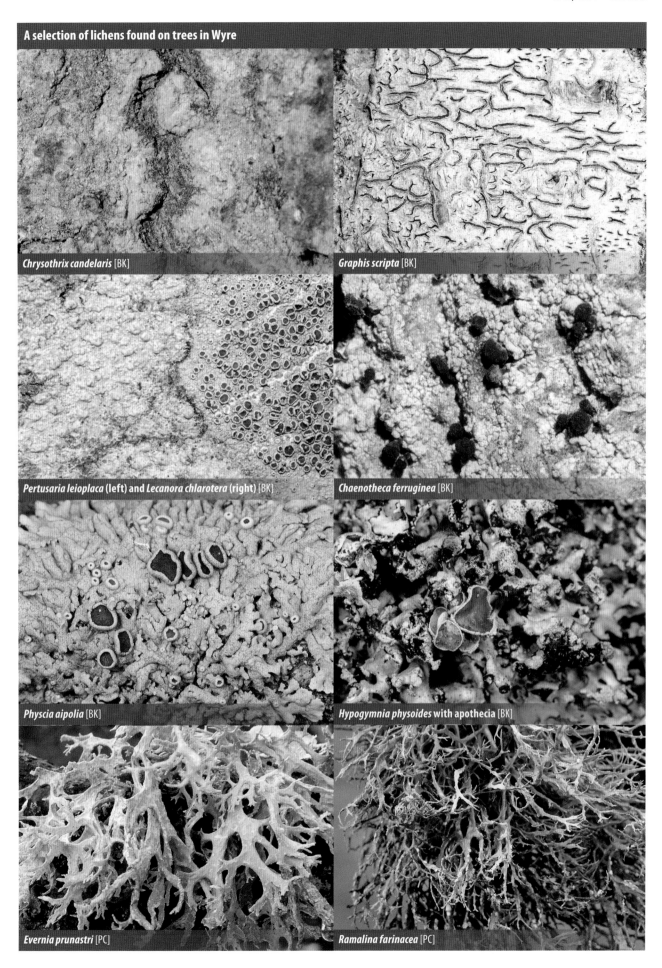

A selection of lichens found on trees in Wyre

Chrysothrix candelaris [BK]

Graphis scripta [BK]

Pertusaria leioplaca **(left)** and *Lecanora chlarotera* **(right)** [BK]

Chaenotheca ferruginea [BK]

Physcia aipolia [BK]

Hypogymnia physoides **with apothecia** [BK]

Evernia prunastri [PC]

Ramalina farinacea [PC]

Chapter 8

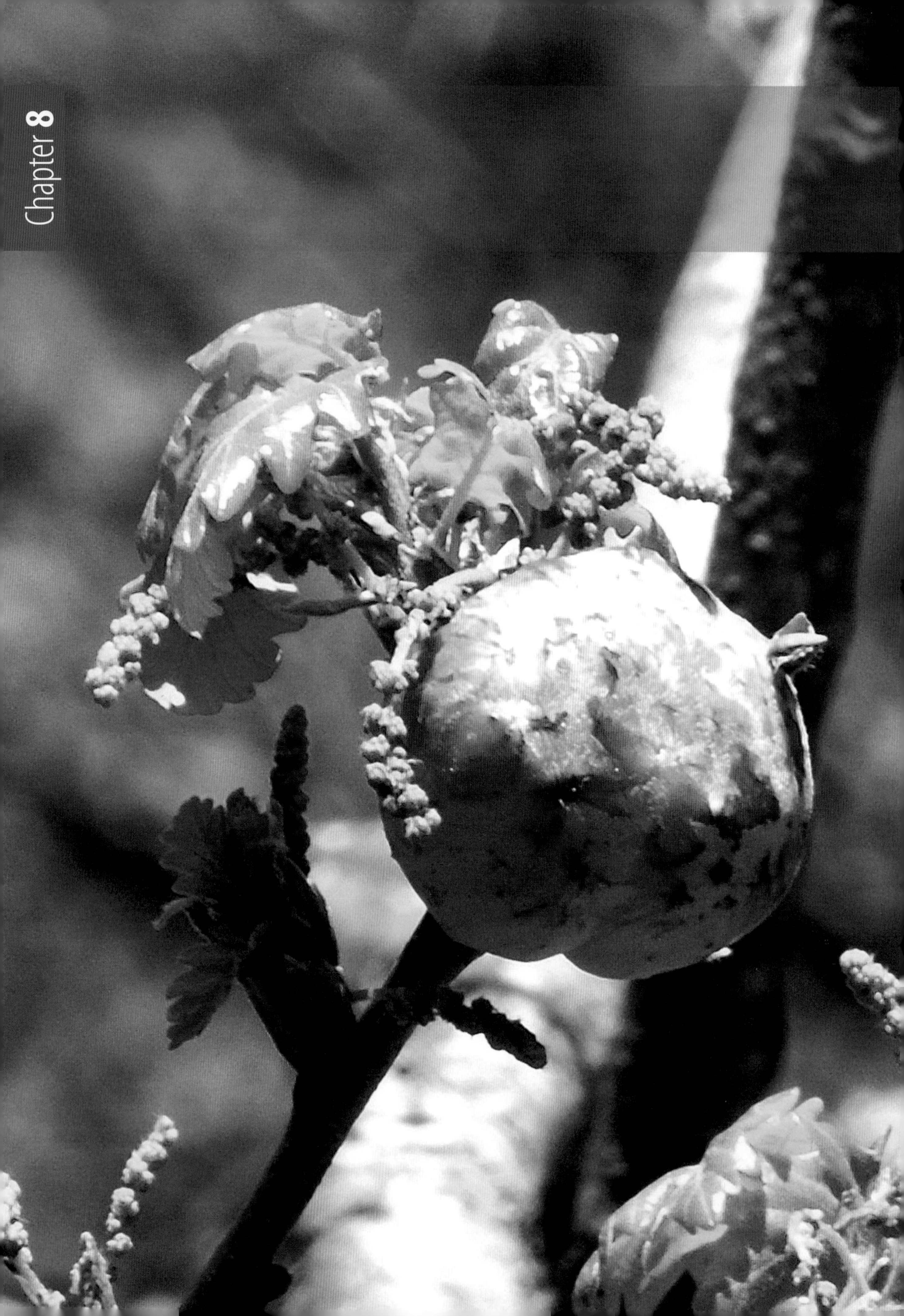

Galls

A walk in any part of the Forest will reveal a plethora of bumps, pimples and strangely shaped objects on the leaves, stems and flowers of trees, shrubs and wildflowers. These are usually galls, most often caused either by fungi or insects and mites. In the case of the last two they provide both shelter and a feast of nutritious tissue on which to feed. Norman Hickin said "The observer of galls will find much to interest him in Wyre". Those words are as true today as when he wrote them over 40 years ago (Hickin 1971). A study of the gall records of the Forest reveals however, that observers have been in short supply. This is despite the fact that Malvern-based biology teacher Arnold Darlington, an early trustee of the Worcestershire Wildlife Trust, was one of the few people championing gall studies in the 1960s and 1970s. For some years his publication *The Pocket Encyclopaedia of Plant Galls* (Darlington & Hirons 1968) was the only easily accessible source of information for the field naturalist. It is hoped that this account of our current knowledge of this eclectic and fascinating group in Wyre will inspire more observations and records.

Galls are growths, often complex and colourful, caused by other organisms, mainly on plants but also on fungi, lichens and algae. In addition to mites, insects and fungi, some nematodes, viruses and bacteria also cause galls. (A very few plants, including Mistletoe *Viscum album*, are gall-causers too.) Many galls are distinctive enough to be identified when the causer is absent, but this is not always so: in these cases the causer must be available for identification to name the gall (Redfern *et al.* 2011).

The biology and ecology of galls is complex: there is often far more going on inside a gall than an external examination suggests. For example, although galls offer protection to their inhabitants, other creatures have evolved ways to muscle in. There are specialist insects, called inquilines, which feed only on the nutritious gall tissue and may or may not bring about the death of the gall's creator. Parasitoids, especially but not exclusively

chalcid wasps, attack the gall-causers, inquilines and each other. The presence of these extra insects makes each individual gall a mini-ecosystem in its own right (Redfern *et al.* 2011).

The geographical position of Wyre Forest, the area it covers, the variety of habitats and land management, and the extensive tree cover, indicate great potential for a rich gall fauna. In Britain there are well over a thousand species of gall-causer (Chinery 2011) and nearly 200 of these have been recorded in Wyre. Although years of extensive coppicing in Wyre militates against fungi which need old, rotting trees, the opposite is the case with galls. They are very much phenomena of active growth, and are therefore often favoured by coppicing, natural succession and the planting of young trees.

Galls on shrubs and trees

Twenty-two galls have so far been recorded on Wyre oaks *Quercus* spp. a much smaller number than would be expected in such an extensive oak-rich forest. This may be partly due to the restricted distribution of Pedunculate Oak *Q. robur,* mainly along some of the valleys, compared to Sessile Oak *Q. petraea* and Hybrid Oak *Q.* × *rosacea.* Sessile Oak bears fewer galls than Pendunculate Oak and this may be true of their hybrid here. The hybrid is known to vary in the intermediate characteristics displayed by individual specimens, some tending to *petraea* and some to *robur.* This variation may well influence susceptibility to gall-causers and their effects. There do not seem to be any records of galls on the few Holm Oaks *Q. ilex* around Wyre. Most oak galls are caused by cynipid gall wasps, although the frequently recorded Psyllid *Trioza remota* is found on oak leaves. This is very insignificant compared to many other oak galls, being nothing more than a tiny pimple on the upperside with a nymph in the corresponding depression on the underside.

Gall wasps generally have two generations a year, each of which causes a distinctive gall either on the same or on different trees, or on different parts of the

A female Chalcid wasp *Megastigmus* sp. (Torymidae), a parasitoid, on the Marble Gall caused by *Andricus kollari*. [RW]

A selection of the 22 galls found on oaks *Quercus* spp. in Wyre

Oak Apple gall of *Biorhiza pallida* [RW]

Cherry Galls of *Cynips quercusfolii* [PC]

Marble Galls of *Andricus kollari* [JB]

Knopper Gall of *Andricus quercuscalicis* [JB]

Redcurrant-like galls of *Neuroterus quercusbaccarum* on catkins [RW]

Galls of the psyllid *Trioza remota* [RW]

Common Spangle Galls of *Neuroterus quercusbaccarum* [RW]

Silk-button Galls of *Neuroterus numismalis* [RW]

Flightless female gall wasp *Biorhiza pallida* [JB]

tree. Those appearing in the spring usually contain males and females of the sexual generation, whilst those appearing later in the year contain agamic females, able to reproduce without mating. Some species, particularly those which have arrived in this country in the last 100 years, require Turkey Oak *Q. cerris* to complete their lifecycle. One generation produces small galls in spring on Turkey Oak, and a second generation generally causes more prominent galls on Pedunculate and Sessile Oak in late summer. There are remarkably few records of these species in Wyre, which may reflect the small number of Turkey Oaks present; most are in Cleobury Coppice. One of the longest established and generally most common of this group is the Marble Gall-causer *Andricus kollari*.

A prominent member of the group which is in Wyre is the well-known Knopper Gall of *A. quercuscalicis*, a species which arrived and spread rapidly throughout the country in the 1960s (Claridge 1962; Darlington 1974). The gall is a mass of twisted tissue erupting from acorns, sticky, green and red at first, later hard and brown. In some years almost every acorn on some trees is affected. The spring generation causes galls on the catkins of Turkey Oak.

Other gall wasps present include *Biorhiza pallida*, which produces the well-known Oak Apples, *Neuroterus* spp. which cause spangle galls on leaves, and *Cynips* spp. which cause Pea and Cherry Galls

on leaves. Most easily recognised are the Cherry Galls of *C. quercusfolii* and the Striped Pea Galls of *C. quercuslongiventris*. An uncommon, but probably under-recorded gall is that of *Trigonaspis megaptera*. This is a waxy, white and pink gall found clustered on trunks and stems, often low down. There are few records but it was found at Ribbesford some years ago.

The *Neuroterus* Spangle Galls are often very numerous on the underside of leaves in the summer and autumn, especially those of another under-recorded species *N. quercusbaccarum*. One of the most attractive galls, which can also be very numerous, is the Silk-button Gall of *N. numismalis* with its covering of silky golden threads. These are all agamic generation galls: the sexual generation galls appear in the spring. The most prominent of these are the redcurrant-like galls of *N. quercusbaccarum* on leaves and catkins.

One of the most spectacular, beautiful and well-known galls of all is the Robin's Pin-cushion, or Bedeguar, gall of *Diplolepis rosae*. This appears on wild roses *Rosa* spp. and consists of a central mass of tissue, usually with dozens of cells each containing a larva, surrounded by branched, wiry hairs, green at first, then bright red and finally brown. The largest galls can be as big as a tennis ball, and old galls persist for a long time. Like oak apples they are often opened by birds, and perhaps by small mammals, searching for any insects left inside. The related *D. nervosa* can produce sputnik-like galls with spiky projections on the underside of leaves on roses.

Little red pustule galls on the upperside of leaves of maples and Sycamore *Acer* spp. are common. These are the work of eriophyid mites, such as *Aceria myriadeum* on Field Maple *Acer campestre*, and *A. cephalonea* and *A. macrorhyncha* on Sycamore *Acer pseudoplatanus*. Mites also cause the elongated pouches known as nail galls on leaves of limes, *Tilia* spp. The two species involved are *Eriophyes tiliae*, found on Large-leaved Lime *T. platyphyllos*, and *E. lateannulatus*, found on Small-leaved Lime *T. cordata*. Another type of mite gall is the felt-like patches of hairs, called erinea, on the leaves of many trees and shrubs. Amongst the most common are *Acalitus brevitarsus* on alder *Alnus* spp., *Acalitus rudis* on birch *Betula* spp. and *Aceria*

Robin's Pin-cushion, the gall of *Diplolepis rosae* on wild rose *Rosa* sp. [RW]

Galls of *Eriophyes torminalis* on Wild Service-tree *Sorbus torminalis* [RW]

Red Bean Galls of the sawfly *Pontania proxima* on willow *Salix* sp. [RW]

Gall of the fungus *Taphrina alni* on Alder *Alnus glutinosa* cone [JB]

nervisequa on Beech *Fagus sylvatica*. The only gall-causer recorded in Wyre on Wild Service-tree *Sorbus torminalis* is the mite *Eriophyes torminalis*. This produces rounded pustules up to 2 mm across on both surfaces of the leaves.

A very distinctive and prominent gall occurs in the petioles of Black-poplar *Populus nigra* and its hybrids. It is a twisted swelling caused by the aphid *Pemphigus spyrothecae*. Curiously the closely related and equally prominent gall of *P. bursarius*, which also occurs in the petioles is not yet recorded. A more unusual gall that has been recorded in Wyre is that of the beetle *Saperda populnea*, usually found on Aspen *Populus tremula*. The larva of the beetle bores into thin stems and causes them to swell. Prominent exit holes are left when the beetle emerges in the spring.

Willows, *Salix* spp., bear many different galls but these are probably the most under-recorded group of all in Wyre. Those that have been noted include the Bean Galls caused by sawflies (see below), midge galls created by *Rhabdophaga rosaria*, *Iteomyia major* and *I. capreae*, and the spindle-shaped stem galls of the tortrid moth Sallow-shoot Piercer *Cydia servillana*.

Rhabdophaga rosaria is found on a range of willows. It causes a very prominent rosette of bunched and distorted leaves in terminal buds, and old, brown galls persist through the winter. *Iteomyia capreae* is commonly encountered, as it names suggests, on sallows and their hybrids. It is easily recognised, causing a hard dome on the upperside of leaves, with a conical, red-rimmed opening on the underside. The gall is green at first, later it may be yellow, brown or red, and initially contains a white larva which turns orange or red before pupating.

The sawfly Bean Galls are caused either by species of *Pontania* or *Eupontania*. Of the four species recorded in Wyre the most easily seen are the Red Bean Galls of *Pontania proxima* found on White Willow *Salix alba* and Crack Willow *S. fragilis*. Each contains a single sawfly caterpillar which, when it is fully fed, bites a hole in the gall, drops to the ground and pupates in the soil.

A very distinctive gall is caused by the fungus *Taphrina alni* on the cones of Alder *Alnus glutinosa* and Grey Alder *A. incana*. It has been recorded in

recent years in the Forest. It grows as a tongue-like projection from the cone, changing from green to red or purple as it does so. It had only been recorded from Cornwall until the end of the 20th century, but now it is widespread in Britain.

The third most-recorded gall in Wyre is that caused by the gall midge *Taxomyia taxi* on Yew *Taxus baccata*: it catches the eye of passing naturalists. This occurs in two forms, one with a one-year and one with a two-year life cycle. They both produce an 'artichoke' gall composed of clusters of leaves in buds containing an orange larva. The gall is tighter and smaller in the two-year form, which is the commoner of the two; the one-year form is better described as an enlarged bud. Less often encountered, but worthy of note, is a gall caused by the moth Scarce Bright *Lampronia fuscatella* on small birches. The caterpillar feeds inside twigs, causing them to swell.

Galls on herbs and grasses

There are plenty of galls on the flowers and grasses around your feet, although they are not so easy to spot as those on trees which tend to be more at eye level. Swollen stems, bumps on leaves and modified flowers and seed pods abound and are often noted by botanists. Many of these are caused by gall midges and other flies. The most recorded gall in Wyre is that of the very common and widespread gall midge *Dasineura urticae*

Gall (centre) of *Dasineura urticae* on a flower bud of Common Nettle *Urtica dioica* [RW]

on Common Nettle *Urtica dioica*. The gall is a thick swelling (often several coalesce) mainly on leaves and petioles, but also on stems. The galls contain one or more white larvae.

Other *Dasineura* galls recorded on herbaceous hosts include: *D. trifolii* on clovers *Trifolium* spp., which causes leaflets to swell and fold into the form of a pod, and *D. pustulans* and *D. ulmaria* on Meadowsweet *Filipendula ulmaria*. The former causes pustules or small swellings on the upperside of leaves with a corresponding depression and yellow patch on the underside, whilst the latter produces rounded, often reddish, swellings on the upperside of leaves with hairy conical projections on the underside.

The second most-recorded gall in Wyre is that of the gall midge *Jaapiella veronicae* on Germander Speedwell *Veronica chamaedrys*. The gall consists of either thickened terminal leaves pressed together to form a hairy pouch, or swollen flower buds, protecting the midge's orange-red larva and pupa.

In Britain the daisy family Asteraceae supports more gall-causers than any other. Amongst the easiest to find are the stem galls of the tephritid fly *Urophora cardui* on thistles *Cirsium* spp. It is a prominent swelling, up to 10 × 3 cm, which persists through the winter, making it particularly easy to find in that season. In summer the gall is green and fleshy, later it becomes brown and woody. This is a southern species becoming less common from the midlands northwards. Other tephritids (picture-wing flies) found in Wyre in the flowerheads of thistles, Musk Thistle *Carduus nutans* and knapweeds *Centaurea* spp. are

Picture-winged flies *Urophora jaceana*, gall-causers of Common Knapweed *Centaurea nigra* [RW]

Urophora jaceana, *U. stylata*, *U. quadrifasciata* and *U. solstitialis*. The galls are obscure, within flowerheads, causing hardened tissue in receptacles and achenes, which means that, although often present, they are easily overlooked. A beetle, *Rhinocyllus conicus*, which causes similar galls in Musk Thistle and Spear Thistle *Cirsium vulgare* has been recorded. This species is thought to be restricted to southern England so may be at its northern limit in Wyre.

Right down at ground level are the only cynipid galls recorded in Wyre that do not occur on oaks or roses. One of those is *Xestophanes potentillae* which has Creeping Cinquefoil *Potentilla reptans* as its host. The galls are swellings 2–3 mm in diameter, often in groups or sausage-shaped chains, in petioles and stems

A stem gall on Creeping Thistle *Cirsium arvense* [RW] caused by the picture-winged fly *Urophora cardui* (pictured below [PB]).

Gall of *Xestophanes potentillae* on Creeping Cinquefoil *Potentilla reptans* [RW]

Apion frumentarium a gall-causing weevil of docks and sorrels *Rumex* spp. [JB]

Galls of Ergot *Claviceps purpurea* on grass [RW]

Gall of *Chirosia grossicauda* on Bracken *Pteridium aquilinum* [RW]

on or just beneath the ground. They persist and may be found at any time of the year. Also close to the ground are the green or reddish galls of the cynipid *Liposthenes glechomae*, and the 'lighthouse gall' of *Rondaniola bursaria*, a midge gall, both on the leaves of Ground-ivy *Glechoma hederacea*. The latter is one of the most frequently recorded galls in Wyre.

There is a smattering of records of beetle gall-causers. These include *Apion frumentarium* which appears as swellings in the roots and stems of docks and sorrels *Rumex* spp., *Rhinusa linariae* and *R. antirrhini* on Common Toadflax *Linaria vulgaris*, and *Mecinus pyraster* on Ribwort Plantain *Plantago lanceolata*. *R. linariae* causes rounded nodules in roots and root collars, *R. antirrhini* affects flowerheads, resulting in papery fruits containing swollen seeds each enclosing a characteristic beetle larva. *M. pyraster* causes swellings in stems and flower stalks.

Some fungi are gall-causers. One is the economically important infestation of grasses (Poaceae) called Ergot *Claviceps purpurea*. This causes purplish projections in the inflorescences of many different species of grasses. It was recorded in Wyre throughout the 20th century and is still common. Another widely and frequently recorded genus is *Puccinia* which, with 25 species, is the most diverse

genus of gall-causers so far recorded here. *Puccinias* are rusts with complex life cycles, sometimes involving more than one plant species. Amongst the hosts are Marsh-marigold *Caltha palustris*, Daisy *Bellis perennis*, Ground-ivy, Nipplewort *Lapsana communis*, mints *Mentha* spp., and Bugloss *Anchusa arvensis*.

Other galls

Finally, there are galls on ferns and one on a fungus. Wyre is home to one of the curiosities of the gall world: a fungus which galls other fungi. This is the Powdercap Strangler *Squamanita paradoxa*. There is an account of this species in Chapter 6 on Fungi (see page 101).

Two galls on ferns caused by Anthomyid flies in the genus *Chirosia* are in the top five most-recorded galls in Wyre. *C. betuleti* occurs on Lady-fern *Athyrium filix-femina*, and on male-ferns and buckler-ferns, *Dryopteris* spp. The gall is a distinctive and prominent mop-head at the end of fronds with a white larva inside. *C. grossicauda* occurs on Bracken *Pteridium aquilinum*. It causes the tips of pinnules to roll downwards; inside the roll a white larva mines the main vein. Also the gall of the midge *Dasineura pteridis*, the vernacular name of which is 'little black pudding', is found on Bracken. As the name suggests the gall is a thickened, black roll which appears on the pinnulets.

Chapter 9

Insects

With the exception of microscopic life, insects outnumber all other species in Wyre, where they have colonised every ecological niche from tree canopy to leaf litter. Many of them are small or inconspicuous and go unnoticed unless found by special searches: others are difficult to identify.

There are 27 distinctive Orders (groups) of insects in Britain and Ireland comprising over 25,000 known species. Those groups containing most species are flies (7,000), Hymenoptera (7,000), beetles (4,000), bugs (1,800) and butterflies and moths (2,500) (Barnard 2011). These groups are well-represented in Wyre which is home to many nationally scarce or local insects. In this chapter, we consider a number of the more familiar insects; the butterflies and moths, dragonflies and damselflies, grasshoppers and crickets, bugs, beetles, flies, ants, bees and wasps.

Butterflies

A sunny spring walk in Wyre is always enlivened by butterflies. Pearl-bordered Fritillaries *Boloria euphrosyne* flit over clearings and streamside meadows and, with luck and the right location, you may see a delicate Wood White *Leptidea sinapis* or a Grizzled Skipper *Pyrgus malvae*. In high summer, the stands of Hemp-agrimony *Eupatorium cannabinum* along Dowles Brook are alive with Peacocks *Aglais io* and Silver-washed Fritillaries *Argynnis paphia*, jostling for nectar on the dusky-pink flowerheads.

The Forest has always been, and still is, well known for its variety of butterflies. Many species common here are now in national decline or have largely disappeared from elsewhere in the Midlands. Visitors are attracted from far and wide to enjoy and photograph these stunning insects.

Dipping into *The Transactions of the Worcestershire Naturalists' Club* makes fascinating reading and offers not only an insight into the butterflies of the day, but also a glimpse of the character of the 19th century Forest. The Club was founded in 1847 and during a field visit in August 1853 members visited the already famous Whitty Pear, the Great Bog and Dowles Brook. There the 'Entomologist-general', who no doubt had his own special top hat to designate his rank, displayed his captures of the day. These included Wood White, Small Skipper *Thymelicus sylvestris*, Comma *Polygonia c-album*, Speckled Wood *Pararge aegeria*, Silver-washed Fritillary, Dark Green Fritillary *Argynnis aglaja* and Black-veined White *Aporia crataegi*. The last species disappeared from Wyre long ago and is now extinct in Britain.

From the contemporary accounts, there is a strong sense of a forest much more open in character than today. "Wyre Forest itself ... is made up of an infinitude (*sic*) of dwarf oaks, cut down at intervals for charcoal, and consequently there are no trees of any magnitude" (Worcestershire Naturalists' Club 1869). Records of Dark Green Fritillary, Black-veined White and even Grayling *Hipparchia semele* (Rae & Fletcher 1901 in the Victoria County History) all suggest that open grassland (including orchards) and heathland must have been much more extensive in and around the Forest. While reports show that plants and fungi appear to have been the main pre-occupations of early visiting naturalists, butterflies, by their sheer abundance, were noticed from time to time. For example, the Worcestershire Naturalists' Club report of a half-day walk in July 1895 records "whilst *Argynnis adippe* (High Brown Fritillary) and *Paphia* (Silver-washed Fritillary) greeted the members'

The Wood White *Leptidea sinapis* prefers open rides and sunny paths where trefoils and vetches, its larval foodplants, flourish. [RW]

sight at every sunny spot hovering on the flowers of *Carduus acanthoides* (Welted Thistle)" (*Worcestershire Naturalists' Club Transactions* 1895).

Changes in the Forest landscape during the 20th century were detrimental. Conifer planting was much lamented by the naturalists of the day: "In recent years this large portion of Forest has been reforested with conifers, and it is feared this will lead to the eradication of several rare plants owing to the altered conditions by the dense growth of the bracken, thistles and other coarse herbs which choke the more delicate ones. It will also undoubtedly change the character and beauty of this primeval forest" (Worcestershire Naturalists' Club 1932). Certainly many coniferised areas became shaded and much less attractive, but the Forest is still one of England's best woodland locations for butterflies. Thirty-four species are regularly seen, around half of the British total. This is a significant number because many of the absentees are restricted to specialist habitats associated with chalk downland, lowland heath, peat bogs and moorland, or are at the edge of their current range in southern England.

The main reasons for the amazing diversity of butterflies are the long history and continuity of management, whether as a result of charcoal burning, coppicing or timber production, ensuring that Wyre has retained an open character. There have always been some sunny glades or clearings, and wide woodland rides and tracks, providing warmth-loving species with nectar and breeding plants. This mosaic of habitats together with the variety of management provides many different ecological niches and habitats for butterflies. Wyre also has a long history as ancient woodland dating back to pre-Domesday times and its 2,600 hectares make it one of the largest intact blocks of surviving ancient semi-natural woodland in the UK.

As a result Wyre still holds many species, such as Pearl-bordered Fritillary and Wood White, which have been lost completely from many parts of the country and are undergoing catastrophic national decline. In addition to Pearl-bordered Fritillary, the Forest is particularly well known for its other fritillaries, including Small Pearl-bordered *Boloria selene* and Silver-washed, both of which maintain relatively strong populations.

Other species have fared less well. Perhaps the saddest loss has been the High Brown Fritillary *Argynnis adippe* which declined drastically in the 1980s and became extinct here soon after. This very striking butterfly, about the size of a Peacock, is splashed with silver on its underwings and Norman Hickin (1971) called the butterfly 'Silver Spangles'. For some of the others, like Marsh Fritillary *Euphydryas aurinia* and Dark Green Fritillary, there are relatively few modern records. Marsh Fritillary has not been recorded since 1948 (Riley 1991).

Another butterfly which has disappeared is the Wall Brown *Lasiommata megera* which used to be relatively common. Like the High Brown Fritillary this has declined nationally as well as locally, and is now virtually extinct in Worcestershire. Hickin's (1971)

Butterflies on the increase in Wyre

White Admiral *Limentis camilla* [RW]

Marbled White *Melanargia galathea* [RW]

book serves as a timely reminder that nothing stands still in the natural world: a number of butterflies, including Dingy Skipper *Erynnis tages*, Grizzled Skipper and Small Heath *Coenonympha pamphilus*, then described as "common and widespread" are now greatly reduced and only found in certain areas.

There have been arrivals as well as departures. During the last 40 years new species have colonised and others have increased. Notable amongst these is the White Admiral *Limenitis camilla*, a graceful species whose soaring flight enlivens dappled rides in summer. This butterfly often visits bramble flowers for nectar and lays its eggs on Honeysuckle *Lonicera periclymenum* growing in semi-shade. It has been slowly moving northwards in Britain, partly in response to global warming, and now appears to be resident in several parts of the Forest including Eymore Wood east of the Severn. Another attractive colonist is Marbled White *Melanargia galathea* which again has spread from the south in recent years. It now seems to be established locally on the Forest fringes and in some of the meadows along Dowles Brook. Occasional reports of Dark Green Fritillary, followed by more regular sightings in recent years, suggest this species is becoming established here again.

Less striking in appearance, but also newly arrived, are Brown Argus *Aricia agestis* and Essex Skipper

Wyre's fritillary butterflies that grace the forest clearings in summer sunshine

Pearl-bordered Fritillary *Boloria euphrosyne* has increased since the woodland has been opened up (male left [RW], mating pair right [JB])

Small Pearl-bordered Fritillary *Boloria selene* may be found in damp areas (male left [JB], underside right [JB])

Dark Green Fritillary *Argynnis aglaja*, a recent coloniser in Wyre (male left [CR], underside right [JB])

Silver-washed Fritillary *Argynnis paphia*, the largest of Wyre's fritillaries (male left [DW], underside right [JB])

Thymelicus lineola both increasingly recorded in recent years. Interestingly, there is a record of Essex Skipper from Arley around 1900 in the collection of Charles Simmonds, a local entomologist living in Kidderminster (Green 1982). The first modern-day record was in 2005 (Grundy 2006) although the butterfly is now well established along rides and in meadows. The Brown Argus, like the Essex Skipper, can be easily overlooked and also seems to have benefitted from climate change. It now lays its eggs on a range of annual crane's-bills *Geranium* spp. and stork's-bills, *Erodium* spp., which occur throughout Wyre, rather than the more typical Rock-rose *Helianthemum nummularium* which is absent.

The national decline of many woodland butterflies, especially the Pearl-bordered Fritillary, is associated with the lack of open space in modern-day woodland. Many species are very selective in their choice of egg-laying sites: for example some butterflies need their caterpillars' food plants to be growing in hot and sunny positions. Once this was provided by normal woodland management, including coppicing, which created a succession of open clearings and rides. As the demand for traditional woodland products declined, woodlands became shadier and, in places, conifers were planted. As a result, many butterflies and other sun-loving insects and plants declined or disappeared.

These processes certainly affected Wyre and led to increased involvement by conservation charities such as Butterfly Conservation which established regular butterfly monitoring by setting up two transects in the late 1970s and early 1980s. Since then it has been actively involved in the conservation of butterflies and moths in the Forest, in partnership with private woodland owners, the Forestry Commission, and Natural England.

The conservation aim is to reverse butterfly declines by restoring a more diverse woodland structure including new clearings and a network of sunny open rides. This should provide ideal conditions for a wide range of wildlife as well as butterflies and moths. Cattle grazing has also been re-instated as it is important in maintaining many of the flower-rich meadows along the main Dowles Valley corridor. These provide important nectar sources for a variety of species, including the sun-loving fritillaries.

Now, as the Forest is being opened up, the butterflies are returning. The year begins with the first Commas, Peacocks and Brimstones *Gonepteryx rhamni* flying in late-winter sun in late February and March. More Red Admirals *Vanessa atalanta* now overwinter in Britain and may be on the wing in January.

In April they are joined by Orange-tips *Anthocharis cardamines*, Holly Blues *Celastrina argiolus*, Green-veined Whites *Pieris napi* and Speckled Woods. In late April and early May the first Pearl-bordered Fritillaries are on the wing in Dowles Valley. As the month unfolds, they are joined by many Common Blues *Polyommatus icarus* and occasional Dingy Skippers, Grizzled Skippers and Small Coppers *Lycaena phlaeas*.

Another springtime butterfly whose appearance is rather unpredictable is the Green Hairstreak *Callophrys rubi*. Its caterpillars have a varied diet and in Wyre are associated with Bilberry *Vaccinium myrtillus*, gorse *Ulex* spp. and Broom *Cytisus scoparius,* and the adults are usually seen flying erratically in heathy places.

The end of May sees the emergence of the first Large Skippers *Ochlodes sylvanus* and Small Pearl-bordered Fritillaries. The latter are generally not as numerous as Pearl-bordered, and within Wyre are associated with more sheltered and damp grassy habitats, such as the area around the Great Bog. June can sometimes be a quiet month for butterflies but generally Meadow Browns *Maniola jurtina* and Ringlets *Aphantopus hyperantus* emerge before the end of the month, sometimes joined by the first Silver-washed Fritillaries.

Brown Argus *Aricia agestis* [KMcG]

Green Hairstreak *Callophrys rubi* [JB]

Grizzled Skipper *Pyrgus malvae* [BK]

In a good year all three of these can be quite numerous. The sight of a group of Silver-washed Fritillaries feasting on the flowers of a patch of brambles or a group of thistles along the old railway line is truly spectacular.

July is generally the height of the butterfly season with the first species of high summer joined by Gatekeepers *Pyronia tithonus*, Small Skippers, White Admirals and Essex Skippers. This is also the month for looking skyward in the hope of spotting the diminutive Purple Hairstreak *Favonius quercus* spiralling around the canopy of the oak trees, and it is worth keeping a look-out near elm for occasional White-letter Hairstreaks *Satyrium w-album* which still occur but are seldom reported. A third member of the hairstreak family, Brown Hairstreak *Thecla betulae*, appears not to have been recorded from the main Forest since 1908, apart from an unconfirmed record from Ribbesford Wood over 40 years ago (Grundy 2006). Locally this butterfly is confined to a small area of east Worcestershire, having disappeared from elsewhere in the region.

Towards the end of July competition for the flowers of thistles and Teasel *Dipsacus fullonum* comes in the shape of newly emerging Peacocks, Commas, Large Whites *Pieris brassicae* and Brimstones. Numbers of the two truly migrant species, Painted Lady *Vanessa cardui* and Clouded Yellow *Colias croceus*, vary from year to year. August is often a good month to spot them as then they are at their most numerous following breeding by early summer arrivals.

Come September, and depending to some extent on weather, the butterfly season begins to wind down. Silver-washed Fritillaries often last until the first few days of the month but the main interest is provided by the occasional sighting of Commas and Red Admirals

Red Admiral *Vanessa atalanta* [RW]

and, if the weather is kind, Green-veined White and Speckled Wood, species which have more than one generation a year.

Prospects for butterflies in the Forest look bright. Local organisations, including Butterfly Conservation, the Forestry Commission, Natural England, the Wyre Community Land Trust and the Wyre Forest Study Group are working together to enhance and extend the habitats on which many of the specialist species depend. The intention is to develop a strategic approach to land management which should result in many long-term benefits for wildlife. Improved connectivity within the Forest will be an important aspect of this work, as will the involvement of local coppice workers to try to encourage more sustainable woodland management. At the same time, great efforts are being made to improve the recording and monitoring of important species and to involve the local community in learning more about butterflies and their requirements.

Pearl-bordered Fritillary—partnership working and monitoring

One successful example of close partnership working is that between Butterfly Conservation, the Forestry Commission, and Natural England relating to the Pearl-bordered Fritillary. This is one of the fastest declining butterflies in the UK with the most recent analysis showing a distribution loss of 43% (the second greatest in the UK), and a similar decline in abundance of 42% between 1995–99 and 2005–09 (Fox *et al.* 2011).

In Wyre Forest monitoring continues today with two original butterfly transects set up in the late 1970s: this has recently increased to include two more transects and a large number of timed counts. Timed counts are particularly suitable in a changing landscape where occupancy of a single site may only last a few years. These increased monitoring levels have clearly shown that Wyre can support a thriving Pearl-bordered Fritillary metapopulation (caterpillar pictured [RW]) through targeted work creating more linked corridors and glades and through good ride-side management. For example, in 2011, 11 large, three medium and 16 small colonies were identified by timed counts.

(Colony size taken from Oates (2003): large equals peak season counts of 50 or more, medium equals 21–49, small equals 20 or less.) This is an improvement compared with no large, four medium and 11 small colonies in 2002. Timed-count population increases were mirrored by transect counts, with annual indices from both the Wyre Forest East and Wyre Forest West routes increasing in 2010 (to 43 and 28 respectively) and in 2011 (to 186 and 318). As a result of these increased numbers, the Pearl-bordered Fritillary population index for the Wyre Forest between 2002 and 2011 increased by 113% in comparison to a non-significant trend across the whole UK during the same time period.

Butterfly Conservation was also able to determine that between 2002 and 2011 the management of open space and ride and track edges was just as important as coppice and clear-fell, and that the amount of occupied habitat had nearly doubled from 27 ha in 2002 to 52 ha in 2011. Targeted management near existing occupied sites within the main Forest block was a key factor in the level of success (Ellis, Bourn & Bulman 2012).

Moths

The Wyre Forest area is one of the most important for moths in the West Midlands and, in terms of numbers, one of the best in the UK. To date 1,187 species have been recorded: 1,112 in the woodland and in-lying orchards and meadows, the other 75 close by in Bewdley and adjacent sites. As well as the large variety of species the number of individual insects is extraordinary: so many come to light traps in the Forest on warm summer nights that they give rise to an atmosphere of increasing anticipation and excitement among those present.

The Forest has been well known as an exceptional place for Lepidoptera since the mid-19th century. The advent of the railway age enabled Victorians to visit and collect insects here. Since then there has been continuing interest and visits from many entomologists especially, in the past, to see Kentish Glory *Endromis versicolora* in its only English site.

There are rarities in Wyre's oakwoods. Common Fan-foot *Pechipogo strigilata* is now nationally rare, having declined across southern and Midland England, probably because of cessation of coppicing, but it occurs widely in the Forest which may be its most important UK site. It often comes to light, can be disturbed during the day, and the larvae feed on wilted oak leaves. Dave Grundy has mapped the moth's distribution in Wyre. He creates larval habitats by snapping small terminal branches of oaks in late spring or early summer. By leaving them hanging he is able to record the caterpillars feeding on the wilted leaves.

Wild Service-tree *Sorbus torminalis* occurs widely in Wyre oakwoods, but is a foodplant for relatively few moths. In 1990 Tony Simpson found leaf-mines containing yellow larvae of a *Stigmella* species on Wild Service-tree. They were reared in captivity and

Drab Looper *Minoa murinata* [RW]

identified as Wild-service Pigmy *S. mespilicola,* which otherwise only occurs in the UK on the Great Doward in Herefordshire, and in Gloucestershire where it has recently been found. Intriguingly, there were also two green larvae which were not reared and may possibly represent an undescribed *Stigmella* species: they remain a mystery and a challenge to future searchers.

Other species of note are listed in Table 5. In addition to these, the bark miners Oak-bark Pigmy *Ectoedemia atrifrontella* and *E. longicaudella* are fairly common in the thin bark of small sapling oaks *Quercus* spp.: the only adults to have been dissected to identify them were *atrifrontella*. Rare Scarce Bright *Lampronia fuscatella* galls occur on small birches *Betula* spp. Flying on late spring and summer days, the beige-coloured Drab Looper *Minoa murinata,* a nationally scarce species has, along with the micromoth Spurge Marble *Lobesia occidentis,* good localised colonies on Wood Spurge *Euphorbia amygdaloides,* which grows

The Common Fan-foot *Pechipago strigilata* is Nationally Scarce but occurs in Wyre, flying in May and June [JB]. The caterpillar (below [DG]) feeds on withered oak leaves hanging from damaged tree branches.

profusely in the early stage of succession after felling and coppicing.

Other notable and characteristic species include Great Prominent *Peridea anceps* and Lobster Moth *Stauropus fagi* which come to light; Blossom Underwing *Orthosia miniosa*, whose attractive larvae initially feed communally on oak; Square Spot *Paradarisa consonaria* are fairly widespread; the beautiful Orange Moth *Angerona prunaria* occurs in its only Worcestershire site; Great Oak Beauty *Hypomecis roboraria* is still frequent (it is nationally local and declining), and Pale Oak Beauty *H. punctinalis* occurs in one of its most northerly UK sites. Among the micromoths Orange-headed Pigmy *Stigmella svenssoni*, Four-spotted Clothes *Triaxomera fulvimitrella*, Gold-bent Midget *Phyllonorycter roboris* and Western Midget *P. muelleriella*, Black-spotted Groundling *Pseudotelphusa scalella*, and Small Buckthorn Roller *Ancylis obtusana* are widespread, and Northern Grey *Scoparia ancipitella*, Rust-blotched Cosmet *Mompha lacteella*, and Dark Roller *A. upupana* are present. Two notable species of 'bagworm moths' Psychidae occur; two larval cases of Shining Smoke *Bacotia sepium* have been found, out of which a male was reared, and larval cases and males of Lesser Lichen Case-bearer *Dahlica inconspicuella* are often found in spring on old posts and tree trunks, mainly along the old railway line.

One of the great challenges in Wyre is finding the Forest's clearwings. These wasp-mimics are notoriously elusive, but the advent of pheromone lures has increased our chances of locating them in the right habitats. Where oaks have been recently felled, Yellow-legged Clearwing *Synanthedon vespiformis* comes to lures in many parts of the Forest, and on hot days can be seen flying around cut stumps. Red-belted Clearwing *S. myopaeformis* occurs in at least one of the orchards, and Currant Clearwing *S. tipuliformis* is found in local gardens. Where young birch abounds in clearings, there is a chance of seeing the Large Red-belted Clearwing *S. culiciformis* which turned up most recently in May 2014.

If the moths themselves are hard to track down, their tell-tale feeding signs can be more obvious. The spectacular Lunar Hornet Moth *Sesia bembiciformis*, which looks uncannily like a giant furry wasp, makes feeding tunnels in Goat Willow *Salix caprea* stems and its large exit holes near the base of the trunk are seen much more often than the adult. One of the more secretive clearwings, the White-barred Clearwing *Synanthedon spheciformis* is now a local species in the British Isles. It seems to occur extensively among the Alders *Alnus glutinosa* along Dowles Brook and in the adjacent meadows. This moth enthused Norman Hickin on a hot June day when he saw it for the first time, searching for egg-laying sites along an alder-lined stream "hardly flying, but hovering like a hummingbird". This encounter inspired him to write that "to be present in the Forest at the emergence time of this rare and beautiful creature was a most

Great Prominent *Peridea anceps* [KMcG]

Lobster Moth *Stauropus fagi* caterpillar [PC]

Orange Moth *Angerona prunaria* [PCI]

Red-belted Clearwing *Synanthedon myopaeformis* [PCI]

stimulating experience such that even though, later that day I drove one hundred and forty-four miles across England to my home in Surrey, I was Forest refreshed." (Hickin 1965)

There are other beautiful and uncommon moths in Wyre and some of the most exquisite species are deadwood-feeding micromoths. Silver-streaked Tubic *Schiffermuelleria grandis* flies in May and June, early in the morning when it gleams like burnished copper with flashes of metallic steely-blue. It was first described from a specimen from 'Bewdley Forest' in 1842 (Devignes 1842) and not found again until recently, but there are now many records from Ribbesford Wood as well as two in the main Forest block.

One of the most spectacular micromoths is Gold-base Tubic *Oecophora bractella* which is widespread in Wyre. Its larvae are easily found under the bark of log piles, stumps and dead branches in sunny positions. The adult moths fly by day or night in late spring and early summer and are recognised by streaks of iridescent blue or purple contrasting with custard-yellow splashes on their forewings. Scarce Forest Tubic *Esperia oliviella* also seems fairly widespread, especially along Dowles Brook. It has been reared in large numbers from rotten oak stumps and dead Pear *Pyrus communis* and Apple *Malus domestica* in orchards. The cream-striped adults sit on young oak regrowth on sunny days or flutter around dead branches. A more modestly marked but local species Tinted Tubic *Crassa*

tinctella has been taken at light, and like the other three nationally rare dead wood feeders mentioned here, is a good ancient woodland indicator.

The small assarted meadows and orchards in the Forest, carved from the original wildwood, are often flower rich, with large numbers of anthills. Day-flying moths can be obvious in these habitats and include Six-spot and Narrow-bordered Five-spot Burnets *Zygaena filipendulae* and *Z. lonicerae*, Mother Shipton *Euclidia mi* and Burnet Companion *E. glyphica*. Where their foodplant Yellow Rattle *Rhinanthus minor* grows there may be Grass Rivulets *Perizoma albulata* and, if there is Pignut *Conopodium majus* in the meadows, look out for the delicate day-flying Chimney Sweeper *Odezia atrata* whose sooty forewings are tipped with white.

Less common species include the beautiful iridescent long-horn moths, Coppery Long-horn *Nemophora cupriacella* and Small Long-horn *N. minimella* which occur locally where their foodplant, Devil's-bit Scabious *Succisa pratensis* grows. A rare grassland micromoth is Confluent Groundling *Caryocolum junctella* which hibernates as an adult. Its larvae have been found in meadows feeding in spinnings on Lesser Stitchwort *Stellaria graminea* growing on anthills often capped with Wild Thyme *Thymus polytrichus* (Simpson 1996). The larvae of Thyme Plume *Merrifieldia leucodactyla* also feeds on Thyme. Downland Case-bearer *Coleophora lixella*, which feeds on Wild Thyme and then grasses, was rediscovered in 1971 having been previously

Six-spot Burnet *Zygaena filipendulae* [RW]

Burnet Companion *Euclidia glyphica* [JB]

Chimney Sweeper *Odezia atrata* [PC]

Some Forest micromoths, common and rare

Brassy Long-horn *Nemophora metallica* [JB]

Gold-base Tubic
Oecophora bractella [PCI]

Silver-streaked Tubic
Schiffermuelleria grandis [RW]

Spurge Marble
Lobesia occidentis [OW]

Currant Shoot Borer
Lampronia capitella [OW]

Yellow-barred Gold
Micropterix aureatella [PC]

Yellow-triangle Slender
Caloptilia alchimiella [OW]

Notch Wing Tortrix
Aclaris emargana [OW]

Green Oak Tortrix
Tortrix viridana [KMcG]

White Plume
Pterophorus pentadactyla [KMcG]

Pearl Grass-veneer
Catoptria pinella [OW]

Beautiful China-mark
Nymphula nitidulata [KMcG]

Common Purple and Gold
Pyrausta purpuralis [RW]

recorded in 1889. One grassland moth which may have disappeared is the Pimpernel Pug *Eupithecia pimpinellata*; it has not been found since 1982.

The oozing patches of wet ground formed by flushes in parts of the Forest have their own special moths. Here Common Skullcap *Scutellaria galericulata* and Lesser Skullcap *S. minor* support the polka-dotted pair Silver-dot Twitcher *Prochoreutis sehestediana* and Small Twitcher *P. myllerana* which are locally common in midsummer. Strawberry Bright *Incurvaria praelatella* is associated with Meadowsweet *Filipendula ulmaria*; Little Slender *Calybites phasianipennella* with *Persicaria* spp.; Bitter-cress Smudge *Eidophasia messingiella* with Cuckooflower *Cardamine pratensis,* and Thin-barred Dwarf *Elachista gleichenella* with sedges *Carex* spp. All occur in these habitats. One former garden pest is the Currant Shoot Borer *Lampronia capitella* whose brown and white adults are now decidedly local. It has recently been found however, feeding on Red Currant *Ribes rubrum* growing along streamsides, where the wilted top shoots of the foodplant in April betray the presence of the larvae.

A number of species have recently been recorded for the first time in Wyre and, excluding known migrants, it is difficult to know whether these were previously overlooked or are new arrivals. A single Welsh Wave *Venusia cambrica* at Bliss Gate was probably only a vagrant, but Devon Carpet *Lampropteryx otregiata* seems to have spread into the West Midlands recently and there are now widespread records here. Little Thorn *Cepphis advenaria* had been last recorded in 1899, but there were records in 2008 and 2013, which may be rediscoveries. This may also be the case with the record of Waved Carpet *Hydrelia sylvata* in 2011. There are single records of Marsh Pug *Eupithecia pygmaeata,* in 2008, and Valerian Pug *E. valerianata* in 2003. John Bingham photographed a single Wood Tiger *Parasemia plantaginis* in 2004, but this moth has never been found since and its origin is unknown. One tiger-moth which is spreading rapidly is the harlequin-patterned Scarlet Tiger *Callimorpha dominula* which now flies by day in Forest clearings. It is well established along the nearby River Severn where its black and yellow larvae feed openly on comfrey *Symphytum* sp.

Not all moth news is as welcome. Although some Wyre species have been lost due to national influences, undoubtedly changes in woodland management have had a great impact on some of the species which have recently disappeared. From the 17th to 19th centuries there was widespread coppicing associated with the need for large amounts of charcoal for industry. This changed woodscapes which had previously been deer forest and woodland pasture but beneficially maintained the open areas. In the 1920s there were major changes with cessation of coppicing and widespread planting of oaks and beeches and later coniferisation. The maturing timber increasingly shaded out much of the Forest. Increasing Fallow Deer

Dama dama numbers may not have helped by reducing coppice regrowth.

Of the 1,187 recorded moth species in Wyre, only 42 have not been recorded since 1980 (Harper & Simpson 2001 & 2003). At least ten of these are probably still present, and could be expected to be found again. Many of the others have declined nationally, often for unknown reasons, and most have not been seen for many years.

Wyre was the last refuge of the Kentish Glory in England. This spectacular moth needs young birches on which the females lay their eggs. The loss of coppicing and reduction in birch regrowth must have been the main cause of its decline and eventual disappearance. The final *coup de grace* was, perhaps, the clearance of rideside birches in the early 1970s with the last record in 1972. The Argent and Sable *Rheumaptera hastata* may also have become extinct in Wyre due to the dearth of small birches, as the last record of this beautiful and conspicuous day-flying moth was in 1998, but the reasons for its decline in southern Britain may also be climatic.

Other losses and reductions include the Small Eggar *Eriogaster lanestris* which probably disappeared as a result of mechanical management of hedgerows. Pale Shining Brown *Polia bombycina* and Bordered Gothic *Heliophobus reticulata* may have died out when their favoured open unmanaged habitats were lost to intensive agriculture. Some species have markedly changed their range in the UK, perhaps due to climate change. For example Sword Grass *Xylena vetusta* is now only resident in northern Britain, and the range of Large Ranunculus *Polymixis flavicincta* has contracted to the south and east.

The decline for another group of moths may be linked to their foodplants. White-spotted Pinion *Cosmia diffinis* has suffered from the loss of large elms

Ulmus spp., on which its larvae feed, to Dutch Elm Disease. Goldenrod *Solidago virgaurea* seems to be much less common in Wyre than it once was, though its yellow blooms may increase again as the Forest is opened up, letting in more light. Of the moths which feed upon it, there have been no modern records of Bleached Pug *Eupithecia expallidata* or the beautiful micromoth, the White-spotted Sable *Anania funebris*. However the Small Golden-rod Plume *Hellinsia osteodactlylus* and Plain Plume *H. tephradactyla* whose larvae feed on Goldenrod are still present. This relationship with a specific group of localised plants is crucial to the survival of moths such as the Campanula Pug *Eupithecia campanulata*, whose larvae were found in 2010 in seedheads of Nettle-leaved Bellflower *Campanula trachelium* and Giant Bellflower *C. latifolia* along the Severn in Eymore Wood.

The larva of the Orange Upperwing *Jodis croceago*, another Wyre speciality, is said to feed on lammas growth on regenerating oak coppice stools and may therefore have been affected by lack of coppicing. It is no longer a resident species in the UK. The False Mocha *Cyclophora porata* is also said to have liked oak coppice and the last local records were in 1974. Silvery Arches *Polia bombycina* is a species of birch woodland and heathland and the increasing high-canopy woodland did not suit it; there is some uncertainty as to the last record in Wyre, but it was not definitely recorded after the 1960s. Similarly, loss of the Forester *Adscita statices* and Small Argent and Sable *Epirrhoe tristata* may have been due to the decline in open habitats, but it is a surprise that the latter is no longer still present.

There is a single specimen of Light Feathered Rustic *Agrotis cinerea* in Worcester Museum collected in the Forest in 1899. This was possibly introduced with limestone ballast in the building of the railway

The day-flying Scarlet Tiger *Callimorpha dominula* is commonly seen along the banks of the River Severn, but can also turn up in gardens and woodland clearings. When disturbed it adopts this startle position, exposing the red underwings to deter predators [RW]. It overwinters as a small caterpillar (below [PC]).

Narrow-bordered Bee Hawk-moth *Hemaris tityus* [JB]

the short term, we may yet find more of our supposedly lost species. That this is very much a possibility was dramatically demonstrated in 2009 when Denise Bingham found a Narrow-bordered Bee Hawk-moth *Hemaris tityus*. This superb moth was last positively identified in Wyre in 1936. Another was seen in the same place the following year and even better, the caterpillars were found on their foodplant Devil's-bit Scabious. The sight of these furry bee mimics zooming along a Forest ride in late spring is a beacon of hope for the future of Wyre's moths.

through the Forest. Historical records of other species usually associated with open calcareous habitats, such as Tawny Shears *Hadena perplexa*, and Reddish Light Arches *Apamea sublustris*, are more puzzling, but perhaps there were more open and disturbed habitats nearby at that time.

Over the past decade large-scale clearance of conifers and felling of large deciduous trees has been deliberately targeted at creating open habitat. This has been of great benefit to many species, especially the butterflies, but it was unfortunately just too late to save some of the rare moths, which now might thrive again in Wyre following the change in woodland management.

The ability of some moths to persist at low levels, and the positive effects of recent forest management, augur well for this nationally important site. Habitat improvements such as the extensive opening up of ride edges and creation of open areas with birch regeneration should bring rewards in the long term. In

Table 5 Woodland moths of note in Wyre	
Common name	**Scientific name**
Plain Wave	*Idea straminata*
Grass Wave	*Perconia strigillaria*
Lead-coloured Pug	*Eupithecia plumbeolata*
Bilberry Pug	*Pasiphila debiliata*
Broom-tip	*Chesias rufata*
Satin Lutestring	*Tetheella fluctuosa*
Alder Kitten	*Furcula bicuspis*
Barred Chestnut	*Diarsia dahlii*
Neglected Rustic	*Xestia castanea*
Beautiful Brocade	*Lacanobia contigua*
Bird's Wing	*Dypterygia scabriuscula*
Suspected	*Parastichtis suspecta*
Angle-striped Sallow	*Enargia paleacea*
Map-winged Swift	*Korscheltellus fusconebulosa*
Yellow-barred Gold	*Micropterix aureatella*
Bilberry Pigmy	*Stigmella myrtilella*
Common Bright	*Incurvaria oelhmanniella*
Hereford Case-bearer	*Coleophora sylvaticella*
Wood-rush Dwarf	*Elachista regificella*
Straw-coloured Tubic	*Pseudatemelia subochraceella*
Bilberry Marble	*Apotomis sauciana*
Bilberry Roller	*Ancylis myrtillana*
Wood-sage Plume	*Capperia britanniodactyla*

Collecting and recording moths

Moth-trapping [RW]

Wyre Forest has been fairly well recorded since the middle of the 19th century. After the arrival of the railways in the 1860s members of the Worcestershire Naturalists' Club visited the Forest and the Worcester recorder, J.E. Fletcher, made a number of microlepidoptera records. He was mainly responsible for the moth records in the Victoria County History of Worcestershire of 1901 (Rea & Fletcher 1901). A greater number of recorders, including H. McNaught and C.H. Simmonds, visited the Forest just before and around the turn of the 20th century, some of the latter's records extending up to 1946. The Birmingham based S.E.W. Carlier collected in Wyre between the wars and his collection is in the Birmingham Museum. Les Evans and other members of the Birmingham Naturalists' Society were regular visitors before and after World War Two.

In recent years John Robinson, former National Nature Reserve Warden, made extensive records. From 1984 to 1991 John Bingham and Mike Taylor recorded the macromoths and produced an annotated list (Bingham & Taylor 1991). Frank Lancaster, Mike Taylor and Neville Wilde recorded regularly at the Roxel site. Rosemary Winnall then organised and led the recording effort of the Wyre Forest Moth Group, later handing over to Dave Grundy, who organised regular moth light-trapping sessions attended by many entomologists; Ian Machin now arranges occasional trapping events in Wyre. A large number of other entomologists, including Colin Plant in the 1980s, have recorded in the Forest. Adrian Riley, Dave Emley, Godfrey Blunt, and Pete Boardman recorded on the Shropshire side. Tony Simpson has visited and undertaken some light trapping but has mainly concentrated on microlepidoptera recording. The Wyre Forest Study Group has included recording work on the Lepidoptera in the past five years.

Male Common Clubtail *Gomphus vulgatissimus* [MA]

Dragonflies and damselflies

The rustle of wings along a forest glade and a gleam of cobalt in the dappled shade of Dowles Brook are both signs that betray the presence of dragonflies and damselflies. Although a relatively small group of insects their size and colour attract attention and epitomise a sunny day by the water's edge. In common with butterflies, they were sought by the early naturalists for their aerial agility and vibrant colours but less often collected because of the difficulty of retaining those brilliant hues.

The Order Odonata covers both the larger true dragonflies, which settle with their wings held out sideways, and the more slender damselflies which hold their wings pressed together over the abdomen when at rest. The features that true dragonflies and damselflies have in common are the possession of two pairs of wings and an aquatic larval stage, the latter with an extendable mouthpart grabbing device used for catching prey.

Dragonfly records in Wyre go back to 1895, though most are much more recent (Averill 2006). Currently 23 species of dragonfly and damselfly have been recorded, a growing list which reflects both changes

in distribution over the last 50 years and an increasing interest in these insects. Among them are species localised in the Midlands, such as Golden-ringed Dragonfly *Cordulegaster boltonii* and Common Hawker *Aeshna juncea*. In addition two species associated with the River Severn are locally important for Shropshire and Worcestershire: White-legged Damselfly *Platycnemis pennipes* and Common Clubtail *Gomphus vulgatissimus*.

The species recorded, 14 dragonflies and nine damselflies, are shown in Table 6. The commonest of these, Southern Hawker *Aeshna cyanea,* Brown Hawker *A. grandis,* Blue-tailed Damselfly *Ischnura elegans,* Common Blue Damselfly *Enallagma cyathigerum* and Common Darter *Sympetrum striolatum,* may be seen wherever there is permanent water.

Damselfly larvae may spend as little as three months underwater, while some true dragonfly larvae can spend almost three years there and only a few months as flying adults. Their intolerance of any level of pollution, makes the presence of dragonflies a strong indication of good water quality. Some species favour standing water, others streams and rivers. The damselflies and the hawker dragonflies lay their eggs into plant material, so emergent and floating vegetation is very important to them. Recently emerged maturing adults may need refuges away from the breeding site, and Wyre provides excellent opportunities for two river species, the White-legged Damselfly and Common Clubtail. They spend much of their adult lives away from the Severn and can be seen almost anywhere in the area. Clubtails are believed to select glades in oak woodland to look for mates.

Wyre's dragonfly habitats are the River Severn, smaller streams, wet flushes and ponds. Almost all of the area drains into the river via Dowles Brook and minor tributaries. Open water is less common and, other than a collection of fishing pools, there is only a handful of pools in the heart of the Forest, the largest being at Uncllys Farm. Nearby there are smaller ponds along the stream at Hitterhill, which provide some limited and rather shady habitat. Whilst natural ponds are in short supply, an increase in new pools, either for fishing or farm irrigation, has provided good breeding sites, although these can be dominated by fish. In the woodlands near Cleobury Mortimer there are more natural, richly vegetated, rushy ponds without fish which hold a wider range of species, including the Emerald Damselfly *Lestes sponsa*, and the Common Hawker.

It might seem surprising that seven new species have been recorded since 1981, but like many insects, dragonflies are responsive to recent climate change. We now find the Migrant Hawker *Aeshna mixta* and Ruddy Darter *Sympetrum sanguineum* in Wyre and, most recently, the Scarce Chaser *Libellula fulva* has appeared on the Severn. This dragonfly is a newcomer to Worcestershire following expansions in other parts of England. It is still spreading to suitable habitat outside its core area on the River Avon downstream of Pershore. Two other dragonflies, the Four-spotted Chaser *L. quadrimaculata* and Black-tailed Skimmer *Orthetrum cancellatum*, were absent from Wyre until their appearance in 1998. This may be due to the increased number of pools constructed for fishing and conservation.

Lack of habitat may explain the rarity of two other species. The Red-eyed Damselfly *Erythromma najas* has a strong association with floating water weeds such as Amphibious Bistort *Persicaria amphibia*. This plant is scarce in the few pools in Wyre, but grows in fishing pools in the north. The Hairy Dragonfly *Brachytron pratense* is very scarce and few records exist for Worcestershire or Shropshire, making the single record for Malpass Wood in 2000 particularly interesting. Was it a wandering individual or is there is an undiscovered breeding site hidden in the Forest?

Two species that epitomise the Forest are the Beautiful Demoiselle *Calopteryx virgo* and Golden-ringed Dragonfly. Perhaps these two species caught the eyes of early naturalists as they embarked on their trips from Wyre Forest Railway Station and walked down to Dowles Brook. The Beautiful Demoiselle is widespread throughout the west of Worcestershire and Shropshire. It is an insect of stony streams which the larvae can tolerate even in spate. The tropical splendour of displaying males as they flash turquoise and cobalt over the eddies can be breathtaking in late spring and summer. They defend sunlit patches of water, darting out from the brookside foliage to chase off rivals or intercept the brown-winged females. In its early adult life the male's wings also have a brownish wash: in the 19th century these younger adults were thought to be a separate species.

The Golden-ringed Dragonfly is mainly a species of the western uplands and lowland heaths so is not common in Worcestershire, but it is found in Wyre because of the proximity of suitable habitat in the neighbouring South Shropshire Hills. These impressive insects can be encountered hawking anywhere throughout the Forest at any time during high summer, so it is hard to predict exactly where they will turn up. They are striking creatures with wasp-like yellow and black markings and can be very confiding as they patrol low over rills and seepages. The females are our longest-bodied dragonfly and are unusual in that they lay their eggs directly into soft stream silt, using their extended abdomen like a gardener's dibber. The larvae are formidable-looking, squat and spiny and can live in the shallowest muddiest rivulets and wet flushes.

The other heathland species found in Wyre is the Common Hawker which, despite its name, is rather scarce here. It is often misidentified from sightings of the smaller but more abundant Migrant Hawker, but unlike that species has a distinctive yellow costal vein along the front margin of each wing. The Common Hawker prefers the acid conditions of heathland, but breeds in pools rather than streams and wet flushes. The rather similar Southern Hawker is much more common and is found in most forest pools and streams, sometimes being the only large dragonfly present, as it can tolerate shade and often flies in dull conditions.

Common Clubtails and White-legged Damselflies occur widely, but breed in the Severn. Both require

Common Hawker *Aeshna juncea* [BK]

Male Beautiful Demoiselle *Calopteryx virgo* [BW]

Male Golden-ringed Dragonfly *Cordulegaster boltonii* [MA]

large clean silty rivers and the Severn makes Shropshire and Worcestershire arguably the two most important counties in the country for them. Fortunately the river water quality, which is the source of drinking water for over six million people, is carefully monitored.

The Common Clubtail is the commonest clubtail in Europe, but in the UK, outside its strongholds on the Severn and Thames, it is restricted to a few outlying rivers in England and Wales (Cham *et al.* 2014). Surveys during its synchronised emergence period between mid-May and mid-June have recorded as many as five individuals per metre of river bank which, considering the length of the Severn represents large numbers along suitable parts of the river. Often enlivening woodland glades with its lemon-yellow and black livery this dragonfly has the distinction of being the only British dragonfly with eyes that are set apart. It can be hard to find as it forsakes the water soon after emerging: adults have been seen up to 10 km from the nearest river. Courtship and pairing usually takes place in wooded areas especially in sunlit rides, but only the females return to the river to lay eggs, lightly brushing the water's surface with their abdomens. The larvae are slightly unusual in that the front legs are comparatively long and the antennae are quite bulbous. It is generally thought that these are adaptations for living and burrowing in silty rivers. The skins, or exuviae, left behind by emerging adults often cling to the quays at Bewdley for several months until they are swept away by floods.

White-legged Damselflies, like Common Clubtails, are normally restricted to large rivers, but they also occur at some of the fishing pools in the area, where

White-legged Damselfly *Platycnemis pennipes* [RW]

the number of breeding pairs will always be lower than at the main river habitat. The powder-blue males have flattened white legs which are very prominent during the breeding season and are used in display when dangled in flight in front of the females. Immature White-legged Damselflies often fly some way from the river and are pale brown which makes them virtually invisible in the riverside cornfields.

Wyre provides an important network of wetland habitats, from wet flush, stream and river, to ponds and lakes. Even small areas of water such as garden ponds offer considerable opportunities for dragonflies and although some of the scarcer species may never choose them, 15 dragonflies and damselflies do. Wetlands, no matter how well protected, can suffer from accidental pollution and so the many isolated private ponds and pools are valuable refuges.

Table 6 Dragonfly and damselfly records for the Wyre Forest 1895–2013

The total number of Wyre Forest records is 2,220, of which 1,615 are from VC37 (Worcestershire), 472 are from VC40 (Shropshire) and 133 are from VC33 (Staffordshire).

Common name	Scientific name	Earliest record	Latest record	No of records	Habitat
Beautiful Demoiselle	*Calopteryx virgo*	1895	2013	100	Stream
Golden-ringed Dragonfly	*Cordulegaster boltonii*	1895	2013	102	Stream/wet flush
Banded Demoiselle	*Calopteryx splendens*	1900	2013	211	River
Common Darter	*Sympetrum striolatum*	1947	2013	176	Pond
White-legged Damselfly	*Platycnemis pennipes*	1949	2013	182	River
Common Clubtail	*Gomphus vulgatissimus*	1950	2013	170	River
Blue-tailed Damselfly	*Ischnura elegans*	1952	2013	128	Pond/river
Large Red Damselfly	*Pyrrhosoma nymphula*	1975	2013	163	Pond/river
Azure Damselfly	*Coenagrion puella*	1975	2013	157	Pond/river
Brown Hawker	*Aeshna grandis*	1975	2013	168	Pond/river
Southern Hawker	*Aeshna cyanea*	1975	2013	256	Pond/river
Emperor Dragonfly	*Anax imperator*	1975	2013	57	Pond
Common Blue Damselfly	*Enallagma cyathigerum*	1978	2013	118	Pond/river
Common Hawker	*Aeshna juncea*	1979	2013	17	Pond
Broad-bodied Chaser	*Libellula depressa*	1980	2013	93	Pond
Emerald Damselfly	*Lestes sponsa*	1981	2013	31	Pond
Migrant Hawker	*Aeshna mixta*	1984	2012	52	Pond/river
Ruddy Darter	*Sympetrum sanguineum*	1991	2012	17	Pond/river
Four-spotted Chaser	*Libellula quadrimaculata*	1998	2013	4	Pond/wet flush
Hairy Dragonfly	*Brachytron pratense*	2000	2000	1	Wet flush
Black-tailed Skimmer	*Orthetrum cancellatum*	2006	2013	12	Pond
Scarce Chaser	*Libellula fulva*	2006	2013	2	River
Red-eyed Damselfly	*Erythromma najas*	2010	2012	3	Pond

Common Clubtail *Gomphus vulgatissimus* emerging [BK]

Grasshoppers, bush-crickets and their allies

Grasshoppers, bush-crickets and ground-hoppers comprise the order Orthoptera and there are about 30 British species (Haes & Harding 1997). They are familiar sun-loving insects, obvious on warm days when their songs boost the soundtrack of summer. In spite of this, there is little information on their presence and behaviour in Wyre: both Norman Hickin's *Natural History of an English Forest* (1971) and Simon Fletcher's *Wyre Forest Diary* (1981) fail to mention them. In wooded spots they live in open sunny glades and rides, but are commoner in hedgerows, fields and riversides.

A notable exception is the Oak Bush-cricket *Meconema thalassinum,* an arboreal species which lives unnoticed in the woodland canopy. In Wyre it is often seen after late summer storms, or during forestry operations, when the crickets are dislodged from trees. Oak Bush-crickets are also found in and around buildings, they are attracted to artificial lighting and often enter houses, where they are sometimes known as the bathroom bush-cricket (Farmer 2007). Despite their fragile appearance, Oak Bush-crickets are, like all other crickets, omnivorous, feeding on vegetation and soft-bodied invertebrates. Unlike many other crickets they do not stridulate, but communicate by drumming their hind legs rapidly on leaves. Often this is the last cricket of the year and a few specimens can survive until late November.

Despite their attraction to domestic lighting, Oak Bush-crickets rarely turn up in moth traps, but in Wyre three female House Crickets *Acheta domestica* were found in a mercury vapour light trap in 2003 (Winnall 2005). This non-native cricket has been at large in buildings and domestic rubbish tips in the south of England for many years, as noted by Gilbert White in his *Natural History of Selborne* in 1789. In the English Midlands it used to be regularly found (along with non-native cockroaches) in bakeries, hospital cellars and domestic hot-air heating systems all of which provided the required warmth and humidity. Because of improvements to heating systems and the introduction of powerful insecticides however, this species has been virtually eradicated from its old haunts along with its cockroach cousins. Escapees from the pet trade, in which crickets are bred to feed reptiles, are probably responsible for the more recent colonies which can persist for a season or two on rubbish tips and in sheltered urban sites. Even this source has now ended as the House Cricket has been replaced in favour of several less hardy non-native species. However, a self-sustaining population is known in buildings near Bewdley which may result in occasional sightings in Wyre, but it seems unlikely that House Crickets will become established in the Forest in the foreseeable future.

Two native species of bush-cricket have increased by leaps and bounds in recent years and have now established a foothold here: Roesel's Bush-cricket *Metrioptera roeselii* and Long-winged Cone-head *Conocephalus discolor* are both colonists from the south of England. They have expanded their ranges dramatically to the north and west in the last two decades. They are now both common insects in many parts of Worcestershire (Green 2007). Long-winged Cone-heads were heard and seen for the first time in Wyre in autumn 2012, when the high-pitched reeling song was located with a bat detector in ungrazed

Female Oak Bush-cricket *Meconema thalassimum*, a species of the forest canopy but which occasionally turns up in houses. [JB]

Speckled Bush-crickets *Leptophyes punctatissima*, male left, female right [RW]

meadows at Snuffmill. Although their stridulations are inaudible to most people, conversion via a bat detector produces a chugging sound like a distant lawnmower.

Roesel's Bush-cricket arrived a year earlier and was first found near Heightington in a sunny spot in long grass on the edge of an arable field. As with all of the Orthoptera, Roesel's Bush-crickets do not have a larval or pupal stage instead hatching from eggs as nymphs, perfect miniature versions of the adults. These were found deep in the Forest in a heathery clearing in June 2014, and several very fresh adults of the long-winged forms were found at Uncllys Farm in July of the same year. This indicates that colonisation is well underway. They are handsome, distinctively patterned insects whose reeling song resembles the buzz of overhead cables.

Two other Bush-crickets occur in Wyre. The Speckled Bush-cricket *Leptophyes punctatissima* is secretive and flightless, living amongst thistles, Common Nettles and other tall vegetation in sheltered sunny areas. Its plump, bright green body is covered in tiny black spots and its wings are reduced to stubs or pads. In summer the wing pads and legs of the male Speckled Bush-crickets turn bright orange-red for just a few days, as they search out the less colourful females. The mating ritual consists of a bizarre sequence of distorted body posturing (Farmer 2012). Its song, like that of most crickets, is produced by rapidly rubbing its wings pads across each other, and consists of single, short chirps which are inaudible to human ears.

In contrast the Dark Bush-cricket *Pholidoptera griseoaptera* stridulates with a loud series of tinny chirps. These can be heard on sunny autumn days, often well into November. This is a bolder and more robust species which basks on vegetation especially in areas such as Rock Coppice, Arley Woods and along the Severn valley. Female bush-crickets have a sword-like structure, the ovipositor, which projects from the rear of their abdomen. Using this the eggs are inserted deep into plant stems or soft ground where they are safe from most predators. Dark Bush-crickets favour brambles and thistles, the spiny plants giving their eggs added protection. All the native bush-crickets and grasshoppers die as temperatures fall in autumn, leaving their eggs to overwinter and hatch the following year in early summer.

Four species of grasshoppers have been found in Wyre. The most common is the Meadow Grasshopper *Chorthippus parallelus*, found in almost all grasslands and especially frequent along the river paths and in meadows. This is typically a green grasshopper with brown wings and a bright yellow underside, although a completely brown form is increasing from the south and may occur here. Females of this species are unusual amongst our grasshoppers in having short wings only half as long as the abdomen. The males, as with all of the Orthoptera, gather in summer leks where they sing to attract females. They stridulate by rubbing their long back legs against the hard edges of their wings. Grasshoppers choose open patches of ground, surfaces of large leaves or even dry cowpats to call from. Most surprisingly, Meadow Grasshoppers have been found courting on active Southern Wood Ant *Formica rufa* nests, apparently unnoticed by the ants which often predate Orthopterans.

Field Grasshoppers *C. brunneus* are more likely to be encountered in dry grassland along well-worn sunny tracks or in heathy areas, such as at Pound Green Common, where they bask on bare ground amongst the broken turf. When disturbed they spread their long wings and part jump, part fly into the longer vegetation. This is our largest grasshopper and is quite hairy, typically mottled brown in colour, although green and even pink forms, have been found.

Grasshoppers lack the long ovipositor of crickets and need soft ground in which to lay their eggs. The sandy soils of heathland are ideal but crumbling banks along sunny tracks, or even the soil mounds of Yellow Meadow Ant *Lasius flavus* nests, are used. Rather than laying single eggs as the crickets do, grasshoppers lay batches of eggs in pellets formed from a foam-like substance which becomes coated with soil particles and quickly hardens. When ground temperatures rise sufficiently in early summer, the eggs hatch and the nymphs wriggle to the surface. In order to protect their delicate antennae and long thin legs, the young grasshoppers start life coated in a thin skin and resemble a maggot. This skin immediately peels off as the nymphs emerge from the ground, revealing miniature grasshoppers, identical to their parents but scarcely bigger than aphids.

Despite its name the Common Green Grasshopper *Omocestus viridulus* is far from common in Wyre, although it is doing well in some places. In Britain it ranges from Land's End to the far north of Scotland (National Orthoptera Recording Scheme). Within that range it is restricted to herb-rich moist grassland and humid heathy grassland. In Wyre it is found only on open heathy areas such as Pound Green Common and some of the meadows along Dowles Brook. The long,

Meadow Grasshopper *Chorthippus parallelus* [JB]

reeling song of Common Green Grasshoppers will be familiar to anyone who has walked through flowery, summer meadows. There is though some suggestion that this species, along with the habitats on which it depends, is declining (Farmer 2013).

Another species restricted by habitat is the Mottled Grasshopper *Myrmeleotettix maculatus*, a sun-loving insect particularly found in heathland. Areas of heathland around Hartlebury are ideal for this little grasshopper where it can be locally numerous, but there are few suitable sites within the Forest and places such as Pound Green Common are important for is survival. This is a small grasshopper and the male has distinctive antennae, shaped like hockey sticks, and a song which sounds like distant roller skates. The females are very variable in colour and patterning and are particularly well camouflaged against the mossy ground of heathlands. Its habitat requirements mean it will never be very common in Wyre.

A species which may soon be found anywhere in grassy habitats in the Forest is the Lesser Marsh Grasshopper *Chorthippus albomarginatus*. This is now common in the English Midlands as part of a dramatic range expansion through England in recent decades (Benton 2012). A photograph taken in Button Oak Meadow in 2014 may well have been of a young nymph, marking the arrival of this grasshopper in Wyre. Originally a wet grassland species, it has now colonised most grassland types across its increasing range. It is similar to the common Meadow Grasshopper but is typically more subdued in colour and often straw-coloured. Unlike the Meadow Grasshopper this species flies very well, which has helped its expansion into new areas. The Lesser Marsh Grasshopper is very likely to become a familiar sight in Wyre's grasslands in the near future.

None of the native Orthoptera mentioned so far overwinter as adults, but Wyre's two species of ground-hoppers do, and appear on sunny days as early as February. The Common Ground-hopper *Tetrix undulata*, and the Slender Ground-hopper *T. subulata*, are associated with sunlit mossy places. The Slender Ground-hopper prefers watery areas and, if disturbed, leaps into puddles or ditches to escape. It swims well and will even dive underwater to avoid capture (Farmer 2005). The species often occur together, but being small and songless they are easily overlooked. After forestry work they are often encountered on and around bonfire sites which have been colonised by moss. These sites are often sheltered by surrounding vegetation and have higher humidity, conditions ideal for these little insects. The ground-hoppers are like small grasshoppers in appearance, but they have an extension to the top of the thorax (the pronotum) which covers the whole of the back including the wings. They do not stridulate, so at courtship sites they can be seen flicking their wings out from under the pronotum when near other adults in a visual display.

Another group of insects closely related to the Orthoptera are often seen; the Dermaptera or earwigs. Two species are known to occur in the Forest: the Lesser Earwig *Labia minor,* a very small, uncommon insect which favours compost heaps and dung piles, and the ubiquitous Common Earwig *Forficula auricularia,* familiar to any gardener. It is not surprising that Lesser Earwigs are seldom encountered, given their small size and habitat choice. They fly well and will come to light, but are likely to be mistaken for a small Staphylinid rove beetle rather than an earwig. Because of this they may be commoner than records suggest. The Common Earwig on the other hand is unmistakable, and is equally at home in buildings, under logs and stones, or in leaf litter. Its liking for flower petals gives this insect a bad reputation among gardeners, but it also eats many insect pests, such as aphids and small caterpillars. Common Earwigs have flight-wings which are intricately folded into small pouches made by its short, hardened outer-wings, but are rarely seen flying.

This is a time of change for Wyre's Orthoptera as some species become restricted or decline due to habitat preferences and climatic changes. Overall though, the picture is positive and several species are thriving and colonising, with more heading this way. With the variety of habitats and continued sensitive management, Wyre's meadows and other grassy places will continue to host the summer soundtrack of grasshoppers and crickets.

Common Ground-hopper *Tetrix undulata* [JB]

Slender Ground-hopper *Tetrix subulata* [GF]

Bugs

Sweep a net along a heathery ride or gently shake the lower branches of a forest oak and you will almost certainly capture a bug. The woodlands, orchards, meadows and ponds of Wyre offer a range of habitats for many bugs, some of them common and widespread, others scarce and localised. Excitingly, in recent years new species have arrived.

Although the word 'bug' is used in many parts of the world as a general term for any insect, true bugs are insects of the order Hemiptera, distinguished by their piercing mouthparts enclosed in a long beak-like structure called a rostrum, through which they suck sap or the internal fluids of prey. A few bugs can pierce human skin: an encounter with an innocent-looking flower bug will convince you of the rostrum's effectiveness.

Bugs are divided into two sub-orders: Homoptera (leafhoppers, treehoppers, planthoppers, aphids and plant lice), and Heteroptera, the 'true' bugs, including leatherbugs and shieldbugs among many others. Many species are attractively marked both as adults and nymphs. Unlike many insects, the bugs have three life stages; egg, nymphs of various instars and adults.

There are approximately 2,000 species of bugs in the UK (British Bugs Website) and about 360 have been identified in Wyre (Wyre Forest Study Group Website from WBRC data). Many of these are small and need microscopic examination to identify them, so although about 10% of the world's insect species are bugs, they are often overlooked. Here we have chosen some of the most typical or notable species.

Shieldbugs

The shieldbugs, called stinkbugs in the USA because of the noxious smell they produce when handled, are often large and colourful, and their habit of sitting in the open means that they can be conspicuous. Green Shieldbugs *Palomena prasina* are often seen on plants in sunny spots in Wyre woodlands and in gardens and hedgerows everywhere. They probe unripe fruits in late summer and autumn and overwinter as adults. The Hairy Shieldbug *Dolycoris baccarum* is fairly common in open areas and easy to recognise by its pink and green colour combination. Gorse Shieldbugs *Piezodorus lituratus* bask in spring in the thorny cradles of their host-plant. In a few places, Woundwort Shieldbugs *Eysarcoris venustissimus*, beautifully marked in soft greys and metallic mauves, cluster on Hedge Woundwort *Stachys sylvatica*. Underneath sheltering birch or alder leaves, gravity-defying Parent Shieldbugs *Elasmucha grisea* guard their broods of eggs and stripy black and green nymphs.

Predatory shieldbugs lurk amongst the oak leaves. The Bronze Shieldbug *Troilus luridus* stalks caterpillars, impaling them on its rostrum then hoisting them into the air as it sucks out their body fluids. Adults are grey-brown, but the nymphs are splashed with iridescent green or bronze. The Red-legged Shieldbug *Pentatoma rufipes,* a similar species

Green Shieldbug *Palomena prasina* [PC]

Hairy Shieldbug *Dolycoris baccarum* [JB]

Gorse Shieldbug *Piezodorus lituratus* [JB]

Bronze Shieldbug *Troilus luridus* [JB]

with red legs, can be very common in oaks and surrounding trees. It feeds on plant sap, honeydew and dead insects. In open grassy places you might see the Spiked Shieldbug *Picromerus bidens*, a large brown insect which has a sharp spike on each 'shoulder'.

Wyre is one of the few places in the UK with a thriving population of the rare and declining Cow-wheat Shieldbug *Adomerus biguttatus*. The adult bug, 5–6 mm long, and black with a white dot on each wing-case, feeds on Common Cow-wheat *Melampyrum pratense*, a plant which is locally common in sunny spots in the Forest. The bug was first recorded from Wyre by Bernard Nau in the 1970s. It was not noted again for 40 years or so until colonies were found in April 2011 at Uncllys in Worcestershire, and in July on the Shropshire side of Dowles Brook at Withybed Wood. At both locations, which were well lit, finding it required careful searching in leaf litter under the host plants. In September 2012, following hot dry weather, a dead adult and two dead nymphs were found under desiccated plants of Common Cow-wheat at the Shropshire location. This is a nationally scarce bug whose distribution in the Britain may be limited by a decline in coppicing and an increase in Bracken *Pteridium aquilinum*, since heavy shading prevents the establishment of its host plant. In Wyre management to widen rides and create clearings could benefit this bug by allowing Common Cow-wheat to flourish.

Forest management may also encourage Wyre's rarest shieldbug, the Heather Shieldbug *Rhacognathus punctatus*. There is a single record of this medium-sized predatory bug from Withybed Wood, on the Shropshire side of Dowles Brook, on 24 July 2010. It was found on Heather *Calluna vulgaris* in an open sunny spot, presumably searching for its main prey, the Heather Beetle *Lochmaea suturalis*. The nearest known colonies to Wyre are probably in Shropshire, where it occurs in the north of the county, but it may occur on the north Worcestershire heaths. Heather Shieldbugs look similar to Red-legged Shieldbugs but are smaller and have diagnostic orange bands on their tibiae. They have a widely scattered distribution across the UK, but are nowhere common.

Some new shieldbugs have recently been found in the Forest, possibly as a result of climate change allowing species to migrate further north. They may have occurred in the more distant past but we have no records to prove either possibility. The Tortoise Shieldbug *Eurygaster testudinaria*, has been spreading from the south of England since the 1990s and was first recorded in the Forest in autumn 2010. Since then it has appeared in several places, usually in damp grassy areas along the Dowles Brook valley. By 2014 Wyre was the only place where it had been found in Shropshire, but no doubt it will soon expand its range further north (Boardman 2014). It is a well-armoured, rotund bug about 10 mm long which overwinters as an adult. Nymphs feed on grasses, rushes and sedges between May and August (Evans & Edmondson 2005). Tortoise Shieldbugs are typically streaked in browns and beiges, but reddish forms are not uncommon.

Another new species, first seen in autumn 2006, is the Bishop's Mitre Shieldbug *Aelia acuminata*. It is around 8 mm long, striped brown and cream and gets its name from its shape. It is now well established on many of the rank grassy ride-edges and along the Dowles Brook valley. It is found throughout the year but is most obvious in spring and autumn. Well camouflaged, the adult bugs often climb up grass or tall herbage to bask. The nymphs feed on the ripening seeds of grasses (Hawkins 2003). It is widespread and common across southern Britain in tall and rank dry grassland habitats, but less common further north.

The smallest new shieldbug is the Small Grass Shieldbug *Neottiglossa pusilla* which has spread from the south and was first recorded in autumn 2006. Only 5 mm in length, and pale brown, it can be hard to see as it lurks in low vegetation along grassy rides and in clearings. Its nymphs feed on meadow grasses. Nationally this is the most locally distributed and scarcest of the three new bugs, but seems to be well established. It has spread along the Severn corridor in Shropshire as far as Telford (Boardman 2014). All three of these new arrivals seem to prefer the south facing and warmer Shropshire side of the Forest. They are sensitive to micro-climates and the future

Cow-wheat Shieldbug *Adomerus biguttatus* [JB]

Bishop's Mitre Shieldbug *Aelia acuminata* [JB]

maintenance of warm open glades and bare ground will be important to them.

Other bugs

Apart from shieldbugs there are several other conspicuous bugs which can be found with a little searching. The Dock Bug *Coreus marginatus* is a large, rusty-brown, fiddle-shaped leatherbug which feeds on seeds of docks and sorrels, and often sits on leaves in open places. Its strange nymphs with their disproportionately long antennae are sometimes seen in clearings or rough ground in summer.

Along rides and in grassy fields there are several common bugs which are also widespread in the UK. They include the plant bugs, some green, others long-bodied, which are numerous in grassy places. By the River Severn in autumn the unripe cones of Alders *Alnus glutinosa* provide food for the attractive red and green plant bug *Pantilius tunicatus*. These often bask on leaves and probe the cones for juices. On Enchanter's-nightshade *Circaea lutetiana* the stiltbug *Metatropis rufescens* is fairly common, sitting on the leaves and resembling a small golden cranefly. These bugs are easy to overlook, but seem to have become more frequent in the Forest in the last few years.

A species which has also been seen increasingly often in recent years here is the striking scarlet and black rhopalid bug *Corizus hyoscyami*. This hairy bug was mainly coastal, but has spread inland in the last two decades and now occurs in woodland clearings, open fields and gardens over much of southern and central England (Whitehead 2008).

Where Heather forms overhangs on paths through the Forest look for the fast-running groundbug *Rhyparochromus pini*. This elegant long-legged species is about 8 mm long and is locally distributed on heaths, mainly in southern England, where it feeds principally on seeds. Although a heathland bug, it is locally common in Wyre which may hark back to a time when the Forest had fewer trees and more heathery open space. Now it is found in sunlit places with dry, bare ground and probably benefits from the conservation practices of tree-felling and ride-widening.

It is always worth searching for bugs on tree trunks. In May and June the jazzily patterned plant bug *Miris striatus* is locally common feeding on aphids. Autumn is a good time to look carefully for another plant bug *Phytocoris tiliae*, a master of camouflage, freckled grey and green like the lichen-blotched bark on which it rests.

One special and rather elusive Wyre species is the spurgebug *Dicranocephalus medius*. This is large, about 10 mm long, and feeds on Wood Spurge *Euphorbia amygdaloides*. Although the host-plant is common in many Worcestershire and Shropshire woodlands, Wyre seems to hold the only colonies of the bug in the two counties. This suggests that it may need quite large areas of ancient semi-natural woodland in which to survive. It is a Nationally Rare insect (Hawkins 2003)

Dock Bug *Coreus marginatus* [JB]

A stiltbug *Metatropis rufescens* [JB]

A rhopalid *Corizus hyoscyami* [KMcG]

A plant bug *Miris striatus* [PC]

A mating pair of spurgebugs *Dicranocephalus medius* on their host plant, Wood Spurge *Euphorbia amygdaloides*, in a Wyre clearing. Restoration of coppicing may lead to an increase in their numbers and range in the Forest. [KMcG]

with most locations in southern Britain, Wyre being near its north-west limit. Wood Spurge is quick to appear after soil disturbance, for example following conifer felling and removal, or coppice management, although it will survive under more closed canopy woodland for some time. When spurgebugs are about, they crawl on the leaves or hide near the base of plants, especially on open, sparsely vegetated ground in warm or sheltered spots along rides or in open glades. They're attractive insects, reddish-black with contrasting black and yellow legs and antennae. Adults overwinter and then mate in May, the new generation appearing from August onwards (Hawkins 2003). Most records are in late spring and early summer and it was seen mating on Wood Spurge in Wyre on 26 May 2007 and in May 2014. In that month it was easy to find in Withybed Wood a few years after conifer removal as this enabled Wood Spurge to bloom in large patches. Conservation management designed for butterflies that favour open sunny conditions may also augur well for *Dicranocephalus* and may extend its range. So far most records are on the Shropshire side of the Forest but, in future, it could become more widespread in Worcestershire following new coppice and ride-widening regimes.

Aquatic bugs

Bugs have successfully colonised water in almost every form. Even in puddles and horsetroughs you may see pondskaters *Gerris* spp. and backswimmers *Notonecta* spp. Both groups feed on insects which fall onto the surface film, but backswimmers also catch tadpoles and fish fry. If picked up they can stab human fingers painfully with a well-developed rostrum. Under the surface of pools, corixid bugs or waterboatmen often swarm and stridulate to attract mates. In the genus *Micronecta* this orchestral performance involves scraping their genitalia against their abdomens.

Harder to see are delicate Water Measurers *Hydrometra stagnorum* which hunt across the surface film of ditches and small ponds. Waterscorpions *Nepa cinerea* are also hard to find, looking like flattened brown leaves, with large pincer-shaped forelegs for catching prey and a long siphon for drawing air from the water surface. Water Stick-insects *Ranatra linearis* have been found in Silligrove Pool. They are several centimetres long and can fly, sometimes landing on open ground or plastic sheeting mistaking it for open water.

Flowing water is home to fewer bugs. The many small streams which drain into Dowles Brook are home to Water Crickets *Velia caprai*, always a welcome sight as they skate on the surface of backwaters in midwinter when so few other insects are visible. One of the most unusual of Wyre's bugs is so specialised that it is hardly ever seen unless it is deliberately sought. The River Saucer Bug *Aphelocheirus aestivalis* is an oval, rather flat species about 10 mm across and resembles a pale brown bed-bug. It lives in well-oxygenated flowing

River Saucer Bug *Aphelocheirus aestivalis* [HG]

Water Crickets *Velia caprai* are active on small streams and rivulets even in the depths of winter. They can double their speed on the water by spitting saliva to reduce the surface tension. [RW]

water where it hunts its prey among gravel and pebbles to a depth of five metres or more. A search in August 2010, in the Severn below Seckley Wood, produced several adults in water about 1.5 m deep. Other adults and nymphs have since been found in the Severn at Bewdley. Unlike other aquatic bugs *Aphelocheirus* never needs to come to the surface for air because its body is coated with microscopic hairs, so small that there are two million of them per square millimetre of its body surface. These extract oxygen so efficiently that *Aphelocheirus* is able to conduct its entire life in the flowing depths of the river, where it catches invertebrates (Dolling 1991).

Hoppers
The Homoptera is a large suborder of the Hemiptera which include leafhoppers, planthoppers and aphids. There are too many species to mention here and many are very small and difficult to identify, but a lot of the more noticeable 'hoppers' are attractive and colourful insects. One very common species, the Common

Froghopper *Philaenus spumarius,* is responsible for most of the gobbets of cuckoo spit which appear almost everywhere in early summer. These protective masses of bubbles are produced by the nymphs as they pump plant sap through their bodies to disguise themselves from predators as they feed. This strategy doesn't fool the solitary Two-girdled Digger Wasp *Argogorytes mystaceus* which plucks the nymphs from their frothy retreats, paralyses them, and stores them in miniature mausoleums under the bark of dead trees. The wasp lays an egg alongside each collection of hoppers and the wasp grub emerges to feast on a glut of succulent young hoppers.

The most obvious hoppers appear in May and June when Red-and-black Froghoppers *Cercopis vulnerata* are common in sunny spots in hedgerows and field corners. Here they bask secure in the protection that their warning colours offer them. In sunlit wet flushes, and other marshy places, one of the most striking leafhoppers is *Cicadella viridis*. Females of this species are bright green whilst males are blueish

Red-and-black Froghopper *Cercopis vulnerata* [JB]

A female leafhopper *Cicadella viridis* [JB]

A planthopper *Issus coleoptratus* [PC]

their jumping legs which synchronise their springing action. *Issus* is widely distributed in the Forest and can be found on woody plants, especially trees, where it feeds on the sap using piercing mouthparts. Adults are present all year round, but are most common in the autumn, when searching tree trunks is often the best way to find them. Up to 30 have been found on the shoots of a single coppiced Alder and they can sometimes be beaten from Hazel *Corylus avellana*. *Issus coleoptratus* is a southern insect which in the UK does not occur much further north than Wyre. Another very similar species *I. muscaeformis*, found mostly in south Cumbria, has not yet been found here (Whitehead and Key 2010).

Britain's largest leafhopper is the spectacular Eared Leafhopper *Ledra aurita* which lives in trees and can be 18 mm long. It is superbly camouflaged in shades of grey and green and almost invisible when sitting on a branch. Sometimes the adults will visit moth traps in late summer giving a chance to admire their Biggles-like 'ear flaps', which probably serve to resemble loose bark and break up the bugs' outline. The nymphs are squat, have no ear flaps and are very hard to see. In Wyre, *Ledra* may occur widely, but is only occasionally seen and when it is, is always a prize.

mauve, or sometimes black. In many places, especially where there is tall vegetation or scrub, you will see the common and highly variable Alder Spittlebug *Aphrophora alni*, which can be banded or flecked in shades of brown, white and black.

An attractive and fairly common treehopper in Wyre is the Horned Treehopper *Centrotus cornutus* which is dark brown and has two curved horns extending from its pronotum. Viewed head on it looks like a tiny buffalo. It feeds on a variety of tall herbs and low shrubs but can also be beaten from overhanging branches.

One of the strangest looking planthoppers found in the Forest is *Issus coleoptratus*. This is about 4 mm long, and is a squat, almost toad-like, prehistoric-looking insect with large eyes and heavily veined exterior wings. The younger instars look even odder and have a long tuft of white hairs extending from their rears. Even the anatomy of the bugs is strange: they possess a locomotive mechanism of gears in

Aphids

There are around 630 species of aphids in the UK but these have not been studied in Wyre. Two large species may attract attention. One is the surprisingly large Giant Willow Aphid *Tuberolachnus salignus* which clusters on the shoots of willows and osiers *Salix* spp. in late summer. It has been recorded from Bliss Gate. The Variegated Oak Aphid *Lachnus roboris* is local in the Britain and in Wyre is occasionally seen in clusters on oak twigs when it is invariably attended by Southern Wood Ants *Formica rufa* seeking honeydew. The male aphids are large and have black-banded wings.

The bugs of Wyre have not been studied in great detail and we anticipate many new species in future, encouraged by changes to the Forest climate and landscape.

Eared Leafhopper *Ledra aurita* [JB]

Variegated Oak Aphid *Lachnus roboris* [RW]

Green Tiger Beetle *Cicindela campestris* [RW] **(male below** [KMcG]**), a common beetle on the bare open pathways in the Forest, they take flight readily.**

Beetles

The order Coleoptera is a large group consisting of over 4,000 species of beetles in Britain, about 750 of which have been found in the Forest. Beetle recording in Wyre has been rather infrequent over the years, perhaps because the area has few large veteran trees and associated deadwood suitable for many species, and therefore was considered lacking in prime habitat. Recent recording however suggests that Wyre is rich in beetles and what follows is a summary of the more typical and interesting species to be found.

Of over 350 British species of ground beetles, or Carabids, about 70 are known from the Forest where they are typically seen scurrying over the ground in search of prey. They are more active at night so often hide under stones, logs or bark during daytime. They occur in a vast range of habitats from the wet shingle stones along the Dowles Brook and River Severn (Brown 2010) to open, bare heathy ground. Most familiar are the larger species occasionally seen

crossing a grassy track, for example the Violet Ground Beetle *Carabus violaceus* and the similar looking *C. problematicus*: both are black with a violet sheen and around 25 mm long. More unusual is the 18 mm long Snail Hunter *Cychrus caraboides*, a snail-killing ground beetle. This is a woodland species and has a narrow head enabling it to specialise in eating snails, although in Wyre where snails are less common, perhaps slugs are more likely prey. It is often found under rotten bark where it overwinters as an adult. Among many other conspicuous ground beetles is the fast-running Copper Peacock *Elaphrus cupreus* which lives on water margins and is marked with wonderful iridescent circular patterns.

Areas of open bare ground are the haunt of Green Tiger Beetles *Cicindela campestris*. These fast-running and flying predatory beetles with enormous mandibles are active by day, especially in hot weather, and take to the air with a flash of emerald when disturbed. The ferocious larvae live in burrows waiting for prey which they grab as it passes near their entrance holes.

A ground beetle *Carabus problematicus* [KMcG]

Snail Hunter *Cychrus caraboides* [JB]

Devil's Coach-horse *Ocypus olens* [JB]

A rove beetle *Scaphidium quadrimaculatum* [JB]

Woodland Dor Beetle *Anoplotrupes stercorosus* [JB]

Rhinoceros Beetle *Sinodendron cylindricum* [JB]

The rove beetles (Staphylinidae) are a vast family of over a thousand species of which several hundred have been found in the Forest. One, the Devil's Coach-horse *Ocypus olens* is known by name to many people, even if they have not seen it. At 25 mm long this black beetle is one of the largest British rove beetles and an impressive sight when it raises its abdomen scorpion-style. Many rove beetles are less than 10 mm long. *Scaphidium quadrimaculatum* looks quite different from the normal long-bodied species: it is black with four large red spots and superficially resembles a ladybird. It feeds on various fungi and is not particularly common in the British Isles.

The special rove beetles of Wyre are well hidden in Southern Wood Ants' *Formica rufa* nests which are numerous in the Forest. They are inquilines, creatures which benefit from the shelter of the nests and feed on the Wood Ants' brood. To avoid detection, they produce various chemicals to mask their presence. The great entomologist Donisthorpe produced the standard reference work on *The Guests of British Ants* (Donisthorpe 1927a). Typical species known from Wyre include *Tachyporus hypnorum, Othius subuliformis, Oxypoda formiceticola* and, in particular, *Quedius brevis*.

Although many species are small and inconspicuous, a visit to Wyre in late summer and

Lesser Stag Beetle *Dorcus parallelipipedus* is not common in the Forest but is worth searching for on rotting wood and large tree stumps. The surrounding hedgerows are good places to look. [JB]

autumn will invariably produce dor beetles, large and rotund, lumbering over forest tracks. There are three species here: Woodland Dor Beetle *Anoplotrupes stercorosus*, by far the commonest; the scarcer Dor Beetle *Geotrupes stercorarius*; and the uncommon three-horned Minotaur Beetle *Typhaeus typhoeus*. Their larvae all feed on dung, especially that of deer and Rabbit *Oryctolagus cuniculus*. The adult *Geotrupes* Dor Beetles, known as 'lousy watchmen' because they usually carry a cargo of mites, sometimes congregate on freshly cut tree stumps to gorge on sap. Although common in the Forest, they are local or absent from many Midlands woods.

Other conspicuous blackish beetles that live in the Forest are the Lesser Stag Beetle *Dorcus parallelipipedus* and the Rhinoceros Beetle *Sinodendron cylindricum*, a smaller insect with a single horn. Lesser Stag larvae live in dead wood and can raise false hopes that the Stag Beetle *Lucanus cervus* has reappeared in Wyre. There are recent historic records of this spectacular, rare and local insect in the surrounding Midlands: if found in Wyre, it would be cause for celebration.

Some of the best-loved beetles are the ladybirds and 23 species are recorded in Wyre. The most frequent species are 2-spot Ladybird *Adalia bipunctata*, 7-spot Ladybird *Coccinella septempunctata*, 14-spot Ladybird *Propylea quattuordecimpunctata*, Pine Ladybird *Exochomus quafripustulatus*, Kidney-spot Ladybird *Chilocorus renipustulatus*, Orange Ladybird *Halyzia sedecimguttata* and the new arrival and very variably patterned Harlequin Ladybird *Harmonia axyridis* (Winnall 2009). Another attractive species, usually associated with pine trees, is the Eyed Ladybird *Anatis ocellata*, a red ladybird with 15–18 black spots each normally surrounded by a pale yellow/orange ring. Not all ladybirds have spots; the Larch Ladybird *Aphidecta obliterata* is a pale brown, spotless beetle found locally in the Forest and associated with larch trees *Larix* spp.

A notable and very special species in Wyre is the Scarce 7-spot Ladybird *Coccinella magnifica*, very similar to the 7-spot Ladybird, but with larger spots, a more domed profile and four white markings below the legs on its underside: the 7-spot Ladybird has only two white marks. Scarce 7-spots are rare and local in the British Isles, mostly confined to southern England where they live in association with Southern Wood Ants. These ladybirds may be found feeding on aphids farmed by the ants for honeydew, and gain from their protection. In Wyre, they are widespread in small numbers, especially in clearings where they usually lurk close to wood ant nests, though never on them. Woodland management to create open areas should encourage both the ants and their associated Scarce 7-spots.

There are other colourful and conspicuous beetles along woodland rides and in flowery grasslands. Several of the 22 recorded species of soldier beetles, Cantharidae, are very common, feeding and mating on the umbel flowers of Hogweed *Heracleum sphondylium* and Angelica *Angelica sylvestris* along

Some Wyre Forest ladybirds

Kidney-spot Ladybird *Chilocorus renipustulatus* [JB]

Orange Ladybird *Halyzia sedecimguttata* [JB]

Eyed Ladybird *Anatis ocellata* [JB]

Larch Ladybird *Aphidecta obliterata* [JB]

Scarce 7-spot Ladybird *Coccinella magnifica* [JB]

the Dowles Brook valley, in meadows or along tracks. The Common Red Soldier Beetle *Rhagonycha fulva* is the most abundant, but several other species often crowd the flowerheads including: *R. lignosa, Cantharis nigricans, C. decipiens, C. nigra, C. rustica* and *C. pellucida*. Soldier beetles have soft wing cases, similar to the soft-winged flower beetles that are occasionally found in similar habitats. One species, the Common Malachite *Malachius bipustulatus*, has a dark green body and wing cases tipped with red. It often feeds on Hawthorn *Crataegus monogyna* blossom and other flowers in spring.

Many plants growing in the Forest, both herbs and shrubs, have nibbled edges or holes in their leaves: damage often caused by the larvae of leaf beetles, Chrysomelidae. This is a large group of more than 270 species in Britain: 75 occur in Wyre, although the list is still incomplete (Worcestershire Biological Records Centre data). Most leaf beetles are rather rounded, dumpy and metallic, or burnished looking, in shades of green, blue or brown. Heather *Calluna vulgaris* plants often host brown Heather Beetles *Lochmaea suturalis* which occasionally become abundant and do considerable damage. Tortoise beetles include *Cassida flaveola, C. rubiginosa* and the commonest species Green Tortoise Beetle *C. viridis* which is normally found on deadnettles *Lamium* spp. They tuck their legs under their green shell-like wing cases, making them difficult to see in grassy places. The large *Clytra quadripunctata*, an orange beetle with four black spots and a black head and thorax, is local in England and Wales, and closely associated with Southern Wood

Ants. In Wyre the adults appear in late spring, often on warm, scrubby banks where they feed on the young leaves of deciduous trees near Southern Wood Ants' nests. From her perch on foliage overhanging the ant nests, the female drops her eggs to the ground where the ants collect them and take them into their nests. Here the *Clytra* larvae hatch and feed on debris, emerging as adults in spring.

Weevils, Curculionidae, and associated families, are a distinctive group of beetles, typically with an extended head forming a beak or rostrum. They are very numerous with over 450 species in Britain characteristically found on trees and shrubs. Within the Forest 130 species are recorded, although many more are probably overlooked. Some are associated with specific plants: in spring for example gorse *Ulex* spp. flowers often attract the tiny, white-striped *Exapion ulicis*. Common Figwort *Scrophularia nodosa* is host to several attractively mottled weevils, the most frequent of which is the Figwort Weevil *Cionus scrophulariae*, often accompanied by *C. alauda, C. hortulanus* and the grey-black *C. tuberculosus*. Adults and larvae feed together in early summer on the leaves of their host. One of the most impressive of Wyre's weevils is the Acorn Weevil *Curculio glandium* which has a very long, needle-like rostrum, a feature shared by the Nut Weevil *C. nucum* which lives on Hazel *Corylus avellana*.

Although many weevils are drab, those in the family Attelabidae, which includes the Oak Leaf-roller Weevil *Attelabus nitens* and Hazel Leaf-roller Weevil *Apoderus coryli*, have red bodies and black heads. They

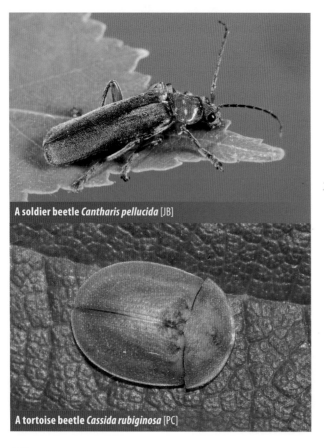

A soldier beetle *Cantharis pellucida* [JB]

A tortoise beetle *Cassida rubiginosa* [PC]

Figwort weevils *Cionus hortulanus* [JB]

Nut Weevil *Curculio nucum* [JB]

roll the leaves of their food plants to create a tubular shelter in which their larvae grow. Not all weevils use plants: the fungus weevil *Platystomos albinus* breeds in fungi on dead trees. The adult beetle is cryptically camouflaged to resemble a broken twig, its brown body contrasting with the white head and wing-case tips.

The Buprestid jewel beetles are brightly coloured, in metallic shades of greens, blues and reds. The adults are bullet shaped with large eyes and short antennae, and fly rapidly in search of freshly exposed or damaged wood in which their larvae develop. One species, the Oak Jewel Beetle *Agrilus biguttatus*, has recently increased owing to the amount of oak dieback occurring in many woodlands. Oak dieback, or oak decline, is a disease caused by *Phytophthora* sp. causing sudden canopy dieback and can kill mature trees. *Agrilus* cannot attack healthy trees, but is attracted by weeping sap runs on affected specimens and soon moves in to colonise them. Until as recently as 1987, Oak Jewel Beetle was listed in the British Red Data Book as 'Vulnerable' and under some threat of extinction (Shirt 1987). Since the great storm of October 1987, when many oaks were damaged, the beetle took advantage of a new supply of suitably stressed or dead wood and is now locally common in many woods including Wyre (Denman *et al.* 2010).

The striking red cardinal beetles also need deadwood for their larvae to develop. In Wyre there are two species. The Black-headed Cardinal Beetle *Pyrochroa coccinea* is widespread here but less common elsewhere in the Midlands. It is often seen on flowers, especially Wood Spurge in May and June, along with the less frequent Red-headed Cardinal Beetle *P. serraticornis*. Wood Spurge is popular with many spring beetles including the click beetles Elateridae; the wireworm larvae of some species are the bane of gardeners. The most common in the Forest is the dull brown *Athous haemorrhoidalis*. Other less-common species are *Denticollis linearis*, the Chequered Click Beetle *Prosternon tessellatum* and *Ctenicera cuprea*.

In 2012 a new species of false click beetle *Epiphanis cornutus* appeared in Wyre. This dark beetle with golden hairs was originally discovered in the Britain in rotten spruce logs in Gloucestershire in 1964. It is probably an import from North America where it is apparently only rarely found. In 2005 it was recorded in Warwickshire and has now reached Wyre where it lays its eggs on freshly cut conifer stumps (Bingham 2012a).

Many other beetles are associated with sap runs or fungi in trees. *Glischrochilus hortensis*, a black beetle with four red spots, is quite common in the Forest on rotten stumps. On birch stumps with fungi, look for the rare *Tritoma bipustulata*.

One of the more unusual-looking beetles using deadwood is *Hylecoetus dermestoides*. This long-bodied orange beetle, sometimes called the Large Timberworm Beetle, is restricted to old woodlands, and is locally common in Wyre. Its larvae farm a fungus, a type of yeast *Endomyces hylecoeti,* which is initially provided by the female beetle. The beetle grubs carry the fungal spores around their burrows, infecting the wood as they go, until the walls of their tunnels are lined with a white layer of fungus. This symbiotic relationship with the beetle enables the fungus to

Oak Jewel Beetle *Agrilus biguttatus* [JB]

Black-headed Cardinal Beetle *Pyrochroa coccinea* [JB]

A click beetle *Ctenicera cuprea* [JB]

Male (top) and female timberworm beetles *Hylecoetus dermestoides* [JB]

colonise pastures new and maintains the larval food supply (Piper 2009).

A night walk in summer through the Forest and its surrounds may reveal greenish-yellow lights along path sides. These are the bioluminescent tail segments of female Glow-worms *Lampyris noctiluca*, hoping to attract a male. Glow-worms are not common in Wyre where they avoid dense forest, preferring woodland edges, meadows or orchards and the disused railway line. Numbers vary from year to year: Sue Hall and Dennis Brooks have monitored a site in Wyre since 2002 where single evening counts have ranged from two to 44 (Winnall & Hall 2009). A warm, still evening in the latter part of June is a good time to look for Glow-worms, but their prehistoric-looking larvae turn up on tracks or among leaf litter at any time of year.

Corpses of small mammals or birds are a happy hunting ground for coleopterists because they attract specialised beetles, such as the carrion beetles *Oiceoptoma thoracicum*, *Nicrophorus vestigator* and *N. vespilloides*. These are often banded in bright red or orange and will buzz past loudly on warm days. Most of their lives are spent beneath corpses which they bury as a food supply for their larvae. The large Black Snail Beetle *Silpha atrata* is a snail killer most often found under loose bark or beneath fallen wood. The similarly shaped *Dendroxena quadrimaculata* is a rare woodland species, yellowish-brown with black blotches; it hunts caterpillars of geometrid moths on oak leaves.

On warm evenings in May and June, Cockchafers *Melolontha melolontha* blunder into lights and

A carrion beetle *Oiceoptoma thoracicum* [RW]

crash against windowpanes. The largest of these heavyweights can be 30 mm long. Cockchafers were once abundant but have declined over much of the British Isles, though they are still fairly common around the Forest. Other chafers in Wyre include the common Garden Chafer *Phyllopertha horticola*, the scarcer Summer Chafer *Amphimallon solstitiale*, Welsh Chafer *Hoplia philanthus* which live in meadows and rough grasslands, and the Noble Chafer *Gnorimus nobilis*, a rare species of old orchards (see box below).

Beetles that need wood as part of their life cycle are called saproxylic and can be used to rank woodland habitats in terms of their national importance for these 'deadwood' species. A very characteristic group of saproxylic beetles are the longhorns Cerambycidae, many of which have strikingly long antennae. Most are

The Noble Chafer

One of the flagship species of old traditional orchards is the Noble Chafer *Gnorimus nobilis* (pictured top right [HG] and bottom right [RW]), a spectacular, bronze-green beetle, about 2 cm long, spotted with white. Its larvae live in old rotting apple, plum and cherry trees. It is known from several orchards in and around Wyre with the first records from the 1930s. Interestingly boxes of insects collected by Norman Hickin discovered in 2000 contained three specimens, one labelled "in house, Newalls, Wyre Forest, 12.vi.1970" (McGee & Whitehead 2003). The adult beetle is rarely seen, emerging from trees between the end of May and mid-July as observed at Bowcastle Farm on 7 June 2004 (McGee 2004). The beetle is often reluctant to fly except on warm days when it visits flowers of Hogweed, Angelica, Elder *Sambucus nigra* and Meadowsweet to feed on pollen and nectar.

The chafer grubs chew their way through decaying fruit trees and take one or two years to develop into adults. Even if the larvae cannot be seen, their distinctive droppings or frass within a decaying tree is a clue to their presence. Noble Chafers are scarce and vulnerable and their UK stronghold is in Worcestershire's old orchards, a habitat also under threat. The chafer is a Biodiversity Action Plan species and the subject of many conservation projects. If this beautiful beetle is to survive in Wyre, we need to conserve and maintain local orchards and value them as important wildlife habitats which support populations of many insects as well as birds such as Redstart *Phoenicuros phoenicuros* and Lesser Spotted Woodpecker *Dendrocopos minor*.

associated with woodland where the larvae feed in dead or living timber, often taking several years to develop. Longhorns are often attractively marked, and many are active by day when they feed from flowers. In Britain there are 59 native or naturalised species (Twinn & Harding 1999). Of these, 32 species have been recorded in Wyre, but others are likely to be present (Bingham 2009). One of the most typical, and perhaps the most obvious, is the Black-and-yellow Longhorn *Rutpela maculata*. This is an elegant wasp mimic 15–20 mm long, and often feeds from bramble blossom in July, but is attracted to many woodland flowers in summer. In warm sunshine the adults fly readily: the larvae feed in rotting wood in a variety of deciduous trees.

Larger, and barred black and orange, the Four-banded Longhorn Beetle *Leptura quadrifasciata* is a much scarcer insect, possibly declining in the British Isles, but still occurring in quite good numbers in the Forest. Adults look very wasp-like as they fly in warm sunshine in midsummer in search of nectar and egg-laying spots in the timber of deciduous trees. The Speckled Longhorn Beetle *Pachytodes cerambyciformis* is smaller and dumpier than its relatives and common in western Britain, though absent from much of the Midlands and east of England. It is widespread in Wyre where adults appear from May to August feeding on flowers: the larvae are polyphagous in deciduous and coniferous trees, especially on the roots.

The finest wasp mimic among longhorns is the Wasp Beetle *Clytus arietis*, abundant over England and Wales, but rare in Scotland. In Wyre it frequently visits flowers and in May and June. It walks jerkily like a wasp as it searches for egg-laying sites on fallen timber or log piles. These can be in deciduous or coniferous timber. Spring in Wyre is heralded by the appearance of two spectacular longhorns, the Black-spotted Longhorn Beetle *Rhagium mordax*, and the Two-banded Longhorn Beetle *R. bifasciatum*. Their shorter antennae, stocky appearance and thoracic spines make them distinctive as does their approachability. Although they fly well, they often allow close inspection as they visit tree stumps or feed on Hawthorn and other blossom. The larvae feed on several species of coniferous and deciduous trees, but the Black-spotted Longhorn Beetle prefers oaks and other broadleaved trees. They become adult beetles in autumn and overwinter under bark, emerging in spring sunshine. Both are widespread in the Forest, but the Two-banded Longhorn is slightly less common.

These larger longhorns may be conspicuous, but the commonest species in the Forest is probably the Common Grammoptera *Grammoptera ruficornis*. Its small size, 3–7 mm long, and funereal colours make it easy to overlook, even though it can be abundant on Hawthorn flowers in early spring, when dozens of beetles congregate on a single bush. Its larvae develop in rotten, fungus-infested branches of deciduous trees. Two other species, the Black-striped Longhorn Beetle *Stenurella melanura*, and the Tobacco-coloured Longhorn Beetle *Alosterna tabacicolor* are often seen on early summer flowers, especially Hogweed. Male Black-striped Longhorn Beetles have chestnut-brown wing-cases with a black central stripe and black tips; females are brown, and markings vary. The adults of both species visit a range of flowers and their larvae develop in small dead branches or rotten tree stumps. Tobacco-coloured Longhorn Beetles are scarce in the main forest block of Wyre, but are sometimes frequent in the Dowles Brook valley or along the Severn at Seckley and Eymore Woods.

The Variable Longhorn Beetle *Stenocorus meridianus* is an impressively large species which, despite its size, can be difficult to find. It is a robust, generally black but often chestnut-coloured beetle, around 20–25 mm long, though it varies in size. The adults emerge in early June when they sit on leaves or wood, but can be local and uncommon. The larvae feed for three years on the dead roots of deciduous trees such as oaks, elms and maples before emerging as adult beetles.

Many British longhorns are restricted by habitat, and most are in decline, mainly due to unsuitable woodland management. Wyre is still remarkably good for many uncommon species, but lacks large amounts of fallen and standing deadwood and a good variety of tree and shrubs. However the introduction of conifers has provided habitat for new longhorns. Four species are of particular interest as they each feed in different conifers: the Larch Longhorn Beetle *Tetropium gabrieli*, the Black Spruce Longhorn Beetle *T. castaneum*, the Pine-stump Borer *Asemum striatum* and the Spruce

Four-banded Longhorn Beetle *Leptura quadrifasciata* [JB]

Black-spotted Longhorn Beetle *Rhagium mordax* [JB]

Shortwing Beetle *Molorchus minor*. None of these seem to be common here, although they have the potential to become pest species. Since they are crepuscular or nocturnal they may be under-recorded.

The Larch Longhorn Beetle, 8–18 mm long, is widely distributed and locally common in Great Britain. Its larvae feed under or within the bark of diseased or dying trees, in standing or fallen trunks, and in thick branches. The few records for the Forest are of adults seen on logpiles on summer evenings. The Black Spruce Longhorn Beetle is also scarce in Wyre. Its larvae feed in various conifers, typically Norway Spruce *Picea abies:* adults have been seen in two places in the west of the Forest. Another beetle to look for on conifer logpiles at dusk is the Pine-stump Borer, a large black insect 8–23 mm long with shorter antenna than many longhorns (Bingham 2011). It frequents Scots Pine *Pinus sylvestris* and other conifers. In Wyre it is an introduction from its native Scotland from where it

Spruce Shortwing Beetle *Molorchus minor* [JB]

Black-clouded Longhorn Beetle *Leiopus nebulosus* [JB]

Welsh Oak Longhorn Beetle *Pyrrhidium sanguineum* [JB]

has spread with the planting of pines. Curiously, most records come from the Rock Coppice area, where pine is uncommon. The Spruce Shortwing Beetle looks more like a spider than a longhorn. This small but distinctive beetle, only 6–16 mm long, has a narrow body, very long antennae, and swollen femora. Although there are only a few records for Wyre it may be overlooked and it is worth inspecting hawthorn flowers by day, especially those in hedgerows near conifer plantations, where its larvae feed on trees such as spruces and firs.

Black-clouded Longhorn Beetles *Leiopus nebulosus*, are native in England and Wales and turn up occasionally in the Forest, most recently on oak logs in Longdon Wood. Their cryptic colouration makes them easy to miss when they sit on bark, but they are genuinely rare beetles whose larvae feed in deciduous trees including Beech, oaks, maples, elms, birches, willows and cherries. The White-clouded Longhorn Beetle *Mesosa nebulosa* is a Red Data Book species, found only in England. There are two records from Wyre, in Ribbesford and Withybed woods where the lichen-patterned adults were seen on scrubby vegetation and tree trunks. The larvae feed on a wide range of deciduous trees, usually preferring oaks. The adults are probably crepuscular or nocturnal.

Two other oak-feeding longhorns are the Greater Thorn-tipped Longhorn Beetle *Pogonocherus hispidulus* and Lesser Thorn-tipped Longhorn Beetle *P. hispidus*. Both are intricately marbled like lichen-covered bark, 5–8 mm long and widely scattered, but local, over England and Wales. The few records from the Forest are from small, often damaged or broken-off oak twigs. The Lesser Thorn-tipped Longhorn Beetle also uses Holly *Ilex aquifolium*, Ivy *Hedera helix* and apple as breeding sites. Their cryptic patterns camouflage them superbly and because they appear not to visit flowers, they are best sought by close inspection of small trees and bushes.

Among the longhorns are some of Wyre's most spectacular insects. The Musk Beetle *Aromia moschata* is an occasional and very welcome find along the Severn where its larvae feed in old pollarded trees, especially willows. This very large, iridescent greenish or purple-black beetle, with long arcing antennae can be 30–35 mm long. Adults appear throughout summer and are said to smell of attar of roses. Away from the river there is a single record from within the Forest in August 2005, from a willow pollard by a pool at the Roxel Rocket site at Kinlet.

In Wyre the Small Poplar Borer *Saperda populnea* is an attractive but uncommon species whose larvae develop in Aspen *Populus tremula* saplings, producing a gall in smaller branches. Its rarity reflects the scarcity of Aspen locally and highlights the need to conserve and encourage a diverse range of trees and shrubs.

By contrast, although oaks are the commonest trees in the Forest, the Tanbark Borer *Phymatodes testaceus*, which depends on them, is a local southern species in Britain. There are two Wyre records of the adults emerging from oak collected from log piles at Uncllys

Musk Beetles *Aromia moschata* are rarely seen in the Forest, but may be seen feeding on umbellifer flowers along the wooded banks of the River Severn. [RW]

Farm and Bliss Gate. This beetle prefers open wood pasture or parkland so the denser woodland in Wyre may not be ideal.

Another oak longhorn is flourishing locally. The Welsh Oak Longhorn Beetle *Pyrrhidium sanguineum* is a Red Data Book species which, until recently, was very rare and almost restricted to the woodlands of the Welsh Marches. In 1970 the only known site was in an ancient deer park at Moccas in Herefordshire. Since then it has spread and is now turning up more widely in England and Wales. It may have been commoner in the past as there are old records scattered over England, nearly all cited as introductions from imported timber. It is a very attractive ruby-red and black beetle felted with fine down. Its larvae feed under the bark of deciduous trees, especially oak within 24 months of felling. The Wyre population first came to light some 40 km to the south when a beetle was discovered emerging from oak logs destined for a wood burner in a house near Bredon Hill in south Worcestershire (Meiklejohn 2007). Detective work showed that the logs had been cut in Bell Coppice in Wyre. This prompted a search in the Forest and a beetle was found in an oak log pile at Uncllys Farm in spring 2008, and another under the bark of a dead oak at Sturt. Since then records have included dozens of beetles under the bark of a dead oak near Dowles Brook. The beetle is now established within the Forest at Lords Yards Coppice and Longdon Wood and probably many other places: to find the adult, look on log piles in May and June.

In modern Wyre, an almost legendary aura surrounds the rare and elusive Small Black Longhorn Beetle *Stenurella nigra*, a Nationally Scarce species recorded by Norman Hickin in the 1970s when he found an adult feeding on Wood Spurge flowers near Brand Wood (Hickin 1971). Unfortunately, since

Colin Plant made more recent records in June 1984 (Worcestershire Biological Records Centre data), it has not been seen. Given its small size and blackish colouration, it could easily be overlooked, and remains a challenge for the dedicated coleopterist.

Perhaps the Holy Grail of modern longhorn seekers is the very rare Red-collared Longhorn Beetle *Dinoptera collaris* recorded from Wyre in 1938, and possibly more recently (Invertebrate Site Register 1997). It breeds in old insect galleries in oaks and the blue-black and scarlet adults visit flowers in early summer. Whoever re-finds this elusive species would boost the reputation of Wyre as a very special longhorn location.

The Saproxylic Quality Index

The Saproxylic Quality Index (Fowles *et al.* 1999) is a scoring system designed to assist with the evaluation of the conservation significance of wooded habitats in Great Britain for saproxylic Coleoptera. In the past Wyre has never been considered important for saproxylic invertebrates because it lacks old mature trees. Nonetheless, it is an ancient forest, even if the more recent history of 300 years of coppicing has removed most of the original ancient trees. The coppice stools are themselves old and provide good habitat, and the surrounding traditional orchards contain decaying and mature fruit trees. For beetles it may be continuity of ancient woodland on the site that is more important than the presence of large veteran trees, although old trees are clearly important for some highly specialist species. Using the most recent species lists, dated to 2014, Wyre is ranked 36 in order (SQI score 507) out of 186 sites on the online Saproxylic Quality Index website database. Wyre does not compete in rank against the most important sites in Britain like the vast tracts of the New Forest or great parklands such as Windsor Park, but for a small forest it is significant. Within the Midlands it is ranked as the 10th most important for saproxylic beetles, but with more study it may prove even richer.

Flies

A very large proportion of the insects the visitor to Wyre sees feeding on flowers in sunny clearings, or swarming in damp and shady places, belong to the Order Diptera, the true flies. Their distinguishing characteristics are a single pair of wings together with a pair of usually knob-shaped balancing organs, known as halteres, placed beside the base of the wings. On a spring or summer walk through the Forest you will certainly see and hear the hoverflies (Syrphidae), suspended in mid-air on whirring wings or decorating sunny flower heads, and often mimicking wasps or bees. Tiny midges haunt damp and shady places or swarm beneath the overhanging branches of trees and those giants of the midge world, the craneflies, bumble through the tall grass.

The varied geology, habitats, vegetation and management of Wyre is reflected by the fly fauna's richness and diversity and a significant proportion of the 7,055 species of fly recorded in the British Isles are likely to be found here. A year-long survey of three orchards on the south-east margin of the Forest in 2004 (Smart & Winnall 2006) identified 441 species, and the total number of fly species for Wyre in the recorders' database currently stands at 1,278.

The larvae of flies, maggots, are found in dark, damp places such as streams, soil, leaf mould, dung and rotting wood, or mining the roots, stems or leaves of plants. The midge families, the more 'primitive' Diptera, have larvae with heads and jaws of the conventional caterpillar type. The more 'advanced' Diptera maggots have no obvious head but a pointed front end and a pair of hook-shaped jaws suitable for burrowing. They often mine plant tissues or rotten wood but are also commonly predaceous or parasitic.

Many flies are associated with particular host plants and are expected where these plants grow. For example small willow catkin flies (*Egle* spp.) emerge in March from fallen catkins of the previous year. After basking in the spring sunshine to harden off, they lay their eggs on the newly opening catkins of the current year. The small maggots feed on the *Salix* seeds. The larger flies of the genus *Chirosia* form tangled galls on the tips of fern fronds. Those commonly met with in Wyre are *C. betuleti* on Lady-fern *Athyrium filix-femina* and Male-fern *Dryopteris filix-mas*, and *C. grossicauda* which forms galls on Bracken *Pteridium aquilinum* (see Chapter 8 Galls).

The tiny but pretty picture-winged flies (Tephritidae) include species whose maggots burrow into the flower heads of thistles and other plants. The common Creeping Thistle *Cirsium arvense* is mined by *Xyphosia miliaria* and *Terellia ruficauda*, while *Urophora cardui* forms many-chambered galls on its stem. Common Knapweed *Centaurea nigra* is mined by *Chaetostomella cylindrica* while *Urophora jaceana* galls its stem. *Euphranta toxoneura* is a most unusual picture-wing as its maggots attack the oval sawfly galls caused by *Pontania* spp. on willow leaves and feed on the sawfly larvae inside.

A female cranefly *Ctenophora pectinicornis* [KMcG]

Common Awl-fly *Xylophagus ater* [JB]

The majority of species are not associated with particular species of plants but with physical features of the habitat such as still or running water, shelter, shade or rotting wood, or the presence of prey species or animals necessary to complete life cycles.

Flies of rotting wood

Some of Wyre's most spectacular flies are the larger craneflies (Tipulidae) many of whose larvae live in rotting wood: their pupal cases are frequently found projecting from the end of the exit burrow. The most striking of these is *Tanyptera atrata*, a large shiny black species with a red and black abdomen and red or ochre legs. The female's impressive sting-like ovipositor adds to her intimidating appearance. After emergence in May, the smaller, yellower males locate the females perhaps using their comb-like antennae to detect pheromones. Two other comb-antennae craneflies *T. nigricornis* and *Ctenophora pectinicornis* are also recorded from Wyre but are seen less often. In decaying logs the Common Awl-fly *Xylophagus ater* breeds and though the adults are rarely seen, the larvae are easier to find lurking beneath rotting bark (Stubbs & Drake 2014).

Macrocera stigma (Keroplatidae) is a fungus gnat often found in the field layer of the woodlands

Male and female *Tanyptera atrata* **craneflies: the striking female (bottom) has an impressive sting-like ovipositor** [JB]

particularly around rotting stumps. The males in particular have extremely long thread-like antennae. Other keroplatid fungus gnats often seen are *Cerotelion striatum* and the large black *Platyura marginata*. Their wormy larvae make webs and trackways of silk beneath bark or under rotting logs to trap fungus spores or small prey. Some of the species use droplets of oxalic acid to make them toxic.

Flies of water and wet places

In May and June, the mottled-winged Yellow-winged Water-snipefly *Atherix ibis* emerges along the Dowles Brook and the Severn. Although it is usually seen singly or in small numbers, female *Atherix* have the strange habit of forming clusters on twigs overhanging the water and, post egglayng, dying in that position, producing balls of dead flies, eggs and jelly which later fall into the water. Its aquatic larva is an ambush predator with a powerfully venomous bite.

The streambed of Dowles Brook is mostly stony with, in places, marginal deposits and bars of sandy gravels or cobbles. In summer these marginal sediments may be teeming with tiny black flies known as lesser dung flies (Sphaeroceridae). The predominant species is generally *Pseudocollinella humida*, with smaller numbers of the closely related *Opacifrons coxata*. They may be joined by the equally tiny marsh flies (Ephydridae) particularly *Ditrichophora palliditarsis* and *Scatella paludum*.

The stony beds and continuous flows of Dowles Brook and its tributaries limit the scope of many midge larvae, but one group of midges which positively prefers the flowing water are the tiny buffalo gnats of the genus *Simulium*, often known as blackflies. Their larvae are usually found anchored to stones or weeds by their rear ends with their bodies projecting into the water flow, straining fine particles with their fan-like mouthparts. It is very likely that several species of *Simulium* occur in Wyre but the adults are very difficult to tell apart. Some species produce extremely painful bites on people, but those in the Wyre have not proved particularly obnoxious to date. They appear

black, but under a lens it can be seen that the sooty black thorax and legs are decorated with short, fine, golden hairs and patches of glossy silver felt.

The *Culicoides* biting midges (Ceratopogonidae) are even tinier, only 1–3 mm long. The females bite people mainly in the later part of the afternoon, but at any time of the day if the weather becomes dull and damp. *Culicoides obsoletus* is the species most commonly met with; it is greyish white with a banded appearance, and in large numbers it can be an irritating biter.

In June 2007 a very unusual water midge (Chironomidae) was collected from the surface of an illuminated sheet being used by moth-trappers in Eymore Wood. It was *Buchonomyia thienemanni*, a member of a relict group at the base of the chironomid family tree. *Buchonomyia* is associated with the larger rivers so the specimen presumably originated in the Severn. Its larvae are thought to be parasitic or predaceous on caddis larvae (Trichoptera). The Wyre specimen is the most northerly record for the species in the UK (Ashe *et al.* in press).

Biting midges such as *Culicoides* spp. are attracted to light and light traps set for moths usually collect large numbers of them. On 8 June 2008 in a wooded lane near Park House four Skinner light traps attracted two species of predaceous biting midge (*Serromyia femorata* and *S. morio* (Ceratopogonidae)). The females of these midges feed on other midges, entering mating swarms and seizing the males with their powerful legs. In less than an hour the prey is reduced to a hollow husk: some of the larger species can capture and digest insects, such as mayflies, many times their own size.

One fly that comes looking for us is the stealthy grey-mottled Notch-horned Cleg *Haematopota pluvialis*, the commonest of the horseflies (Tabanidae). It is abundant in most of the Wyre Forest, but before you squash one it is worth pausing to appreciate the its extremely beautiful eyes of remarkable red and green iridescence, banded horizontally with squiggly lines of dull purple. Its relative the Splayed Deerfly *Chrysops caecutiens* is even more strikingly beautiful. Its body is

A wet patch in the Great Bog. Areas such as these are usually rich in fly species. [RW]

Splayed Deerfly *Chrysops caecutiens* [JB]

Golden-haired Robberfly *Choerades marginatus* [KMcG]

Small Yellow-legged Robberfly *Dioctria linearis* [KMcG]

yellow and black; its wings boldly patterned in blackish brown, and its eyes a brilliant iridescent green with dark purple spots. Its larvae are usually associated with mud on the margins of streams (Stubbs & Drake 2014). Among other horseflies, the Dark Giant Horsefly *Tabanus sudeticus*, at up to 24 mm in body length, the largest and most spectacular in the UK, is occasionally seen, usually in the more southerly parts of Wyre.

The most powerful predatory flies are the robberflies (Asilidae). They have strong spiny legs, a stabbing proboscis which can inject a powerful toxin, and a large bushy 'moustache'. The most abundant species is the Kite-tailed Robberfly *Machimus atricapillus* which is widely distributed in Wyre. It is usually seen resting on low- or medium-level vegetation in sunlit spots, its body tilted to one side to soak up the sunshine. The Golden-haired Robberfly *Choerades marginatus* and the Common Awl Robberfly *Neoitamus cyanurus* are two other large robberflies which are regularly seen in

Kite-tailed Robberfly *Machimus atricapillus* with Notch-horned Cleg *Haematopota pluvialis* [JB]

clearings and along rides. The Kite-tailed Robberfly ambushes other flies while the Common Awl Robberfly seems to prefer small moths (Stubbs & Drake 2014). The *Dioctria* robberflies are more delicate. The Small Yellow-legged Robberfly *D. linearis* is the most abundant species in the shaded woodland areas while the Violet Black-legged Robberfly *D. atricapilla* is associated with more open areas such as Pound Green Common, Experimental Pool Meadow and Breakneck Bank.

Flies in flushes

One of the groups most typical of wet flushed areas is the craneflies, both the large ones of the family Tipulidae and the small species of the Limoniidae and Pediciidae. One day's collecting on a large flush at Holy Well in Wyre on 14 June 2010 yielded 15 Limoniidae and two Tipulidae species. A large and very striking cranefly often seen in flushed and damp areas is *Pedicia rivosa* whose wings are attractively patterned with chocolate brown hieroglyphs. Another family of flies typical of the flushes are the Dolichopodidae, somewhat unfortunately referred to as 'dollies' or 'dolly flies'. They are small- to medium-sized flies, mostly predaceous, often blackish in colour glossed with green. The males in many species have gigantic sexual organs curled under the rear of their abdomens.

Wyre flushes containing tufa deposits have particularly interesting and important species. The most notable is *Ellipteroides alboscutellatus*, a very small black-and-yellow cranefly, classified as nationally Endangered. It is the subject of two papers by David Heaver (2006 & 2014) in which he documents its association with the calcicole moss *Palustriella*.

E. alboscutellatus is widely distributed in Wyre, mostly in very small numbers associated with patches of mud, usually with flecks of tufa and sparse clumps of moss, high on the steep sides of the tributary valleys. Two Wyre sites have produced large populations of the species. The 'Great Bog' had at least one tufa patch but this has partly dried up recently and the fly has all but disappeared. A grassy flush in Shelf Held Coppice on the slopes above Park Brook contained hundreds. This flush is particularly interesting as it contains a buried tufa deposit several centimetres thick. The flies were usually found in the tall grass on the upper parts of the flush. This population also appears to have declined, probably because of the encroachment of bracken, though small patches of moss are still present in a rivulet draining the flush margin.

Other cranefly species are also particularly associated with the tufa flushes and their associated streams. The tiny *Molophilus corniger*, an uncommon cranefly with furry wings, has been found around the Shelf Held Coppice tufa flush above Park Brook, but not elsewhere in Wyre. Two more small craneflies, *Paradelphomyia ecalcarata* and *Ellipteroides limbatus* have been have been found close to small streams into which tufa flushes are draining (Blythe 2010). In these stretches the pH of the stream water is between 8.0 and 8.5 (Limbrey pers. comm.). *P. ecalcarata* is nationally Vulnerable, *E. limbatus* is nationally Endangered (Falk 1991).

Two tiny flies of the family Psychodidae (the hairy-moth-flies), *Tonnoiriella pulchra* and *Paramormia decipiens* have been found at the lower end of the flush near the Park Brook. Both species have associations with tufa, and *P. decipiens* larvae are described as encrusted with lime (Withers 1989). *Telmatoscopus britteni* is another unusual moth fly regularly met there.

The Sciomyzidae are the snail-killing flies: many of the 70 British species attack water snails whilst others specialise in terrestrial snails. The species most commonly met with in Wyre is *Tetanocera hyalipennis* an aquatic snail killer which occurs most commonly around wet flushes and roadside ditches. Its close relative *T. elata* kills slugs which are more mobile than snails and present a greater challenge to infect. The fly maggot waits in ambush to attack a passing slug and older maggots can rapidly immobilise their prey with a toxic bite (Knutson & Vala 2011).

The particular Wyre speciality amongst the Sciomyzidae is *Renocera pallida*. This fly is regularly met with in the wet flushes (both with and without tufa) where its larva feeds on tiny freshwater pea mussels (*Pisidium*) and orb mussels (*Sphaerium*). The little maggot prefers to attack mussels that are at least partially exposed to the air and so it may be favoured by fluctuation of water levels in the flushes. The mussel is somehow prevented from closing its shell so the rear end of the maggot remains exposed to the air while it is feeding. The first stage maggot feeds on a single mussel, and the subsequent two stages will kill about 50 more between them (Horsáková 2003).

Great Pied Hoverfly *Volucella pellucens* [RW]

Chrysotoxum arcuatum [KMcG]

Hoverflies

Hoverflies (Syrphidae) are some of the most obvious and attractive flies in Wyre. Either visiting flowers or hovering nearly motionless over a ride, they can suddenly vanish as if by magic, only to reappear in the same place a few moments later. Among the most obvious are the large *Volucella* species including the striking black and white Great Pied Hoverfly *V. pellucens*, which holds territory at about head-height in sunny spots and visits brambles. It is one of a select group of hoverflies with larvae which develop in wasp nests and which also includes the wasp-mimicking *V. inanis*, a new arrival which often turns up in gardens.

The Drone Fly *Eristalis tenax* is one of the commonest and most conspicuous species. Its larvae are 'rat-tailed maggots'. They have a long breathing tube attached to their rear ends, allowing them to live in wet manure heaps, sewage pools and deep mud. In winter the adults enter diapause and hide in crevices, but often fly on sunny days even in January. *E. pertinax* was found to be one of the commonest pollinators of the fruit trees in the Wyre orchards and *Melangyna lasiophthalma* was an early visitor to flowering cherry trees. The male of *E. nemorum* shows a fascinating courtship activity in which it repeatedly hovers over a female which is resting or nectaring on flowers.

The larvae of many hoverflies feed on aphids. The black and yellow *Syrphus ribesii* is a very common species and with a little searching its larvae (or those of closely related species) are found on a variety of plants

Xanthogramma pedissequum [JB]

Chriorhina ranunculi [JB]

Male Ramsons Hoverfly *Portevinia maculata* [PC]

where aphids are common. A few species have larvae which prey on subterranean root aphids. The larvae of *Chrysotoxum arcuatum*, *Xanthogramma pedissequum* and *X. citrofasciatum* have been found in ants' nests and *X. citrofasciatum* has been shown to feed on root-feeding aphids which are being farmed by the ants.

A smaller set of hoverflies feed on plants. *Cheilosia illustrata* is a good example, easily recognised as it visits the flowers of Hogweed and its larvae tunnel in the plant's roots. Other *Cheilosia* species have similar lifestyles: *C. bergenstammi* larvae feed in the lower stem of Common Ragwort *Senecio jaobaea,* while the larvae of the local and elusive *C. chrysocoma* feeds on

Angelica. Sunlit patches of Ramsons *Allium ursinum* are invariably visited by the Ramsons Hoverfly *Portevinia maculata*, a distinctive black and grey hoverfly which basks on the leaves and flowers during April and May; its larvae munch the garlic bulbs.

Perhaps the most exciting hoverfly hunting grounds are ancient woods and woodland glades, especially when larger mature trees, old fallen logs, streams and marshy areas are present. These often provide sunlit flower-rich verges and, a most important element, shelter from intrusive winds. For instance *Chalcosyrphus eunotus* the nationally scarce honeybee mimic may be seen where sunlight strikes partially submerged logs in the Dowles Brook. The larvae are found in decaying sap under the bark of smaller tree trunks that have lodged against the stream bank and remain partly in the water. The adult males are dark and inconspicuous flies, but once their favourite spots are found, they can be located in May and June where they hold territory on the choicest logs in dappled light. A brassy fly with flecked wings *Ferdinandea cuprea* is usually seen resting on tree trunks and its larvae are recorded from sap wounds in oak or Ash.

Spring is an excellent time for hoverfly watching in Wyre and *Criorhina* hoverflies are spectacular early insects which mimic bumble bees. From early March onwards, white- and red-tailed forms of *C. ranunculi*

The honeybee mimic *Chalcosyrphus eunotus* (below) may be seen along the Dowles Brook where sunlight strikes partially submerged logs. [Both BK]

Xylota jakutorum [KMcG]

Sericomyia silentis [PC]

Helophilus hybridus [PC]

in damp areas. The conifers host their own set of associated hoverflies including *X. abiens* and *X. jakutorum.*

As summer progresses one of most conspicuous hoverflies in Wyre is *Sericomyia silentis*, a dramatic wasp mimic which basks in heathy spots and is especially fond of knapweed and Devil's-bit Scabious *Succisa pratensis* flowers in meadows. In some years there is a mass migration of common species from the continent such as the Marmalade Hoverfly *Episyphus balteatus* and *Scaeva pyrastri* that become locally abundant. Occasionally *Helophilus hybridus* and migrant *H. trivittatus* join the common *H. pendulus* in damp flower-rich areas.

Wyre's hoverfly fauna is constantly changing with habitat and climate and some species are expanding into new territory. For example *Rhingia rostrata,* with its long pointed snout, has recently increased. The Hornet Hoverfly *Volucella zonaria,* one of the largest British flies, has been making spectacular progress northwards after being a southern species for many years and is now widely met with in Worcestershire, while *Callicera rufa,* a pine plantation specialist, has been found just a few kilometres away. There are mysteries too, enigmatic species which remain very scarce or are eagerly awaited. There is even an old Wyre record for the striking wasp mimic the Phantom Hoverfly *Doros profuges*, whose rediscovery would be remarkable.

Other flies

Empis tessellata (Empididae) is one of the large dance flies often seen on Hogweed flowers in the late spring and summer. It is brownish, with an orange tinge to the wing bases and in spite of its long powerful 'beak' and strong spiny legs, is a nectar feeder, though the male makes an exception at mating time in spring when he kills another insect, often a very large one, as a wedding present for his bride. While the female sucks the juices of his gift he mates with her. One special dance fly species is *E. limata*, recorded in July 2010 from pond-side vegetation on the western edge of Wyre. This is a Nationally Endangered species and a UK Priority Species with a national biodiversity action plan (Falk & Crossley 2005). Its previous known locations have almost all been on the South Wales borderlands to the west.

Hilara is a large genus, with 70 British species, closely related to the Empididae. They are a familiar sight in Wyre skimming over ponds or puddles, their long dangling hind legs brushing the surface, perhaps regulating their distance from the water's edge, and leaving a fine wake behind them. The skimmers are mostly males, searching for floating food items such as dead insects or emerging midges. These they will wrap in silk, spun from the enlarged joints of their front legs, creating a gift to be presented to the female in the mating swarm. Males not carrying a parcel are usually rejected. The parcel may contain an inedible item such as a fragment of plant tissue or even in some

buzz around sallow bushes visiting catkins, and in May hawthorn blossom attracts *C. berberina*. In sunlit glades in ancient woodland look out for *C. asilica* which is an excellent honeybee mimic. All *Criorhina* species feed as larvae on damp rotting wood: an important habitat for many invertebrates.

Rot holes in trees are irresistible to several elusive species of hoverflies. Rotting deciduous logs are the larval habitat of species such as the golden-tailed *Xylota sylvarum*. Sap-runs in spring attract *Brachyopa* species, small orange and grey hoverflies whose numbers vary widely from year to year. *Xylota segnis* is regularly encountered especially on flowers and rotting wood

species nothing at all. In many cases the females appear to find males more attractive if they are carrying larger gifts (Plant, pers. comm.). *Hilara fuscipes* is frequently encountered in light shade over the beaches of sandy gravel bordering Dowles Brook, sometimes in company with *H. longifurca*.

When visiting the flower-rich open clearings or flushes in the Forest from May onwards the visitor is likely to see a tough-looking, rufous brown, shiny fly with a bright yellow head and a strangely curled abdomen feeding on nectar. This is *Sicus ferrugineus* (Conopidae) and it needs to be tough as it intercepts and tackles formidable and heavily armoured bumble bees in flight. *Sicus* seizes the bee with its muscular legs, uses its strange, bottle-opener abdomen to lever apart the plates of the abdomen of the bee and slips a single egg into the gap. The egg hatches into a lollipop-shaped maggot with a fat round body and a slender front portion. As the body becomes fatter and rounder the more agile and extensible front section seeks out and feeds on the stored food reserves of the bee. When the bee weakens the maggot begins to feed on more important structures in the classic parasitoid fashion. It has been suggested that even the gut of the bee is penetrated and the food there is eaten before the bee has had a chance to absorb it or take it back to the nest (Clements 1997). The bee responds with a strange behavioural change. Although it forages and goes in and out of the nest in the daytime, it does not return to it in the evening. It stays out all night, and a common sight in the Forest is of dew-drenched drowsy bees on flower heads early in the morning. It is thought that cold nights in the open may slow down the development of the parasite and so prolong the useful working life of the worker bee (Müller & Schmid-Hemple 1993). For its final act, the *Sicus* maggot pushes its narrow head through the bee's 'wasp-waist' into the thorax where the flight muscles form its final banquet. It then pupates in the hollow corpse, but before the bee dies it is forced to dig its own grave. Quite how the fly produces this response at such an inappropriate time is not known.

Several other conopids are recorded from Wyre including two early spring *Myopa* species which resemble *Sicus* but are hairier, with shaggy beards.

Physocephala rufipes has a slender ichneumon-like appearance. It also parasitises a range of bumble bees and is commonly found visiting flowers in late summer. The *Conops* species are black and yellow. The largest and most spectacular of these is the uncommon *C. vesicularis* which is regularly seen nectaring on tall flowers in open areas in spring. Its host is as yet uncertain but it has been suggested that it parasitises hornets.

The Tachinidae are another group of parasitic flies, mostly specialising in the caterpillars of butterflies and moths but also attacking beetles, craneflies, bugs and even earwigs. *Tachina fera* is one of the more distinctive visitors to flowers in the mid- to late summer. It is a bristly fly the size of a bluebottle and has an orange-yellow abdomen with a median blue-grey band. The eggs are laid on oak leaves. They hatch and the maggot then lies in wait, resting with its tail end in the empty egg shell, until it detects the vibrations of a passing caterpillar. Then it rears up and begins to cast about with its head. After contact the maggot penetrates the cuticle of the caterpillar and develops inside it, feeding first on its body fat, and later its vital organs.

A typical sight in Wyre in spring on early flowers, including willow catkins, is the furry brown *Tachina ursina* which appears from mid-March onwards. It will often obligingly return to the same perch making it easier to photograph than many flies. This is a rather local tachinid whose hosts have yet to be identified, but are probably moth larvae. On late summer flowers, you may see *Phasia hemiptera* a late-summer tachinid. The male has striking iridescent wings while the female is smaller with clear wings. Its hosts include the larger shieldbugs.

A recent arrival in Wyre is the tachinid *Sturmia bella*, one of the grey-black spiny species. It was first recorded from the Holy Well flush on 9 September 2009. This is a new arrival in Britain, having been recorded for the first time from Hampshire in July 1998, bred from a Peacock butterfly *Aglais io* (Allan 2005). It specialises in the parasitism of butterflies of the Nymphalidae, including Comma *Polygonia c-album* and Small Tortoiseshell *Aglais urticae*. It has also been recorded from the Meadow Brown *Maniola jurtina*.

A conopid *Conops vesicularis* [RW]

A male tachinid *Phasia hemiptera* [PC]

Bees, wasps, ants, sawflies and woodwasps

Over four hundred species of Hymenoptera have been recorded in the Wyre Forest and surrounding area, and with nearly 7,000 species on the British list, there are certainly more to find. Those here range from one of Britain's largest flying insects, the Giant Woodwasp or Horntail *Urocerus gigas* measuring 4.5 cm from head to the tip of the ovipositor sheath, to the smallest, a braconid wasp about 0.25 mm long which parasitises butterfly eggs. The most familiar are bees, wasps and ants, though gardeners especially will be aware of sawflies because of their larval depredations on gooseberries and other valued plants.

About 4,500 species are parasitic and, being difficult to identify, are not well recorded in Wyre. The exceptions are some cynipid wasps which cause conspicuous galls, largely on oak *Quercus* spp. (see Chapter 8 Galls). The use of Malaise traps (essentially netting tents) in the orchards has given an indication of the huge numbers of parasitic species. The rest of the order Hymenoptera include the sawflies and the 'aculeates'. Aculeates are easily recognised as bees, wasps and ants, having four membranous wings (except worker ants) and the typical 'wasp waist'.

Here, as elsewhere, different species prefer different habitats. Most bees, wasps and ants prefer fairly open, sunny situations with flowers for foraging and suitable substrates for nesting. In Worcestershire the heaths in the north-west, including some parts of Wyre, have the highest number of species and are of regional, if not national, importance. The parasitic and cleptoparasitic species (those which take over the nests of other hymenopterans, rather like cuckoos) are tied to the nest sites of their prey, whilst sawflies are most abundant in damper, shadier habitats. In general, few hymenoptera have acquired English names but these are indicated where possible.

Social bees

Social bees are those species that establish a colony with an egg-laying queen, workers to maintain and defend the nest and to collect nectar and pollen to feed larvae, and males whose sole function is to fertilise new queens when they appear later in the season. Feral Honey Bees *Apis mellifera* establish colonies which can persist for several years and originate from domestic hives or other 'wild' nests. Bumble bee nests last for a single season, only newly mated queens hibernating over winter to found colonies in spring. Honey Bees and bumble bees are ubiquitous throughout the Forest and occur in most warm, open sites. Studies of the orchards around Wyre have underlined the importance of social bees for pollinating the fruit crop (Smart & Winnall 2006).

Six species of bumble bee are common throughout most of Britain and this is also true in Wyre. They are the Small Garden Bumble Bee *Bombus hortorum*, Red-tailed Bumble Bee *B. lapidarius*, White-tailed Bumble Bee *B. lucorum*, Early Bumble Bee *B. pratorum*, Buff-tailed Bumble Bee *B. terrestris*, and the Common

Red-tailed Bumble Bee *Bombus lapidarius* (top) and Vestal Cuckoo Bee *B. vestalis* (bottom) [BW]

Carder Bumble Bee *B. pascuorum*. Generally, the remaining species are in serious decline nationally, but one, the Brown-banded Carder Bumble Bee *B. humilis*, has recently been recorded close by at Burlish Top and Hartlebury Common. Although not so far recorded in Wyre it may well be found in the more open heath-like areas in the future.

Two other species recorded near Wyre deserve mention. The Red-tailed Carder Bumble Bee *B. ruderarius* was first recorded in Wassell Wood in 2004 and, more recently, in April 2014 on White Deadnettle *Lamium album* on the riverbank at Stourport-on-Severn. This bee is best distinguished from the common Red-tailed Bumble Bee by red hairs on the pollen basket on the hind leg, though queens of *B. ruderarius* are noticeably smaller. It has probably been missed and may well occur in the Wyre area. A new arrival that is hard to miss is the Tree Bumble Bee *B. hypnorum* which was first recorded in Britain in Wiltshire in 2001 (Goulson & Williams 2001). It has since spread to nearly all of England and much of Wales and is now one of the commonest bees in Worcestershire. Records in Wyre are frequent and overwintered queens are among the first bumble bees to emerge in spring, often flying in the last week of February.

Cuckoo bumble bees have no workers: the females lay their eggs in the nests of other bumble bees, usually killing the incumbent queen, but occasionally living alongside her. Seven species occur in Wyre and in midsummer the flowers of thistles along forest rides are often crowded with jostling males of the Hill Cuckoo Bee *B. rupestris*, Four-coloured Cuckoo Bee *B. sylvestris* and Vestal Cuckoo Bee *B. vestalis*. The Hill Cuckoo Bee was considered Nationally Rare (Nb status) until relatively recently, but is now a common insect locally. The shaggy-looking red-tailed males are often widespread in sunny places in July. Rarer or, more probably, overlooked species in Wyre are Barbut's Cuckoo Bee *B. barbutellus*, Gypsy Cuckoo Bee *B. bohemicus* and Field Cuckoo Bee *B. campestris*.

Grey-haired Mining Bee *Andrena cineraria* [JB]

Tawny Mining Bee *Andrena fulva* [PC]

Solitary bees

Solitary bees are those that have no worker caste: the mated queens leave eggs in prepared nests which are provisioned with honey and pollen and then sealed up. The emerging larvae feed on the stored food and, when mature, pupate before emerging as adults. Some species have only one generation per year whilst others have two. Mining bees excavate their nest holes in vertical faces or in the ground, whilst other species modify hollow stems, holes made by beetle larvae in dead wood, or holes in masonry or natural stone. Some species nest colonially in favoured areas where each female has her own nest among many other burrows, whilst others nest singly.

So far 71 species of solitary bees have been recorded in Wyre, almost a third of the British total. Some are small and black, and unlikely to be noticed by the casual observer, but others are more striking. In spring obvious species include the fiery orange Tawny Mining Bee *Andrena fulva* and the beautiful black and white Grey-haired Mining Bee *A. cineraria*. Locating solitary bees involves a bit of luck, though the odds of finding them can be improved by looking for the nest holes of mining bees on bare sunny ground, or carefully examining flowers such as dandelions or umbellifers during warm sunny weather. In March willow catkins are an excellent hunting ground for bees such as *A. clarkella* and *A. apicata*.

Like social bees solitary bees have their share of cleptoparasites. The most conspicuous of these are the nomad bees of the genera *Nomada* and *Sphecodes*. Nomad bees are commonly confused with wasps as many are black and yellow striped, but unlike wasps their larvae feed on pollen and honey provided by their hosts. The females can often be seen quartering the ground near mining bee nests, searching for any which have been provisioned, but not sealed. When she finds a nest the female *Nomada* nips in quickly to lay her egg while the host is away.

The status of 21 uncommon or rare solitary bees (out of the 71 recorded in Wyre) is given in Table 7. Some of these species, for example *N. lathburiana*, are increasing in numbers and range and are not as rare as the national status suggests. Others such as the mining bee *A. lapponica*, whilst not rare nationally, are local in the Midlands. This neat black and ginger bee forages mainly from Bilberry *Vaccinium myrtillus*, a scarce plant which is widespread in Wyre but rare elsewhere.

A mining bee *Andrena lapponica* [JB]

A nomad bee *Nomada lathburiana* [KMcG]

Hornet *Vespa crabro* nest in tree cavities or bird boxes and are increasingly seen in woodland clearings and local gardens [MA]

Social wasps

The Social wasps are the archetypal wasps, striped with black and yellow to advertise non-palatability and danger, and a nuisance to us when they attack our picnics and nest in our homes and outbuildings. Like bumble bees they build nests which last only one season. The nest is initiated by a queen which has overwintered, but most of the work of nest building and maintenance is carried out by workers. Males are produced late in the season and mate with newly emerged queens. Social wasps can be broadly divided into two groups: those which nest in hollows and holes in trees or in roof spaces, and those which build hanging nests in trees and bushes. The nests are marvels of paper engineering with layers of hexagonal cells encased in an outer shell, all made from masticated wood or bark taken from trees and outdoor woodwork. Identification of some social wasps is a challenge and can require microscopic study.

Eight species have been recorded in Wyre. The largest of these by far is the Hornet *Vespa crabro* which has increased nationally both in numbers and range in recent years and is now common here. Hornets build their nests in holes in trees or masonry and are particularly fond of bird nest boxes. Often the nest will be so large it cannot be contained in the box and spreads to the outside as well. Hornets often patrol flowering ivy clumps in autumn when they mingle with other species such as the Common Wasp *Vespula vulgaris* and the German Wasp *V. germanica*. Three other longterm residents in Britain are all seen in Wyre: the Tree Wasp *Dolichovespula sylvestris*, the Norwegian Wasp *D. norwegica* and the Red Wasp *Vespula rufa*.

There are also two species which arrived in Britain in the 1980s, the Median Wasp *Dolichovespula media* (Falk 1982) and the Saxon Wasp *D. saxonica* (Hammond *et al.* 1989; Allen & Archer 1989). Both have spread throughout most of England and east Wales and Median Wasp has a few more records in northern England, southern Scotland and west Wales than Saxon Wasp. Both species build hanging nests in bushes and trees and both occur in Wyre.

The best time to see social wasps is in spring, when emerging queens are looking for nest sites, and in autumn when workers and males will be found on rotting fallen fruit.

Solitary wasps

As with solitary bees there is a huge variety of solitary wasps whose females prepare nests and provision them with food for their larvae. The food includes small bugs, beetles, aphids, spiders and larvae of various insects. In Wyre 74 species of solitary wasp have been identified, including 12 species of spider hunters. Table 7 lists nine of the 74 species which are designated as rare (Baldock 2008, 2010; Bees, Wasps and Ants Recording Society 1997–2012).

The pompilids, or spider-hunting wasps, provision their cells with spiders caught and paralysed with their stings. Unlike most species pompilids are most often seen on warm patches of bare ground, where they hunt their prey. In spring one of the most obvious spider hunters in Wyre is *Priocnemis perturbator*, a black and red wasp which often visits the flowers of Wood Spurge *Euphorbia amygdaloides* in May and June. Here it is sometimes seen with the elegant black and yellow Two-girdled Digger Wasp *Argogorytes mystaceus*, which provides its larvae with a selection of leafhopper nymphs, paralysed and neatly arranged in cells under loose bark.

A spider-hunting wasp *Priocnemis perturbator* [KMcG]

Two-girdled Digger Wasp *Argogorytes mystaceus* [KMcG]

Median Wasp *Dolichovespula media* queen [KMcG]

The mason and potter wasps, which use mud to make nests or to make vertical tubes covering the entrance to subterranean nests, are also of great interest. The purpose of the tubes remains unclear, but they may deter cleptoparasites from entering, or shelter the nest entrance during inclement weather.

Inevitably solitary wasps have their cleptoparasites too. Among these are the tropically brilliant jewel or ruby-tailed wasps which gleam as they scurry over dead wood in summer sunshine searching for the entrance holes of potential hosts. These small wasps are the peacocks of the hymenopteran world, displaying vivid metallic greens, blues and reds, although being just a few millimetres long and fast-moving, they are easily missed.

Table 7 Status of uncommon or rare solitary bees and wasps		
Mining bees	**Cleptoparasites**	**Solitary wasps**
Andrena apicata Nb	*Sphecodes niger* RDB3	*Chrysura radians* Na
Andrena congruens Na	*Sphecodes rubicundus* Na	*Tiphia minuta* Nb
Andrena falsifica Na	*Nomada ferruginata** RDB1	*Monosapyga clavicornis* Nb
Andrena fulvago Na	*Nomada fucata* Na	*Anoplius caviventris* Nb
Andrena humilis Nb	*Nomada fulvicornis* Na	*Priocnemis coriacea* Na
Andrena labiata Na	*Nomada integra* Na	*Mimesa bicolor* RDB3
Andrena marginata Na	*Nomada lathburiana* RDB3	*Podalonia hirsuta* Nb
Andrena trimmerana Nb		*Ectemnius ruficornis* Nb
Andrena varians Nb		*Pemphredon morio* Nb
Dasypoda hirtipes Nb		
Halictus confusus RDB3		
Lasioglossum brevicorne RDB3		
Lasioglossum pauxillum Na		
Lasioglossum xanthopus Nb		

Status
Nationally Notable species (known from less than 100 10-km squares since 1980)
Na = known from 16–30 10-km squares; Nb = known from 16–30 10-km squares
Red Data Book species (known from less than 15 10-km squares)
RDB1 (in danger of extinction) = known from 5 or fewer 10-km squares;
RDB3 (rare) = known from 11–15 10-km squares
* This species is known to be extending its range and probably should no longer be classed as RDB1 (Allen & Archer 1989).

A potter wasp *Ancistrocerus nigricornis* [JB]

A jewel wasp *Chrysis viridula* [KMcG]

Southern Wood Ants nest, Postensplain [RW]

Southern Wood Ants *Formica rufa* [JB]

Ants

In many places ants tend to be inconspicuous creatures, but Wyre and the Southern Wood Ant *Formica rufa* are almost synonymous. Their large and very conspicuous conical nest mounds made of fragments of vegetation are found throughout the Forest, usually in clearings or at the edges of rides and some are very large indeed, up to 1.2 m or higher. In warm weather the worker ants are seen scurrying about on the nest and radiating from it along well-defined paths to collect prey and building materials, such as small twigs and pine needles, to add to the nest. Ragged lines of ants ascend into the trees to capture prey which includes almost any invertebrate, or to tend to clusters of aphids for their honeydew.

Southern Wood Ant nests are usually positioned to receive maximum spring sunlight and little shading, which at that time of year is important. In late February and March the surfaces of many nests are covered by a dark, seething carpet of ants, absorbing the sun's rays. However, the ants can tolerate some shade later in the year because the thick insulating thatch traps their metabolic heat in the nest where it can raise the temperature by 10°C. Some shade is also useful as protection from heavy rain which can destroy nests. However, too much shade, from bracken for instance, is unwelcome and may cause the ants to decamp to a sunnier site.

Hickin (1971) found it difficult to picnic without being invaded by Southern Wood Ants and stated that in 1965 he found 35 nests along three-quarters of a mile of ride (approximately 1,200 m), or about 46 nests per mile (46 nests per 1,600 m or approximately 29 nests per kilometre). Wilson (2011) derived a similar figure from his studies of rides adjacent to conifer plantations, but was careful to point out that despite the similarity

The hummocks of Yellow Meadow Ant *Lasius flavus* under fruit trees at Lodge Hill Farm. Well-drained and raised above the surrounding grassland, these venerable nests are a micro-habitat for meadow flowers. [RW]

suggesting a stable population there is no baseline or wide-ranging study to substantiate this. Southern Wood Ant nests in Wyre tend to be more frequent on the north side of the Dowles Brook where the slopes are south facing and to be on the north sides of rides facing south. Many are on ride edges or along footpaths and can be at risk from winter ride-side clearance of vegetation. This can destroy nests, although as these are partly underground some may survive. Along rides which are less than 20 m wide, the rule seems to be that the narrower the rides, the fewer the nests. There are however no more nests in rides wider than 20 m (Wilson 2011). Ride creation and widening is important as a conservation measure to protect not only the ants, but also sun-loving invertebrates, such as butterflies. Southern Wood Ants are poor colonisers of new habitats and, although they seem numerous in Wyre, are very local in central England. Because they often build nests at the edges of rides or clearings widening rides may destroy a large number of colonies at onc time, so clearing rides in short sections and not all at once could be an important conservation measure (Wilson 2011; Girling 2005; Pontin 1996).

Another local ant depends on Wood Ants for a home: the diminutive Shining Guest Ant *Formicoxenus nitidulus*, lives with impunity in Southern Wood Ant nests. If you are prepared to risk personal invasion by Southern Wood Ants you can sometimes see the tiny 3 mm ants moving about on the nest surface, dwarfed by their hosts. They are easily recognised by the polished appearance of their abdomens and are most obvious in early autumn. When *F. nitidulus* was found in 2006 (Green & Westwood 2006) the records were the first for over a century, though it had probably been in Wyre all along. They build their own tiny nests within the Southern Wood Ants' nests, but why they are not attacked is a mystery.

In addition to Southern Wood and Shining Guest Ants another 23 ant species have been recorded in Wyre (Green 2009). Many are common species found widely in appropriate habitats in the countryside and gardens. These include the Yellow Meadow Ant *Lasius flavus* whose nest mounds are common in old meadows and orchards: some particularly fine examples are in the orchard at Lodge Hill Farm. Other common ants are the Small Black Ant *L. niger*, the larger dark-coloured Negro Ant *Formica fusca*, and the red ants *Myrmica rubra* and *M. ruginodis*.

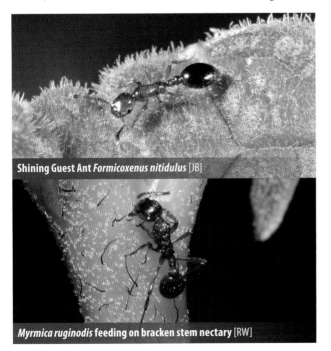

Shining Guest Ant *Formicoxenus nitidulus* [JB]

Myrmica ruginodis feeding on bracken stem nectar [RW]

Three other species have been recorded in Wyre almost exclusively within the woodland area: the Slavemaker Ant *Formica sanguinea*, Slender Ant *Leptothorax acervorum* and *Myrmica scabrinodis*. Whilst *M. scabrinodis* has only been found locally in Wyre, *L. acervorum* seems to be widespread but local in dead wood, especially fallen tree trunks. It is probable however that both are under-recorded and may well be more widely distributed.

The Slavemaker Ant is uncommon nationally, with colonies in southern England and Scotland but very few in between. It has been known in Wyre for many years and was recorded here by myrmecologist Donisthorpe who, in 1908, watched a raid on a nest of Negro Ants take place on railway banks near Bewdley (Donisthorpe 1927b). Hickin (1971) thought it 'common'. In recent years naturalists feared for the survival of the sun-loving Slavemaker as plantations matured and the Forest became heavily shaded. It has survived, although probably in much lower numbers than in Donisthorpe's day, and several nests have been found during recent ant surveys (Bloxham 2006). They are often in sunny spots on dry banks, sometimes under stones or within old tree stumps and, if disturbed, the occupants are fast-moving and very aggressive. For much of the time, the Slavemaker's life-style is similar to other *Formica* species but, from time to time, workers go out to attack the nests of other ants, frequently the Negro Ant, from which they remove pupae. These are taken back to the Slavemakers' nests

and the emerging adults become part of their colony, carrying out the tasks normally done by the host workers. This is a species which is likely to benefit from opening up clearings and the removal of shade from banks and tracksides.

Rarer species, found both in Wyre and elsewhere in Worcestershire and Shropshire, are *Lasius alienus*, the Brown Ant *L. brunneus*, the Jet Ant *L. fuliginosus* and *L. umbratus*. The Brown Ant presents an interesting conundrum. Over most of Britain this small bi-coloured species is rare, seeming to be confined to the catchments of the Rivers Severn and Thames. In Worcestershire it is fairly common, though local, and is present, though probably under recorded, in Shropshire (Jones & Cheeseborough 2014). It seems to especially like the fissured bark of fairly isolated or hedgerow oaks and old orchard trees. The nests of the Jet Ant are often underneath the base of trees or in other structures on the ground. At one site members of Wyre Forest Study Group watched a continuous stream of them marching along the top of a fence (looking thin and empty), up an oak tree to the canopy and then returning along the same route fat and swollen with honeydew produced by aphids on the tree leaves.

Recently two new species have been added to the British list, *Lasius platythorax* and *L. psammophilus* (Trevis 2004). *L. platythorax* is morphologically very similar to *L. niger* and *L. psammophilus* to *L. alienus*. The status of these two species has yet to be established in Wyre.

Finally there is a group of enigmatic records of uncommon or nationally rare species which have been located only once or twice, often many years ago (Green 2009). These include *Lasius mixtus* (one record from 1971), *Formica cunicularia* (one record from 1916), and the Narrow-headed Ant *F. exsecta* (two records from 1901 and 1971). The last is especially intriguing as it occurs on heaths and open woodlands at a site in Devon, but otherwise only in Scotland. Its distinctive flattish nests are built of similar materials to those of Southern Wood Ants and should be obvious, but none have been seen so it seems unlikely that it persists in Wyre. Other species with old records are *Myrmica lobicornis* (one record from 1971), *M. sabuleti* (one record from 1971), *M. schencki* (one record from 1946), *M. sulcinodis* (one record from 1971) and *Stenamma westwoodii* (one record from 1971). Although the last was named as *S. westwoodii* modern work suggests it could have been the similar species *S. debile* which has been found in Worcestershire in recent years.

Many of these records came from the late Norman Hickin, professional entomologist and well-known Wyre Forest naturalist. They hint at species to be uncovered and underline the need for more exploration and study of the Forest's ants. For example in 2014/2015 *M. lobicornis* was rediscovered at Pound Green Common and in a Bell Coppice meadow, and *M. sabuleti* at Pound Green Common, Longdon, Bliss Gate and Button Oak Meadow.

Slavemaker Ant *Formica sanguinea* [JB]

Negro Ant *Formica fusca* [JB]

Some of the many sawflies found in Wyre

Abia sericea [KMcG]

Turnip Sawfly *Athalia rosae* [JB]

Strongylogaster multifasciata egglaying [PC]

Figwort Sawfly *Tenthredo scrophulariae* [JB] and larva [RW] (right)

Sawflies and woodwasps

Serious study of this group (the Symphyta) has been undertaken only relatively recently in Wyre but already 71 sawflies and two wood wasps have been recorded. Little is known of sawfly status and distribution but we can say that two of them, *Abia candens* and *A. sericea,* are considered uncommon. A number of sawflies cause galls on willows (see Chapter 8).

The Giant Woodwasp *Urocerus gigas* is widespread, but not common nationally and has occasionally been recorded from New Parks in Wyre and more recently at a Forest timber yard. It is a large insect with a prominent ovipositor which looks dangerous but is harmless to humans. It is used to drill into solid timber when laying its eggs. These hatch into larvae which will feed on the wood for two to three years before pupating and emerging as adults. Not all reach adulthood as this insect is host to the equally impressive Sabre Wasp *Rhyssa persuasoria.*

Parasitica

The parasitic species of Hymenoptera are, for convenience and the purposes of this chapter, divided into two groups with very different life styles. Some

Giant Woodwasp *Urocerus gigas* [JB] is host to the equally impressive ichneumon the Sabre Wasp *Rhyssa persuasoria* (see overleaf).

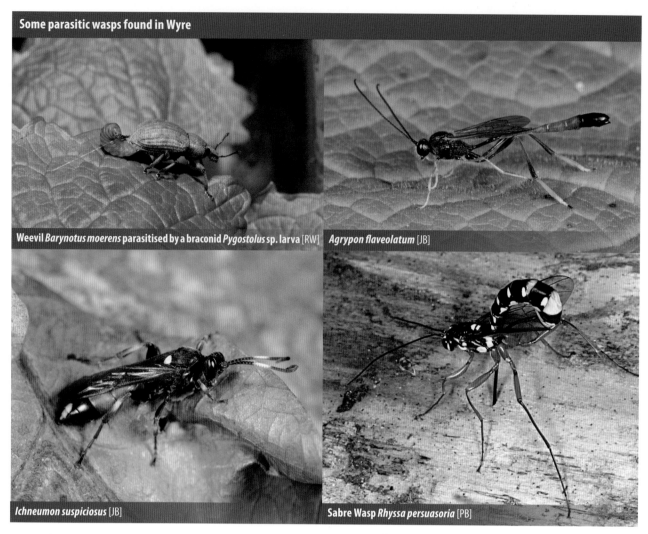

Some parasitic wasps found in Wyre

Weevil *Barynotus moerens* parasitised by a braconid *Pygostolus* sp. larva [RW]

Agrypon flaveolatum [JB]

Ichneumon suspiciosus [JB]

Sabre Wasp *Rhyssa persuasoria* [PB]

cynipid wasps lay eggs on various parts of plants and the emerging larvae cause gall formation, and some Chalcid wasps also cause galls. An account of galls is given in Chapter 8.

The second group are parasites or parasitoids on other insect species, often the larvae of other Hymenoptera. The larvae may be either ectoparasites, which remain on the outside of the body of the host, or endoparasites, which emerge from eggs laid within the body of the host. The endoparasites in particular have many bizarre and interesting adaptations to their lifestyle. A common feature is that they complete most of their development feeding on the haemolymph (internal body fluid) of the host, only attacking the vital organs and causing the host's death when close to pupation (Gauld & Bolton 1988). Altogether 23 cynipids and 89 other parasitica have been recorded in Wyre.

If we know little of the status and distribution of sawflies, the situation with the parasitica is even worse. Of the 89 recorded species by far the largest group is the Ichneumonidae, or ichneumon wasps. Most of the parasitic wasps are difficult to identify, are rarely seen or recognised, and many fly at night. One easy way to collect them is to attend moth recording nights as the wasps are attracted to the light traps. There were few records prior to 2004 when

Malaise traps were used in local orchards, adding 78 species to the list.

The adults of this group attack a wide range of hosts for the development of their young. Whilst larvae are primary targets, other stages, including eggs and adults, are not immune. Ichneumons and their allies, of which there are more than 2,400 species, play a crucial part in regulating population size in many invertebrates and therefore have great ecological significance.

Bees, wasps and ants are characterised by having the females' ovipositors modified into stings. In the parasitica however the ovipositor is used to lay and deliver eggs. It can be used as a weapon though, so don't pick up larger members of this group.

Perhaps the most well-known ichneumon is the very large and spectacular (up to 10 cm) Sabre Wasp *Rhyssa persuasoria*. Its extremely long hair-fine ovipositor is capable of drilling into the solid wood of tree trunks and branches to lay eggs on the bodies of wood boring larvae, especially sawflies. Exactly how the ichneumon locates the position of the larva is still unclear though it may involve vibrations, sound, scent or all of these. In high summer, they may occur around timber yards and conifer log piles on hot days, when they are often approachable. Other species have lengthy and highly flexible ovipositors to reach larvae in situations where one would imagine they would be safe. Many ovipositors are much shorter and have evolved to deliver modified eggs as in the large and common *Dyspetes praerogator*, which also targets the larvae of sawflies, mostly *Tenthredo* species. Her eggs are armed with an anchor-like process to ensure they remain in place.

Whilst the visitor to Wyre is surrounded by a host of small and inconspicuous parasitic wasps during a normal summer walk, sightings of really large ones are uncommon. Many of these larger species are ichneumons. *Dolichomitus tuberculatus* may be found with its ovipositor inserted in a pine stump; its target perhaps the Pine Weevil *Hylobius abietis*, a favoured host.

In some species, several wasp larvae can develop within a single host. The collections of silky white cocoons sometimes found on vegetation result from a mass emergence from a single host caterpillar. This is a typical breeding strategy for many small braconid wasps which can reproduce in quantity by using a large host. In order to assign these parasitic wasps to species, it is important to collect or rear them from hosts that have been identified as such in the wild. For example, Tony Simpson found a weevil *Barynotus moerens* parasitised by an unknown larva near Lodge Hill Farm (Simpson 2012). The specimen was kept, the parasite emerged and was identified as a braconid wasp *Pygostolus* sp.

A number of nocturnal ichneumons which visit light traps include the large and impressive *Ophion obscuratus*. It is more easily distinguished from its close relatives by its yellow markings and like them lays its eggs on moth caterpillars which are more active after dark. There is evidence that some parasitic wasps have evolved finely honed antennae which allow them to locate the caterpillars in pitch darkness. By hunting at night they are also less vulnerable to predation.

The extraordinarily wide range of form and adaptation to parasitic life exhibited in many families is beyond the scope of this account. Often exceedingly small in size, their identification and the exploration of their life histories is the province of dedicated specialists. Here are just two examples of remarkably tiny insects observed in the Forest.

Discovered at Bliss Gate on a tree trunk, *Cleonymus laticornis* is a magnificent but tiny wasp which appears to be a parasitoid of various beetles developing in timber. The Spruce Shortwing Beetle *Molorchus minor* has been recorded as a likely victim. As is so often the case minute parasitoids bring about the downfall of much larger hosts in an entomological David and Goliath contest. *Cleonymus* is widely distributed, having been recorded from a number of European countries (Bouček 1972). Maybe wind dispersal is an important factor in assisting its parasitic progress in Wyre and elsewhere.

During August 2010, during a study group visit to Hawkbatch, Geoff Trevis caught a miniscule parasitic wasp hovering over a nest of wood ants. This was a *Neoneurus* species, a member of a small family whose members parasitise adult ants.

Other terrestrial insects

Take a walk in Wyre Forest in summertime and some insects are hard to miss. Butterflies flit through the dappled shade, dragonflies pursue their prey and path-side patches of flowers attract a variety of insects from flies and beetles to bugs and bees. But this obvious life is only the tip of the iceberg: much more is hidden away.

Lacewings are typically gauzy-winged insects, often disturbed from foliage. Their larvae are predatory with curved sucking mouthparts and many have the gruesome habit of camouflaging themselves with the remains of their prey. Lacewing eggs are supported on long white stalks attached to vegetation as protection against predators. *Chrysoperla carnea*, a familiar green lacewing is most often seen, but other green lacewings in Wyre include: *Chrysopa perla* and the rarer *Cunctochrysa albolineata, Chrysotropia ciliata, Dichochrysa ventralis* and *Nineta vittata*. Several brown lacewings also occur, notably *Hemerobius lutescens* and *Micromus angulatus*. The most spectacular lacewing in Wyre is the Giant Lacewing *Osmylus fulvicephalus*, with a wingspan of up to 50 mm. Its size, orange head and broad mottled wings make it obvious when flushed

Green lacewing *Chrysopa perla* [JB]

Lacewing larva [PC]

Giant Lacewing *Osmylus fulvicephalus* [JB]

from its retreat amongst streamside vegetation. Its larva lives in damp mosses and preys on small invertebrates, using scythe-like mouthparts to wound a victim before injecting poison and sucking out the vital juices. (Hickin 1971; Plant 1997). Two of the three British sponge flies, Sisyridae, have been found in Wyre, the common *Sisyra nigra* and *S. terminalis* which appears to be nationally rare (Plant 1994). The larvae are aquatic, living in freshwater sponges. The tiny white-winged wax flies are small and rarely seen: three species have been identified in Wyre. *Coniopteryx pygmaea* and *Semidalis aleyrodiformis* were recorded in the 1980s by Colin Plant and the latter was also found during the special orchard survey at Bowcastle Farm in 2004 (Smart & Winnall 2006).

Psocopterans (Barkflies) are some of the least recorded insects. They browse on algae, lichens, moulds and fungal spores found on trees. A Wyre oak tree examined for invertebrates in 2012 harboured six psocid species on the branches and leaves. The

commonest was *Ectopsocus briggsi*, a species often abundant on foliage. The search also produced *Stenopsocus immaculatus* and *Graphopsocus cruciatus* (Winnall *et al.* 2012).

Rhaphidioptera (Snakeflies) seize their prey like serpents using their flattened heads with forward-facing mouthparts supported on an extended thorax (McGavin 2001). They are almost always associated with trees and the canopy-dwelling adults are not often seen. The eggs are laid in cracks and crannies in bark and both larvae and adults prey mainly on small invertebrates such as aphids. Adults hunt in foliage, the larvae in leaf litter or under bark. There are four British species and two of them, *Phaeostigma notata* and *Xanthostigma xanthostigma,* have been recorded from the Wyre Forest.

Male scorpionflies hold their genital capsules curved, scorpion-like, over their backs. Of the three British species, *Panorpa germanica, P. communis* and *P. cognata,* the first is commonly seen in the Forest and the others may occur. Adult scorpionflies and their larvae eat dead and dying insects. The strangest scorpionfly is the Snow Flea *Boreus hyemalis*, a 5 mm long flightless insect first recorded in Wyre in the 1970s and not seen again until December 2009. Since then it has been discovered in several places, usually on mossy banks in open woodland. Snow Fleas are active from October until April often in very low temperatures, and even in snow. They jump well and are easily mistaken for outsized springtails, but are longer-legged, brassy in colour and have a prominent 'beak'. Both sexes are flightless and the male uses spine-like outgrowths of his vestigial wings to hold the female during mating. Like its winged relatives the Snow Flea eats the dead remains of invertebrates (Winnall 2009; Bingham 2012b, 2014b).

Springtails are common in leaf litter and soils. Some species catch the eye when disturbed when they shoot several centimetres into the air, powered by the furca or spring organ located on the underside of the body. All springtails are small, the largest just a few millimetres long, and are either globular or have a longer abdomen. There are about 250 species in 19 different families in the British Isles, found in a wide range of habitats from leaf litter to water. They are not easy to identify, although some of those living in litter are quite brightly coloured (Hopkin 2007). *Pogonognathellus longicornis* is one of the largest and frequently noticed in the Forest. *Orchesella cincta* with its distinctive abdominal patterning is another common species. Recent classification includes springtails not as insects, but as non-insect Hexapods (Brock 2014).

Bristletails are often found in leaf litter (where they eat plant debris), and usually only attract attention when uncovered by day, but by night are regularly found on tree-trunks. These primitive, scaly, hump-backed insects are about 12 mm long and gleam with coppery iridescence under a lens. Their tapering body bears a long terminal filament flanked by two others, giving a three-tailed appearance. In Wyre the only woodland species appears to be the Southern Bristletail

Barkfly *Graphopsocus cruciatus* [JB] Barkfly *Stenopsocus immaculatus* [RW]

Female snakefly *Phaeostigma notata* [RW]

Male scorpionfly *Panorpa germanica* [JB]

Mating Snow Fleas *Boreus hyemalis* [JB]

A springtail *Orchesella villosa* [JB]   A bristletail *Dilta* sp. [JB]

Dilta hibernica. A second species in the area is the Silverfish *Lepisma saccharina* which is more familiar in bathrooms where they forage on floors at night, running rapidly into crevices under skirting boards when disturbed.

Other insects associated with freshwater

Many insects, other than dragonflies, occur by ponds and streams, including those known collectively as river-flies: mayflies, stoneflies, alderflies and caddisflies. Most of these spend much of their lives underwater as larvae, often called nymphs, and many are important indicators of unpolluted water. Dowles Brook is rich in these and other invertebrates and they form a significant part of the diet of Dippers *Cinclus cinclus* foraging underwater. Emerging river-flies and other insects are an important food for other birds nesting along watercourses. The free-flying adults have brief lives mainly devoted to dispersal, mating and egg-laying, but generally not to feeding.

Mayflies are well known for synchronous hatching in huge numbers, a strategy that improves the odds of finding a mate. Mayflies are unique among insects in having a short pre-adult stage. When hatching occurs the larval nymph comes to the surface and a sub-adult, or dun, rapidly emerges from the nymphal skin. It looks very like the adult and can fly. Shortly afterwards its skin splits again and a full adult, or spinner, emerges (see photograph below). Both duns and spinners have only rudimentary mouthparts and do not feed. Males form dancing swarms over water, seizing a partner and mating: after this the female drops her eggs into the water. The nymphs may take several years to reach adulthood and are often easier to identify than the elusive and flighty adults. One large and obvious species in Wyre is the Green Drake *Ephemera danica* whose larvae live in the mud of rivers and streams; adults emerge in May and June when the males dance as if tugged upwards by invisible threads—a spectacular sight. Other mayflies commonly recorded in Wyre include: Iron Blue Mayfly *Baetis muticus, Ecdyonurus dispar, E. torrentis, E. venosus,* Blue-winged Olive *Serratella ignita, Paraleptophlebia submarginata* and *Rhithrogena semicolorata.*

Alderflies, with their heavily veined wings, often settle on waterside vegetation, where they mate and lay their glutinous eggs. On hatching the larvae fall into the water, where they live in burrows and are predaceous, catching mainly small crustaceans and worms. Of

the three British species only *Sialis lutaria* has been recorded in Wyre.

Stoneflies are active mainly at night when the female attracts a mate by drumming her abdomen on a hard surface. The male answers briefly and homes in on the sound. Mating quickly follows after which the female lays a sticky egg mass in water. A special study of Dowles Brook in 2004 found 14 species of flying stoneflies (out of a national total of 34) at two sites. For anywhere in the West Midlands this is a highly significant result: such totals are more usually associated with unpolluted upland streams in mid Wales. Two of the species found are relatively uncommon: *Capnia bifrons* and *Amphinemura standfussi* (Pryce 2004). Other recorded species are: *Brachyptera risi, Isoperla grammatica, Leuctra fusca, L. hippopus, L. nigra, Amphinemura sulcicollis,* the Common Small Yellow Sally *Siphonoperla torrentium, Nemoura cinerea, N. avicularis* and *N. cambrica.*

Green Drake mayfly *Ephemera danica* with skin of sub-imago [RW]

An alderfly *Sialis lutaria* [JB]

A stonefly *Isoperla grammatica* [PC]

A male long-horned caddis *Mystacides azurea* [PC]

A caddis *Brachycentrus subnubilus* [KMcG]

Caddisflies or Trichoptera, named for their hair-covered wings, are somewhat moth-like and mainly nocturnal, hiding away amongst vegetation during the day. They have two pairs of wings, held tent-like over their back at rest, and have forward-pointing antennae. They fly well, and are usually encountered when disturbed from bankside vegetation during the day, or when they come to light. They are often the first nocturnal insects to arrive at a moth-trapper's light, sometimes in good numbers.

Caddisfly larvae are one of the most conspicuous of the invertebrates in Wyre streams and the adults are often noticed by naturalists, though few people attempt to identify them. There are passing references to them in Norman Hickin's books on Wyre Forest (1965, 1971) and he describes how he prepared the drawings for his *magnum opus* (Hickin 1967) on caddisfly larvae in *Forest Refreshed*. Ian Wallace (pers. comm.) tells us that the National Caddis Recording Scheme currently has records for 57 UK species (out of 198) from Wyre Forest. Knowledge of larval habitats suggests some have flown from more distant parts but most originate in the Forest. Many of the records are from David Pryce who collected river-flies in Wyre using Malaise traps on sites along the Dowles Brook and its tributaries (Pryce 2004, Pryce 2006). This trap is a tent like structure open at the base and sited next to or suspended over the brook. Insects rise to the sloping roof and fly or crawl along it to a collecting bottle. In 2004 Pryce trapped nearly 2,000 caddisflies of 36 species.

The females of most Wyre Forest caddis enter the water to lay eggs within a sheet or string or blob of jelly attached under a stone, according to the species.

Caddis larvae, like lepidopteran larvae, produce silk. Most use this to assemble pieces of plant or sand grains, or a mixture of both, into a case that covers the body. When feeding or moving the head and three pairs of legs emerge from the front end of the case. Some caddis however, do not carry their cases with them, but construct fixed shelters on stones associated with nets, with which they ensnare prey. Others use their nets to filter out passing particles from the stream. A significant group of Wyre caddis larvae construct a meandering tube which covers them as they graze algae from the rock surface.

Most of the larger case-building caddis in Wyre grow throughout winter and spring, feeding on leaves that fall into the streams. By summer they seal up their cases, emerging as adults in autumn. One species, *Stenophylax vibex*, breeds in winter-wet temporary streams and is Nationally Scarce. Two commonly recorded case-building caddis in Wyre are *Agapetus fuscipes,* which builds small tortoise-shaped cases of coarse sand grains, and *Silo pallipes* whose well-constructed cases have larger ballast stones attached along their sides to help prevent them being swept away in spates. Both these species graze diatoms and other life growing on the stones.

The net-making larvae of *Hydropsyche* are well represented in Wyre both in numbers of individuals and species. These include the very local *H. fulvipes,* whose larva has a beautiful lyre-shaped pale mark on its head and lives in several of the smaller streams, and the nationally scarce *H. saxonica*, yet to be found as a larva in Wyre. Some of the most intriguing caddis in Wyre are the gallery-making *Tinodes*. The galleries are conspicuous all along the edge of Dowles Brook and many of its tributaries but the national distributions of the various species are still not completely known. *T. pallidulus* is probably the commonest here, although it is known only from a handful of British sites including another ancient wooded area at Charnwood Forest in Leicestershire. It seems to prefer shaded areas as probably does another rare species, *T. rostocki*. Although their galleries can be obvious, it requires at least a strong hand lens to determine the species: the adults are typical 'small brown jobs' and a microscope is recommended.

Another Wyre caddis is *Plectrocnemia conspersa*, the 'trickle tiger' whose larva makes a large tangled web to trap other invertebrates. This caddis, whose speckle-winged adult is often common at moth-trapping lights in the Forest, may be the top predator in very small streams.

One caddis however, is special to Wyre and the surrounding countryside. A search in the Forest's leaf litter soon reveals a species absent from most of the rest of the British Isles, the Land Caddis *Enoicyla pusilla*. For anyone used to seeing caddis in water, it is a surprise to see its small, cylindrical and slightly curved cases moving jerkily on the woodland floor. This is always a privilege though, because this inconspicuous insect is unique among the caddisflies of Britain and Ireland.

The Land Caddis

The Land Caddis *Enoicyla pusilla* was first discovered in Britain at Worcester by John Edward Fletcher in 1858. His discovery was confirmed and reported by Robert McLachlan (1868), the great Victorian European Trichopterist, with later brief notes by Fletcher (1869; 1878; 1901). Of 196 species of caddisflies occurring in the British Isles (Barnard & Ross 2012) only Land Caddis larvae live on dry land. The species has a widespread but discontinuous distribution throughout much of Europe. It and two other European species are wholly terrestrial, living amongst leaf litter. Males fly but females are wingless. The Land Caddis appears to be a species of ancient woodland or its remnants, though it may indicate undisturbed countryside as it has been found on Catherton Common on Titterstone Clee Hill in Shropshire away from trees. The larvae eat fungus-conditioned fallen tree leaves, including oak, and other decaying vegetation. Fletcher succeeded in breeding the adult insects from larvae found near Worcester and some of his adult specimens are in the Natural History Museum in London, including those he sent to McLachlan, all dated October and November 1868; others are in Fletcher's collection of insects in the Worcester City Museum.

Twentieth century Worcestershire naturalists probably first heard of the Land Caddis from books written by Norman Hickin (1965; 1971) on the Wyre Forest. In *Forest Refreshed* he describes how the cased larvae appeared in his daughter's tent on 22 April 1957 during a camping weekend. Hickin was an eminent trichopterist and this was the first time he or anyone else had knowingly seen Land Caddis in Britain since John Edward Fletcher's observations.

Following Hickin's reports David Harding, with colleagues and students at the University of Wolverhampton, started researches on Land Caddis in 1975. Their work "focussed on the distribution, phenology and population dynamics of *Enoicyla pusilla*, which is locally abundant" (Harding 1995, 1998). Their intensive studies were based in Chaddesley Wood, near Bromsgrove, and Shrawley Wood, north of Worcester, both ancient semi-natural woodlands. They also looked for Land Caddis in other woods, and found them in a dozen 10 × 10 km grid squares within a 25 km radius of Wyre Forest. David Harding made many appeals for records elsewhere in the British Isles but none were forthcoming. Michael Taylor found Land Caddis in many 1 × 1 km squares in Wyre Forest and these records are in the Worcestershire Biological Records Centre database. Based on this work the Land Caddis is designated Red Data Book 3 (locally common, nationally rare, not likely to exist in more than 15 10 km squares) by Wallace (1991).

Life cycle (male top right, female below top, larva below bottom [all HG])
Males and females emerge from their larval cases between late September and early November. The flightless females station themselves in prominent places, such as tufts of moss, and laboratory experiments suggest that they probably lure the males by scent. Mating is brief and takes place with one or several males (Green & Westwood 2012). The eggs are usually laid in an amber-coloured gelatinous mass very soon afterwards. In Worcester in 1868 Fletcher observed a female laying her eggs on moss close to the ground and Kellner-Pillault (1960) saw a French specimen begin laying at the tip of a moss leaf.

The eggs hatch after about 30 days, often in late November and early December. Young caddis larvae quickly build their first case by spinning silk with which they wrap their abdomens, attaching tiny wood fragments to this silken belt. Small particles of grit or sand are attached with a second band of silk. Having built its first case the larva starts feeding, usually on decaying tree leaves. As it grows more materials are added and the full-grown case is 7 or 8 mm long and

about 2 mm in diameter. In England Harding's research showed that the larvae passed through five instars. The case also changes shape from a simple cylinder to a horn-of-plenty, thickening in the process. In some locations large numbers of small larvae can be found, but fully grown ones can be scarce. The number in leaf litter varies markedly from year to year (Harding 1998).

From the early 1990s Green & Westwood (2005a; 2005b) spent many years searching woods in Worcestershire and neighbouring counties for Land Caddis, and encouraging other people to do the same. Since Fletcher's records (and including them) Land Caddis larvae have been found in over 250 1 × 1 km squares within 14 adjacent 10 × 10 km squares of the national grid. Although there are probably other sites within these boundaries this appears to be the national distribution of Land Caddis. So far none have been found elsewhere.

By 2005, despite many years of looking for Land Caddis larvae, the main searchers had not seen adult Land Caddis. From Fletcher's reports and specimens the flight period seemed to be October, so in 2005 visits were made to several woods where larvae were common. On 14–15 October 2005 flying males and a flightless female were found in Chaddesley Woods and Wyre Forest. These were thought to be the first seen in Britain since Fletcher's day, although we later heard that David Harding had seen one or two during his studies. The knowledge gained has led to more records of both sexes at different sites in Wyre in recent years (Green & Westwood 2012).

Chapter 10

Other Invertebrates

The general term 'invertebrates' includes a vast array of animals: insects, crustaceans, worms, molluscs, spiders and many more. Many are 'arthopods' with hard exteriors and jointed legs like insects, others are soft like slugs, and large numbers are microscopic. This chapter concerns the less well-known invertebrates, plus spiders and molluscs.

Hidden worlds

Stroll through the Forest and you walk on the roof of an invisible world. The ground may be covered by a layer of decaying leaves and twigs, the rich leaf litter of the woodland floor. Gather a few handfuls into a white tray and wait and watch for movement amongst the fragments. Woodlice crawl, centipedes (the fast-moving hunters of the litter) rush about. Slow, snake-like millipedes amble through the debris on a multitude of legs. Snails, some as small as 1 mm, start to stir. A hand lens reveals roving eight-legged mites, and in the darkness of the decaying wood, there may be delicate, white, many-legged animals, the Pauropodans and Symphylids. In damper places there are worms: segmented worms (like earthworms), very small slim white nematodes, and flatworms. Small spiders are legion and with luck you may see pseudoscorpions. All these leaf litter organisms are vital to the Forest's ecosystem.

There are five common species of woodlice and all can be found in Wyre, in leaf litter, under fallen wood, beneath stones and under detached bark. They are: Common Shiny Woodlouse *Oniscus asellus* which is large (up to 16 mm long) and found in damper places; Common Rough Woodlouse *Porcellio scaber* (up to

17 mm long) seen commonly under bark; Common Striped Woodlouse *Philoscia muscorum* (up to 11 mm long) a fast-running species with a stripe down its back; and Common Pygmy Woodlouse *Trichoniscus pusillus* (5 mm long) which moves very quickly when disturbed and is the most abundant woodlouse in woodland leaf litter. The Common Pill Woodlouse *Armadillidium vulgare* (up to 18 mm) is found less frequently than these others—when it rolls up, it forms a perfect sphere hiding all its legs and antennae. *Porcellionides pruinosus* and *Porcellio dilatatus* have been found in farm dungheaps. One which is occasionally seen is the 4 mm blind white Ant Woodlouse *Platyarthrus hoffmannseggii* which lives in ant nests and has been recorded in the Forest in the nests of Negro Ant *Formica fusca*, Yellow Meadow Ant *Lasius flavus* and Small Black Ant *L. niger*. The Water Hoglouse *Asellus aquaticus* resembles a woodlouse and lives amongst aquatic vegetation and debris. It is common in most areas of still water in Wyre.

About 10 species of millipedes have been identified from Wyre. One of the largest is *Tachypodoiulus niger*, a common black species with white legs, which is often found in leaf litter and also in gardens. At night, torchlight will pick out large numbers of millipedes trundling up tree trunks, probably to graze on algae or fungi. Among them will be the Striped Millipede *Ommatoiulus sabulosus*, another large species and an ancient woodland specialist, which is common in the Forest. It is brown with two distinctive pale stripes along the back. The Blunt-tailed Snake Millipede *Cylindroiulus punctatus*, nationally the most common

Common Shiny Woodlouse *Oniscus asellus* [RW]

Common Striped Woodlouse *Philoscia muscorum* [JB]

Common Rough Woodlouse *Porcellio scaber* [PC]

Ant Woodlouse *Platyarthrus hoffmannseggii* [JB]

Striped Millipede *Ommatoiulus sabulosus*, with two bright orange stripes, commonly found in the Forest [PC]

and widespread millipede, may be found in decaying wood in spring, returning to leaf litter in autumn and going down into soil in cold weather (Lee 2006). Millipedes need to moult as they age and to do so they make a web nest. These have been found inside old acorn cups in the Forest. The numbers of eyes increase with each moult. Flat-backed millipedes, usually of the genus *Polydesmus*, are often found under loose bark and have flat, well-sculptured dorsal segments. A damp log turned over gently might reveal the tiny, delicate Spotted Snake Millipede *Blaniulus guttulatus*, pale with pink spots. The Bristly Millipede *Polyxenus lagurus*, only 2–3 mm long, is not often recorded, and looks more like the Cobweb Beetle larva *Ctesias serra* with its amber colour, bristles and long hair tufts which keep spiders beyond biting distance. The millipede has been found on stumps and walls in the Forest and under moss. Paul Whitehead (1998) found large numbers (estimated at around 12,000) on two senile pear trees in Wyre, a finding possibly unique in Europe. This huge population had probably developed alongside an abundant food source, where the lichen *Parmelia perlata* encrusted the branches. *Ophyiulus pilosus* and Pill Millipede *Glomeris marginata* are both found in leaf litter. The latter is distinguished from pill woodlice by having many more legs (up to 19 pairs) a large shield covering the first segment behind the head, and a more glossy appearance.

The carnivorous centipedes have poison claws behind the head derived from the first pair of legs. Few people have searched for them in Wyre, but several species have been found in soil and leaf litter. These include the sinuous, yellow *Geophilus truncorum*, *G. insculptus*, *Stigmatogaster subterraneus* and the shorter brown *Lithobius microps*. *Cryptops hortensis* may be seen around habitations and *L. forficatus* is common in gardens, but in the Forest the somewhat similar *L. variegatus* is more frequent. This is a centipede often associated with ancient woodland and, if it remains still for long enough, is easily identified by the darker brown bands on its legs.

Pseudoscorpions are quite often seen but rarely specifically identified. They are 4 mm long and, like spiders, have a cephalothorax (head and thorax combined) carrying four pairs of legs. Their most striking features are the huge modified palps by the mouth, ending in lobster-like claws. Two species recorded in the Forest are the Common Chthonid *Chthonius ischnocheles* and the Common Neobisid *Neobisium carcinoides*.

Spotted Snake Millipede *Blaniulus guttulatus* [RW]

Bristly Millipede *Polyxenus lagurus* [GF]

Pill Millipede *Glomeris marginata* [JB]

A centipede *Lithobius variegatus* [RW]

Aquatic crustaceans

Turn over almost any stone in Wyre's streams and you will see a number of wriggling crustaceans. These are Freshwater Shrimps *Gammarus pulex,* and they are found throughout the Dowles Brook catchment, often in very large quantities and even in the smallest trickles. They are important food for the Dipper *Cinclus cinclus*, Water Shrew *Neomys fodiens* and many fish. In the Severn, and the lower reaches of Dowles Brook, another freshwater shrimp, the Northern River Crangonyctid *Crangonyx pseudogracilis* is common. This species, introduced from North America, is now widespread in the British Isles and is greyish, often with a dark lateral stripe. Unlike *Gammarus*, which swims on its side, *Crangonyx* swims in an upright position.

Both shrimps have a larger relative, the native White-clawed Crayfish *Austropotamobius pallipes* which is part of the reason for designating much of the Wyre Forest as a Site of Special Scientific Interest (SSSI). Some streams still contain a nationally important population of this species. In recent years it has been threatened with extinction partly because of the arrival of the alien Signal Crayfish *Pacifastacus leniusculus* (see box).

The White-clawed Crayfish is the largest of Britain's native freshwater invertebrates. To thrive, it needs high water quality, shelter from predators, and food in abundance. It is currently classified as 'Endangered' by the International Union for Conservation of Nature (IUCN 2015), and is one of the Government's top species of concern: the very survival of White-clawed Crayfish in Britain is in doubt.

White-clawed Crayfish are nocturnal and most active during the warmer months of spring through to late autumn. They mate in autumn and the females carry their eggs, followed by the hatchlings, under their tails until the following June or July. Crayfish require alkaline, calcium-rich, clean and well-oxygenated water. They favour shallow, clear, fast-flowing streams with slow-moving sections and coarse substrate. They are also found in deeper lakes and rivers if the water quality is good (Holditch 2003).

Only 30 years ago the species was common throughout most of Britain. Stories are told of people in the Wyre Forest collecting half a bucket of crayfish in half an hour for dinner. Now they are strictly protected and it is a criminal offence to take them from the wild.

Their decline is caused by several factors: decreasing water quality, habitat loss and introduction of alien crayfish species. From the perspective of the native crayfish water quality has decreased in recent decades making many watercourses unsuitable. Streams in arable farming areas are affected by silt carried from fields growing potatoes, maize or winter wheat. Incidents of chemical pollution by pesticides, fuel leaks or farmyard slurry can wipe out crayfish populations at a stroke. Many streams and rivers have been subjected to engineering works to increase flood capacity or reduce erosion so killing crayfish directly during the work or indirectly through habitat degradation. Even more seriously the most important cause of the decline stems from the introduction of alien crayfish to the Britain in the late 1970s. Many species of crayfish occur worldwide.

In 1987 native crayfish were widespread throughout the Dowles Brook catchment. Crayfish Plague was first reported in Dowles Brook in 1988 and soon afterwards the White-clawed Crayfish population crashed and was assumed to have been lost.

Coincidentally at this time, members of the Wyre Forest Study Group were looking for cave spiders in a stream culvert in the Forest and noticed several White-clawed Crayfish in the stream. A survey carried out under licence established that a good population of native crayfish was present.

In the following year, within the Grow with Wyre project, a survey of Wyre streams was undertaken to establish if, and where, native crayfish were present. In the summer of 2011, 74 crayfish surveys were conducted and just under a quarter of the 74.6 km of watercourses was assessed for habitat suitability:

The White-clawed Crayfish *Austropotamobius pallipes* is our only native crayfish. It hides under stones and logs, and in holes in the stream bank during the daytime and emerges at night to feed on small water creatures and plants. [JR]

The American Signal Crayfish

The American Signal Crayfish *Pacifastacus leniusculus* (right [RW]) grows more quickly, breeds more readily and thrives in a wider range of habitats than our native crayfish and was introduced as a source of food. It carries a parasitic fungus, Crayfish Plague *Aphanomyces astaci*, to which it is immune, but which is always fatal to the White-clawed Crayfish (Holditch 2003). The Signal Crayfish clearly likes British waters and is now found in most parts of the country: in southern Britain it has all but replaced the native crayfish. Signal Crayfish are quite capable of walking overland and of climbing obstacles to invade new places. Several were seen to climb a waterfall in one of the streams in the Forest by Graham Hill in summer 2014.

In 2010 a conference was organised at Bristol Zoo on the plight of the native crayfish and one outcome has been the capture and relocation of some to 'Ark Sites' away from outside threats, whilst Bristol Zoo itself has an active captive breeding programme. Then, as now, there is no known way of removing alien crayfish from a stream once they are there (Peay 2001).

crayfish surveys were undertaken where suitable habitat was found. This involved hand-searching 430 refugia, placing 105 crayfish traps, and 14 hours of 'night torching' as crayfish are active at night. The results showed that four streams, all tributaries of Dowles Brook, had populations of native crayfish; one had a high population, one a good population and two had small populations. This was very welcome news. The survey also showed that Dowles Brook and several other tributaries had populations of Signal Crayfish whilst some streams had no crayfish at all. The lower reaches of Lem Brook have excellent physical habitat for crayfish but none have been found, suggesting that water quality is poor there (Hill 2011).

Monitoring surveys have been conducted each year since. More details are given in reports in *Wyre Forest Study Group Reviews* (the most recent in Hill & Hill 2014) and *Worcestershire Record*. These surveys have established that one stream still holds an excellent population of White-clawed Crayfish, and that the range of body sizes (and therefore age) suggests a stable breeding population. Another stream has a small population of native crayfish with an abundance of juveniles, again suggesting that there is a breeding population. However, it is still recovering from the drought in summer 2012 when many individuals died or were rescued. Both of these streams flow through woodland and are little impacted by agricultural practices. The two other streams holding populations of native crayfish flow through land with a mixture of arable and woodland uses, are noticeably more turbid, and are carrying a heavy load of silt. They have small populations of native crayfish, which must be considered more vulnerable to extinction.

The principal reason for the absence of Signal Crayfish in the four streams is, in the author's view, the presence of man-made barriers between Dowles Brook and the parts of the streams containing native crayfish. In each case the lower reach of the stream is culverted (piped) under a track and, on the downstream side of the track, water falls between 0.5 and 1.5 m into the lower streambed creating an apparently unclimbable barrier that has (so far) prevented upstream migration of alien crayfish. The streams that do contain Signal

Crayfish do not have any such barrier making upstream migration from Dowles Brook feasible.

As part of the Water Framework Directive (European legislation intended to improve the quality of rivers) many of these barriers are being removed – to allow fish to pass upstream for example (Environment Agency 2010). The experience within Wyre Forest and Dowles Brook shows that culverts and waterfalls, unnatural as they may be, benefit some species and removal should be undertaken only when these factors have been considered.

Before the White-clawed Crayfish declined so rapidly, they occurred in a wide range of habitats, but it is now becoming apparent that they persist largely in small headwater streams, preferably in a wooded setting and away from farmed catchments. This is true of the streams in Dowles Brook but also of streams in similar settings across Worcestershire and Herefordshire.

What of the future? The big issue is to remove the alien species, although that has yet to be achieved and is a daunting prospect. It is also necessary to improve water quality, although with current farming practices adding large quantities of soil and silt to watercourses this is a considerable challenge. On an individual level we can all help to prevent the spread of alien species or infections when we visit these watercourses. All footwear, clothing and equipment should be checked to ensure that no animals are attached (and later transferred), be cleaned to remove mud and stones to ensure that parasites or diseases are not transferred, and either air-dried or properly disinfected (using a chlorine- or iodine-based product; (GB Non-native Species Secretariat 2015). The spores of Crayfish Plague will die if they dry out, but could survive in wet mud in a boot sole. Whether you are an angler, cyclist, boater, walker, or you have been using heavy digging equipment in the river, you can help by disinfecting, cleaning and drying your clothing and equipment.

Although we can be proud that Dowles Brook still has native crayfish, they remain vulnerable to extinction. It only takes one careless or deliberate act to kill all the native crayfish in any of the streams. The health of the four White-clawed Crayfish populations will continue to be monitored, although, sadly, that cannot guarantee their survival.

Spiders and harvestmen
Spiders

We are all familiar with frosted spiders' webs in winter sunshine and autumn fields covered in linyphiid gossamer, but most of us are unaware that Wyre is home to hundreds of different spiders (British Arachnological Society (BAS) data). Even the more informed naturalist who comes in search of flowers and butterflies is only likely to notice a few species, such as the wolf spiders scampering over the Forest leaf litter, the large webs of the Garden Spider *Araneus diadematus* strung between foliage, and crab spiders lurking with intent amongst the flower heads.

At the time of writing greater Wyre has 262 spider species recorded, compared with 347 for Worcestershire, and approximately 650 for the United Kingdom (BAS data). There is certainly scope for more discoveries in the Forest. Survival of specialist species depends on suitable habitat and a large enough area, so that local disturbances do not threaten the entire population of a particular species: in this respect Wyre is well blessed.

The earliest group of spider records for Wyre appears to be by Peter A. Walker in 1978, who recorded 109 species. He was followed by Michael N. Taylor who added another 84, plus 18 in conjunction with Peter Hobson, mostly in 1988, although he carried on recording for some years after this (BAS data). Other new records have been added by Colin Plant, Peter Harvey, John Partridge and, more recently, by members of the Wyre Forest Study Group, and Shropshire Spider Group.

Wyre has a number of spiders which are locally, or even nationally, scarce and one of the more obvious of these is the striking leaf-coloured Green Huntsman Spider *Micrommata virescens*. It prefers damp, sheltered woodland and is often found on the lower branches of oak saplings and on tall grass or sedge tussocks where it sits, head down, waiting to pounce on passing insects. It is widespread but very scattered in the southern half of Britain, with few records in the north (BAS data). The Wyre population seems to be quite isolated. The dated records are mainly from April to October, peaking in the summer (Bingham 2012c). The male is quite a lot smaller than the female, has a yellow abdomen with scarlet longitudinal bands, and is less often seen. Females deposit their egg cocoons inside a leaf enclosed with silk, and when the tiny spiderlings hatch they are the same grass-green colour as their mother. The first record of this species in Worcestershire was published in 1933. The 'captor' is listed as R. Arkwright, and the authority as T.H. Savory himself, leading national expert at the time, with a date of 1925 (Savory 1933). Although there is no attribution to Wyre, this is the most likely location for this record.

The large and colourful Strawberry Spider *Araneus alsine* was first recorded in Wyre by Peter Harvey in 1988 (BAS data). It has been found occasionally since then, mostly by accident, although members of the Wyre Forest Study Group added a few new locations for this species in 2013 (Bingham 2013) and 2014 (Scott 2014). It gets its name from the pale spots on the abdomen resembling the pattern of seeds on a strawberry and is rare in Britain and locally distributed. In Wyre it appears to favour low vegetation in damp, but fairly open woodland clearings, often in association with Purple Moor-grass *Molinia caerulea*. The spider spins its web in low herbage, occupying a small conical retreat at the top of the web inside one or two curled, dry leaves. Even though the adult spider is a conspicuous orange or reddish colour it is easy to overlook in its habitat, unless you are prepared to lie down and gaze up into its leaf-funnels. Females are adult from June to October whilst mature males are generally found in June and July (Roberts 1995).

The Filmy Dome Spider *Neriene radiata* has a national distribution suggesting that this is the most isolated of the Wyre's four special spiders. Its main stronghold is in Scotland. It was first recorded in Wyre by Peter Merrett in 1980 (BAS data) who mentioned it was widespread and frequent within the Forest, and Colin Plant found it in 1984 (BAS data). It was Mike Taylor who drew attention to it when he discovered it in several sites within the woodlands after his first record from Longdon in 1987 (Taylor 1989). At that time Wyre was the only site outside Scotland for this species. Mike suggested that it may have been imported with conifer seedlings from Scotland which had been planted out in the Forest (Taylor 1989), although this has not been proved and may not be the case. Our dated records are from June, July and August (Worcestershire Biological Records Centre), and females are more often recorded than males. At only 5–6 mm long, hanging upside down under its web, the spider has markings rather similar to a number of other species: it is the distinctive domed web rather than its maker which is likely to be noticed first. In Wyre it seems to occur particularly in heathy woodland clearings, but more local habitat information is required (Winnall 2012).

The small Triangle Spider *Hyptiotes paradoxus* was first found on the Shropshire side of Wyre in September 2013 (Bingham 2013). The females are 5–6 mm long, but the males are only 3–4 mm, and these have huge balloon-like pedipalps which are easily seen with a hand lens (Roberts 1995). The species is locally distributed in the British Isles, found mainly in the south on evergreen trees and shrubs (particularly Yew *Taxus baccata*) (Bingham 2013). This six-eyed spider, which has no venom, relies on its specialised capture technique to secure its prey. It spins a triangular segment of orb web (containing two radial threads) within the tree foliage, and keeps it taut by holding on to one corner of the triangle from its sitting position (see photographs). When an insect is caught in the web the spider alternately slackens and tightens the tension of the web until its prey is fully entangled in silk before advancing to wrap it securely (Dalton 2008). Spiders are mature in late summer but do not mate until the following spring. There is only one known location

Some of the locally and nationally scarce spiders found in Wyre

Green Huntsman Spider *Micrommata virescens* can be found on low vegetation (female left [RW], male right [JB])

Strawberry Spider *Araneus alsine* is difficult to find in damp places in its rolled leaf refuge (left [KMcG], right [JB])

Filmy Dome Spider *Neriene radiata* and its distinctive domed web are found in heathy clearings (female left, male right [both JB])

The Triangle Spider *Hyptiotes paradoxus* has been found in Wyre by careful searching on Yew trees. The male (left and right [JB]) has large inflated palps

A jumping spider *Evarcha falcata* [JB]

Female *Heliophanus cupreus* [JB]

A crab spider *Diaea dorsata* [JB]

Toad Spider *Nuctenea umbratica* [RW]

The horizontal sheets of the webs [RW] **spun by** *Linyphia triangularis* **(below** [JB]**) are especially noticeable in the autumn stretching across the tops of Heather.**

for this species in the Forest so far, but no doubt other sites remain to be found. A search in Yew trees is recommended, although it may occur in other conifers.

Wyre has a wide variety of other spiders. A visit to one of the heathy areas within the Forest might result in the discovery of the small *Episinus angulatus*, whose abdomen is oddly truncated, lurking beneath the Heather *Calluna vulgaris* where it spins a very simple 'H'-shaped web. The colourful jumping spiders *Evarcha falcata* and *E. arcuata* are often seen on Heather and young oaks in open areas and by ridesides, from where they peer at the observer with remarkably acute eyesight. The yellow legs and palps of the female *Heliophanus cupreus* can be conspicuous, although close examination is required to avoid confusion with other species. *Araneus marmoreus* var. *pyramidatus* is rarely seen but has been spotted on a gorse bush near

the Experimental Pool. *Linyphia triangularis* is usually the commonest spider in this habitat, its horizontal webbing stretched widely across the top of the Heather.

In the trees there are more species. Although small, one of the easiest to see is the female *Paidiscura pallens* when she is protecting her conspicuous white spiky eggcase on the underside of leaves, especially oak, in the summer. The attractive *Diaea dorsata* is a green and brown crab spider that can be identified easily from its markings. Tree bark fissures often hide the Toad Spider *Nuctenea umbratica*, although these are much easier to see at night-time when they emerge from their refuges to spin webs and feed. Their orb webs contrast with the very fine webs made on tree bark by *Drapetisca socialis*. This delicate webbing is used to catch small items of prey and the male also uses it to communicate with the female by drumming on it with his palps (Roberts 1995).

Cyclosa conica [JB]

Tetragnatha extensa [PC]

Female Nursery Web Spider *Pisaura mirabilis* carrying egg sac [RW]

A crab spider *Misumena vatia* [PC]

Egg sac of *Agroeca brunnea* (left [JB]) is later covered with soil (right [JB])

Stalked egg case of *Ero furcata* [JB]

A range of different spiders may be seen on ground vegetation or low shrubbery, such as *Cyclosa conica* with its distinctive triangular body, *Tetragnatha* spp. lying outstretched on grass stems, and the Nursery Web Spider *Pisaura mirabilis* basking in the early spring sunshine. The male *Pisaura* presents the female with a silk-wrapped love gift, usually a fly, so that he is able to mate with her whilst she eats it (Roberts 1995). The female carries her egg sac underneath her body; when the eggs are due to hatch she attaches the sac to low vegetation and constructs a complex nursery web around it, over which she stands guard.

An immobile bee or fly on a flowerhead is a clue that the crab spider *Misumena vatia* has claimed a victim. This pale yellow or white spider is at the northern edge of its range in Wyre (NBN Gateway), although it is common here. The females lurk on flowers, immobile with forelegs outstretched as they wait to grab their prey, an unlucky bumble bee, fly or butterfly that can often be larger than the spider itself. Studies in America (Morse 2007) have shown that the female needs to consume the equivalent of three large bumble bees before she is able to lay a batch of eggs.

Some egg cases are found more frequently than the spiders that constructed them. The females of *Agroeca* spp. create white chambered egg sacs that look like inverted wine glasses on low vegetation. The females then painstakingly cover them with soil particles to provide a good insulating cover, and for camouflage. The delicate stalked egg cases of *Ero* spp. with their wiry outer silk, are found occasionally. Near to water the untidy *Tetragnatha* cocoons, with their topping of dirty green silk, may be seen attached to reeds and grasses.

Down at ground level the webbed tunnels of the Labyrinth Spider *Agelena labyrinthica* are very common in the Forest. The greyish occupants lie in wait at the mouth of the tunnel, which in autumn is littered with the husks of their prey. In the summer many of the female Lycosid wolf spiders *Pardosa* spp. carry their egg sacs on their spinners until the young hatch. The tiny spiderlings then climb up onto the mother's back, hunch together, and are carried around for a week or more (Roberts 1995).

One of Britain's largest spiders, the shiny brown Cave Spider *Meta menardi*, has been found lurking

Labyrinth Spider *Agelena labyrinthica* [RW]

Cave Spider *Meta menardi* with egg case [RW]

A female wolf spider *Pardosa* sp. carrying spiderlings on her back [RW]

in a few dark damp places within Wyre (Winnall 2009). The adult spiders are averse to light and so live in complete darkness. When the young emerge though they move towards the light, enabling them to disperse and colonise new sites (Bristowe 1958). Their large white egg cases, which hang down by silken threads, look like small lightbulbs and are conspicuous indicators that this species is present. More colonies may yet be undiscovered in house cellars and other dark places around Wyre.

A few spiders are found only in and around habitation, such as the tiny *Oonops domesticus* (1.2–2 mm) which is bright pink, and has only six eyes. The species is nocturnal and easily overlooked, although it has been recorded from The Newalls in 2014 (Limbrey 2015). The Daddy Longlegs Spider *Pholcus phalangioides* is now commonplace throughout much of greater Wyre. It cannot survive outdoors but flourishes in the warmth of our centrally heated homes and outbuildings. *Pholcus* may be a flimsy-looking spider, but catches its prey by flinging cobwebs to trap it before parcelling it up. In this way, it can catch the much bulkier *Tegenaria* species, and may also be cannibalistic (Dalton 2008).

Harvestmen

The Opiliones are not true spiders. Their abdomen and cephalothorax are merged into a single oval body, they have only two eyes, and they cannot make silk or produce poison, (Hillyard 2005). At the time of writing the Wyre Forest area has 17 recorded species, compared with 21 for the whole of Worcestershire, and 27 for the United Kingdom (BAS data).

Many harvestmen have very long legs and *Leiobunums* (the males of which have legs ten times the length of their bodies (Jones 1983) are most conspicuous. They mature in late summer and are often seen around harvest time, hence the name harvestmen. *L. rotundum* may sometimes be seen *en masse* on tree trunks when it is easy to distinguish the males and larger females. *L. blackwalli* looks similar, but close inspection with a hand lens will reveal white rims around its eyes.

Dicranopalpus ramosus, first found in the UK in 1957 (Hillyard 2005) is now common throughout Wyre. On walls and fence posts it is often conspicuous because of its distinctive posture when resting, with legs stretched out at right angles to the body. It can be easily identified as it has forked pedipalps. *Megabunus diadema* is a species that is not always easy to find as it blends in so well with lichens on trees and rocks but its raised eye turret, with impressive prominent spines, makes this easy to identify. Very few males are ever found and this species is known to be able to reproduce parthenogenetically (Hillyard 2005).

Some of the middle-sized harvestmen are difficult to distinguish and need practice and often microscopic examination to separate. However, two of our smallest species can easily be identified when discovered after a careful search amongst leaf litter.

Male *Leiobunum rotundum* [RW]

Female *Dicronopalpus ramosus* [RW]

Megabunus diadema [JB]

Nemastoma bimaculatum [JB]

Anelasmocephalus cambridgei [RW]

Female *Sabacon viscayanum* subsp. *ramblaianum* [RW]

The black *Nemastoma bimaculatum* measures only 2.0–2.8 mm and is often found, and the less common *Anelasmocephalus cambridgei* with its unusual granular body is only a little larger.

It was with some surprise that a second English record of the rare *Sabacon viscayanum* subsp. *ramblaianum* was discovered in the Wyre Forest in Hawkbatch by Nicki Farmer in October 2013 (Winnall & Farmer 2013). A second individual was found on the Shropshire side of Dowles in Longdon in 2015. This species was first found in the UK in the 1980s, and other confirmed records are all from the South Wales area, the nearest being near Presteigne (BAS data). This harvestman is easily recognised by its unusual pedipalps which are longer than its body and covered in many spines and hairs. It will be interesting to see if other individuals can be found in the Forest and more information collected about its habitat and distribution.

The future of spider recording

A comparison of the species lists for greater Wyre and Worcestershire shows that many of the 'missing' spider species come from the Linyphiidae, which most people will know as money spiders. Nearly all of these, as well as many of the larger spiders, need to be viewed under a microscope for accurate identification, often by careful examination of the genitalia.

Although the Spider Recording Scheme is gradually assembling habitat data on many of our British species, it is still surprisingly difficult to predict which species will be found where. The choice of site is determined by food availability, but even if the food is present, the spider either needs a structure on which to build its web, or suitable hunting territory. In addition some species appear to have distinct humidity preferences.

The discovery of the *Sabacon* harvestman shows that the unexpected can turn up. More species will undoubtedly be added to the spider and harvestmen lists for Wyre by local enthusiasts with the time, patience and expertise to pursue this interest.

Molluscs

There are over 200 species of land and freshwater molluscs in Britain, ranging from the familiar Common Garden Snail *Cornu aspersum* through the Brown-lipped Snail *Cepaea nemoralis* subsp. *nemoralis* and White-lipped Snail *C. hortensis*, with their variable colour bandings, to minute exquisitely marked objects of beauty only found by diligent searching in leaf litter. Some are typically snail-shaped, others are long spirals, some are flat, some have translucent shells, and some are brown and remarkably ridged and grooved, whilst others are smooth and glossy. Search in water and a whole new range of shapes appear: coils, spirals, disc, hooked shells clinging to rocks, and freshwater mussels from small pea-sized creatures to huge burrowers in river mud. Wyre is also home to a large number of slugs, including species typical of ancient woodlands and ranging in colour from midnight black to canary yellow.

Although it is rich in snails, slugs and mussels Wyre does not always deliver them easily. Most of our species require damp or freshwater habitats, and snails and mussels also need lime to form their shells. Much of the Forest is dry, acid, oak and birch woodland with Bracken *Pteridium aquilinum*, Heather *Calluna vulgaris* and Bilberry *Vaccinium myrtillus* on the sandstones, clays and shales of the Coal Measures.

At first glance, this may not seem promising, but there are a number of specialist species which revel in acid places. These include the Hollowed Glass Snail *Zonitoides excavatus* (Cameron & Riley 2008; Anderson 2005) and the Hedgehog Slug *Arion intermedius* (Rowson *et al.*2014). The former has a very large umbilicus (the depression on the underside of the shell) showing the coiling of the earlier whorls. The slug lives under logs or in leaf litter in moist places and, when hunched, the soft spikes on the tubercles make it appear prickly, hence its name. The Brown Snail *Zenobiella subrufescens* also occurs in undisturbed damp acid areas and has a shell so thin that you can see the beating heart of the animal through its whorls.

Turn over a log in Wyre's woods and copses and you may find the carnivorous Garlic Snail *Oxychilus alliarius*, which has a warm-brown shell. If tickled with the tip of a blade of grass, the animal within releases a pungent odour of garlic. Other common species found under dead wood or in leaf litter are the Rounded Snail *Discus rotundatus* subsp. *rotundatus* and the Dusky Slug *Arion subfuscus*. The Dusky Slug is orange-brown and may be identified by dabbing the rear of the head (the mantle) with a piece of white paper, which will come away smeared with the characteristic bright orange slime.

Down in the valley bottoms, which receive mineral nutrients from run off, there are more stable wet and fertile patches. Here there are often streams bordered by Pendulous Sedge *Carex pendula*, and these damp places support sparse numbers of a wider range of species. These include the Smooth Glass

Hedgehog Slug *Arion intermedius* [RW]

Garlic Snail *Oxychilus alliarius* [JB]

Snail *Aegopinella nitidula*, the Cellar Snail *Oxychilus cellarius*, the mottled, chestnut-coloured Copse Snail *Arianta arbustorum* subsp. *arbustorum,* which has a dark brown spiral band around the periphery of each whorl, and the Large Black Slug *Arion ater* agg. which, despite its common name, comes in a variety of colours including brick red, orange, cream and grey. These large and impressive slugs can hybridise with closely related species and are familiar if unwelcome inhabitants of gardens as well as many other habitats.

Other common garden species found in the less acidic habitats include the White-lipped Snail and the Brown-lipped Snail. Typically both are very variable and are often banded in various shades of yellow, cream and maroon. The White-lipped Snail is more frequent in shadier areas than the Brown-lipped, and both will climb trees in suitable damp weather. They are often attracted to wasp-damaged fruit in the Forest's orchards. Where there is little lime in the soil, their shells may be very thin and even flexible. One of our larger and most familiar snails is the Common Garden Snail which is associated with town and country gardens and orchards in Wyre. It is not a species of the high Forest although it may have been introduced to the banks of the River Severn by eggs carried on the boots of walkers.

Less acidic rock, and other areas where there is tufa present, host species with a more marked requirement for lime. This is the favourite haunt of the Lapidary Snail *Helicigona lapicida* subsp. *lapicida,* whose flattened and keeled shell enables it to hide in deep rock crevices in Wyre. The shell of the minute Prickly

Rounded Snail *Discus rotundatus* subsp. *rotundatus* [RW]

Large Black Slug *Arion ater,* pale form [RW]

Copse Snail *Arianta arbustorum* subsp. *arbustorum* [RW]

White-lipped Snail *Cepraea nemoralis* [RW]

Snail *Acanthinula aculeata* is only 2 mm across, but has extraordinary spiny ribs which allow it to accumulate leaf debris for camouflage.

Land molluscs are well known for their lack of mobility and some species can be poor colonisers. This means that several are useful indicators of ancient, undisturbed woodland (Kerney 1999). In Wyre the Lemon Slug *Malacolimax tenellus* may be found feeding on fungi in the late autumn. A visit by night to favoured areas can produce dozens of these attractive canary-coloured slugs with soft grey tentacles, munching on a range of fungi. They are particularly common in woodland with Beech *Fagus sylvatica* where their autumnal colours blend in well with newly fallen leaves. During the rest of the year the slugs remain below the soil surface, feeding on fungal mycelia. Unusually, this slug, which is tolerant of poor acid soils, may survive in replanted conifer forest if there are plenty of fungi, though not in recent commercial forestry plantations. Wyre is a stronghold for this very attractive species which is sparsely distributed in old woodlands in Great Britain.

Lemon Slug *Malacolimax tenellus* is only found in established woodlands. It is common in Wyre when it can be found feeding on fungi in the autumn. Its body is soft and flaccid, the antennae always dark, and when moist it can leave a trail of yellow sole slime. [RW]

Ash-black Slug *Limax cinereoniger* [BW]

Tree Slug *Lehmannia marginata* [RW]

River Limpet *Ancylus fluviatilis* [RW]

Another good indicator of ancient woodland in Wyre is the Ash-black Slug *Limax cinereoniger*, a nocturnal species which shelters under logs and loose bark during the day. It may often be found in groups of all sizes and ages, or as individuals, and may reach 30 cm in length making it the UK's longest slug. Most are jet black and easily recognised by the dark-bordered pale band on their sole, but grey and even fawn individuals turn up regularly in Wyre. At night 'courting couples' are sometimes seen on tree trunks along with the much commoner Tree Slugs *Lehmannia marginata*. Because Ash-black Slugs frequent old mossy woods and steep dingles, often in very attractive locations, the species was described by Boycott in 1936 as "a wonderful judge of scenery".

Base-rich wet flushes within woodland may contain the small English Chrysalis Snail *Leiostyla anglica* which, in the few sites where it is present in central and southern Britain, is an indicator of ancient woodland that has never been clear felled. The even smaller Point Snail *Acicula fusca* (2.2–2.5 mm) is also present in selected wet places that are not heavily shaded. It may have been washed out of at least one site by the severe flash flooding in June 2007. Intolerant of disturbance it is declining at its remaining sites in central England, though it can be hard to find at low population densities, so there is hope that it will recover.

An exciting recent discovery in a wet flush in Wyre made by Rosemary Hill is the Plated Snail *Spermodea lamellata*. This is its only location in Worcestershire and there is only one other record in the same 100 km square. This diminutive but attractive snail with projecting plates, or lamellae, on its shell is a useful indicator of ancient semi-natural woodland that has never been clear-felled. The bulk of records for this species, apart from four in relict sites approximately on or below a line from the Thames estuary to the Bristol Channel, are in coastal west Wales or north of Leeds. This indicates that the find in Wyre is very special, emphasising the quality and ancient origin of the site. Since the original discovery a further five sites have been found for this species in the Forest, all within a relatively small area and all characterised

Freshwater Nerite *Theodoxus fluviatilis* subsp. *fluviatilis* [RW]

Common River Snail *Viviparus viviparus* subsp. *viviparus* [RW]

Great Pond Snail *Lymnaea stagnalis* eggs [RW]

by the predictable availability of moisture at all times of year.

The variety of flowing water habitats in Wyre ranges from tiny trickles and flushes to small springs and brooks, the larger Dowles Brook, and the River Severn. Water arising in or passing over base-rich areas, transports lime to the larger water bodies, to the benefit of the shelled molluscs that may be found in them. These include freshwater snails, orb, and pea mussels. Unsurprisingly, freshwater molluscs appear to be more resilient to the effects of flash flooding than land molluscs which may be overwhelmed before they can crawl out of reach of rising water.

In streams and rivers with fast-flowing clean water the River Limpet *Ancylus fluviatilis,* which has a conical shell with a hooked apex, may be found on the undersides of rocks. Another species favouring this type of habitat is the Freshwater Nerite *Theodoxus fluviatilis* subsp. *fluviatilis* which specifically requires lime-rich waters. It has been recorded from the Severn but not from its tributaries in the Wyre area. On the other hand the Common River Snail *Viviparus viviparus* subsp. *viviparus* has been found in both Dowles Brook and the Severn. Of the large freshwater mussels (Killeen *et al.* 2004), the Painter's Mussel *Unio pictorum* and the Duck Mussel *Anodonta anatina* have been found in the Severn, as has the Nut Orb Mussel *Sphaerium rivicola*. The Horny Orb Mussel *Sphaerium corneum* is also found in Dowles Brook. Ponds and larger water bodies, such as the Uncllys Reservoir provide another habitat for those freshwater molluscs which do not require flowing water with its higher oxygen levels. The ponds in the Forest differ in age and in the quality of their water. Uncllys Reservoir adds a number of molluscs to the Wyre list, including the Lake Limpet *Acroloxus lacustris,* White Ramshorn *Gyraulus albus* and Flat Ramshorn *Hippeutis complanatus*. The Wandering Snail *Radix balthica* occurs in almost all freshwater habitats but changes its form to suit its circumstances. The shell is streamlined in flowing water, but grows larger and has

a much wider opening in the muddy backflow areas of Dowles Brook.

The natural history of all areas is prone to change as new species colonise. When these are brought in by human activity, they tend to be species of disturbed places and gardens, rather than species of the high forest. Here these include the Girdled Snail *Hygromia cinctella*, Iberian Threeband Slug *Ambigolimax valentianus* and Caruana's Slug *Deroceras panormitanum,* which have spread rapidly across Britain. The slender, grey Worm Slug *Boettgerilla pallens* was first found in 2014 under stones near Dowles Brook. This is probably a species introduced into Britain through garden centres. It can successfully colonise stream valleys deep into natural forest and is likely to do so in Wyre. The Durham Slug *Arion flagellus* was first recorded from Wyre in orchards in 2008 and has been found in the Forest at a few more sites since. The Zebra Mussel *Dreissena polymorpha*, which was introduced to Britain in the 1820s, probably with Baltic timber imports, has found its way to the Severn. There is every possibility that the mollusc species list for Wyre will change in the future as new species colonise and other hitherto unseen species are discovered.

Worm Slug *Boettgerilla pallens* [RW]

Chapter 11

Fish

The main body of water in Wyre is the River Severn and, together with its main tributaries, it is described in Chapter 3, Watercourses section (pages 24–25). Map 5 in that chapter shows the main watercourses. The Severn enters the northern edge of our area at Upper Arley, flows through Bewdley and on to the southern edge of the Forest through Stourport.

In addition to flowing water there are bodies of water ranging from tiny forest pools to the large artificial reservoir at Trimpley, which provides a public drinking water supply. The majority of these are artificial, created by impounding small watercourses. Historically they were constructed for irrigation, water power, and as flight ponds for wildfowl. More recently some have been used for angling, and newer pools have also been constructed for that purpose. Fish species present in Wyre are listed in Table 8.

The habitat

In Wyre the Severn is in its middle reaches and has a wide variety of habitat types, ranging from rapids, shallow, fast glides and riffles, to deep pools and slower glides. Much of the riverbed is bedrock and at low water rocky shelves and ridges are clearly visible. There are also areas of cobbles and gravel with sand and silt in the margins and quieter reaches. Water depth varies from 30 cm or less in the wide gravelly riffles

(historically used as fords) to 6 m in some of the deeper reaches above Stourport and in the deep dubs at Arley and Trimpley.

In-stream vegetation is quite sparse, with some beds of water-crowfoot *Ranunculus* spp. in the gravelly glides and pondweeds *Potamogeton* spp. in the margins and shallower parts of the slower flowing areas. There are mosses in areas of boulders and cobbles. The catchment consists mostly of siliceous rocks and the pH of the river is broadly neutral; calcium, an essential building block for plant and animal growth, whilst not especially plentiful as is the case in chalk and limestone rivers, is not scarce. Water quality is generally good; although there was quite severe industrial pollution in the Ironbridge Gorge area during the 19th century (Ironbridge Gorge Museum), there are now no major inputs of pollution to the river upstream of Wyre. The river is slightly enriched by sewage and diffuse agricultural inputs, and there are occasional algal blooms, but not at levels that would directly harm fish.

The tributaries rise in mixed farming and broadleaved forest in the north and west of the Wyre Forest area and follow quite steep courses towards the main river. They support typical upland stream habitats with gravel riffles, pools and some small cascades where they cross bedrock outcrops. An important

feature is that there are artificial impoundments, typically dammed ponds and weirs. These interrupt the natural connectivity in the catchment and restrict migration and movements of fish and other creatures.

In contrast to most of their length the lower reaches of the Dowles and Gladder Brook, close to where they enter the main river, are at a much lower gradient, with silty, sandy beds and lots of woody debris. Apart from river mosses there is little or no in-stream vegetation. As the catchments of these streams drain large areas of broadleaved and coniferous woodland, they tend to be slightly acidic at times and not especially biologically productive. Due to their small size they are vulnerable to small pollution incidents from a variety of sources, and to drought, the effects of which can be exacerbated by over-abstraction for agriculture and other purposes.

The ponds in Wyre, mostly artificial, vary in size and depth; apart from Trimpley Reservoir none would be considered large. They offer typical pond habitats with vegetated shallows supporting plants such as pondweeds and water-starworts *Callitriche* spp. in generally silty beds overlaying bedrock or clay. Those in the Forest areas are usually heavily shaded and have high input of leaf litter, which renders them slightly acidic at times and prone to de-oxygenation in extended periods of ice-cover.

The River Severn at Bewdley. With its shallows and deeper pools, this is a productive stretch for anglers in search of Barbel *Barbus barbus* and other fish. Kingfishers and Goosanders regularly hunt here. [RW]

The River Severn

In Wyre the Severn supports a wide range of fish species. They reflect the diversity of habitat and, very importantly, its connection with the sea, over 160 km to the south. It is generally very difficult to observe fish in the main river due to its size and depth, particularly the more cryptic species and those that live on the riverbed. Most of what we know about their distribution comes from anglers and from surveys undertaken by the Environment Agency and its predecessors (see below). Some species may not have been formally recorded even though they are known to be present.

Fish can sometimes be spotted at the surface under good light conditions and may be identified by a trained observer; equally, the juvenile stages of many species can sometimes be seen in the shallow margins but at this stage all species appear very similar. Even if caught with a hand net and observed in a jar or tank of water they are quite difficult to distinguish.

Migratory species

Atlantic Salmon *Salmo salar* pass through the Forest reaches on their way to the major spawning grounds in Wales, and the lucky observer may spot a Salmon leaping, though those in the Severn are noted for rarely showing at the surface. Not all Salmon travel to the headwaters—some spawning takes place in the middle reaches around Bewdley and has been noted in Dowles Brook. Juvenile Salmon (parr) are present in the brook and in the main river. Salmon populations in the Severn, in common with those in many other western seaboard rivers, are considered to be well below their potential size (Environment Agency 2012). Why this is so is uncertain, although there is evidence that changes in the marine environment affecting the abundance of their food may be responsible.

The Severn is famous for its European Eel *Anguilla anguilla* stocks and significant commercial fisheries for the elvers (glass eel) exist in the lower reaches around Gloucester (Environment Agency 2010). Eels spawn in the Sargasso Sea in the Gulf of Mexico and the larvae (leptocephali) move with ocean currents towards Europe, entering our rivers in early spring, migrating upstream in stages as they grow. They may remain in freshwater for up to 40 years (usually 10–15 years) as yellow eels where they grow and become sexually mature. They then migrate downstream, returning to the sea as silver eels to make their way back to the Sargasso to spawn. Eels are present principally in the main river and in the lower reaches of Dowles and Gladder Brooks, favouring the slower-flowing, deeper areas. They are also able to reach some of the stillwaters despite obstructions to their migration.

Sea Lampreys *Petromyzon marinus* enter the Severn in small numbers in spring and spawn in gravel areas in early summer. They excavate shallow depressions (redds) which can sometimes be seen, but are often confused with those created by Barbel *Barbus barbus* which spawn at a similar time. After spawning the Sea Lamprey adults die and drift downstream, but the

Table 8 Fish species in Wyre

Sea Lamprey *Petromyzon marinus*	Gudgeon *Gobio gobio*
River Lamprey *Lampetra fluviatilis*	Barbel *Barbus barbus*
Brook Lamprey *Lampetra planeri*	Bleak *Alburnus alburnus*
Common Sturgeon *Acipenser sturio*	Silver Bream *Blicca bjoerkna*
Twaite Shad *Alosa fallax*	Common Bream *Abramis brama*
Atlantic Salmon *Salmo salar*	Crucian Carp *Carassius carassius*
Brown Trout *Salmo trutta*	Goldfish *Carassius auratus*
Smelt *Osmerus eperlanus*	Common Carp *Cyprinus carpio*
Pike *Esox lucius*	Stone Loach *Barbatula barbatula*
Roach *Rutilus rutilus*	European Eel *Anguilla anguilla*
Dace *Leuciscus leuciscus*	Three-spined Stickleback
Chub *Squalius cephalus*	*Gasterosteus aculeatus*
Minnow *Phoxinus phoxinus*	Perch *Perca fluviatilis*
Rudd *Scardinius erythrophthalmus*	Ruffe *Gymnocephalus cernuus*
Tench *Tinca tinca*	Bullhead *Cottus gobio*

juveniles (ammocoetes) remain in the river for up to eight years, feeding on detritus and small invertebrates before becoming Sea Lamprey transformers (Davies *et al.* 2004). These migrate to the sea and take up a parasitic lifestyle, sucking the blood of other fish.

The smaller River Lamprey *Lampetra fluviatilis* is present in the Severn, though its population is not thought to be large. They ascend the river in autumn, overwintering unseen until spring. They then become active and can sometimes be seen at the surface and in the margins whilst spawning. They too die after spawning and, as with the Sea Lamprey, their young live in beds of sediment, feeding on small items for up to five years, before becoming transformers and moving seawards in autumn.

Other migratory species that used to frequent the middle Severn, but which are now restricted to the lower reaches of the river, include the Twaite Shad *Alosa fallax*, Smelt *Osmerus eperlanus*, and Common Sturgeon *Acipenser sturio*. The steady increase in

barriers to migration posed by weirs on the main river has led to the demise of these species, a trend reflected across Europe. A Sturgeon 2.59 m long was caught at Worcester in 1813. Sturgeon were still being caught in the lower reaches of the Severn in the 1950s and the last sighting in the Severn was in the late 1980s (British Marine Life Study Society website). Such fish are now considered as vagrants rather than as part of a viable UK population.

Resident fish species

Resident fish species are faring rather better in the Wyre Forest reaches of the Severn. They include not only the classic middle river, flow-loving species but also those typical of more sedate river reaches. Fish of all species move over significant distances according to the season and day-to-day conditions; few are absolutely confined to any one habitat type.

During the summer the faster, shallower, river reaches contain good numbers of Chub *Squalius cephalus*, Barbel, Dace *Leuciscus leuciscus*, Gudgeon *Gobio gobio*, Minnow *Phoxinus phoxinus* and Bleak *Alburnus alburnus,* as well as the more sedentary Bullhead *Cottus gobio* and Stone Loach *Barbatula barbatula*. Roach *Rutilus rutilus*, Pike *Esox lucius* and Perch *Perca fluviatilis* are able to thrive in a wide variety of habitats and are also found close to these faster flowing sections but also frequent the steadier areas.

Barbel is an iconic Severn fish for which the river is nowadays perhaps best known. Paradoxically they are not native to the Severn, being historically confined to the catchments of the Trent, Yorkshire Ouse, Great Ouse and Thames, thought to be tributaries of a post-glacial North Sea river of which the modern river Rhine was probably the main stem (Whitton & Lucas

Pike *Esox lucius* [JR]

1997). Barbel were introduced to the Severn in the 1950s by the then River Board for angling. The original stock came from the Hampshire Avon, to which it is believed they were introduced from the River Kennet (Wheeler & Jordan 1990). Since then the species has followed a classic species-invasion pattern in the Severn, thanks to the near-perfect Barbel habitat. The 1970s saw massive proliferation of small Barbel in the main river and colonisation of all the major tributaries well into the Welsh headwaters (Churchward *et al.* 1984). Since then the population has matured with a variety of ages and sizes present. Although Barbel are still abundant and widely distributed, their range is contracting and they no longer dominate the river as they once did: they are now taking their place as another component of the river ecosystem.

The deeper parts of the Severn through Wyre, such as the stretch from Ribbesford to Stourport, support resident shoals of Common, or Bronze, Bream *Abramis brama*, the smaller Silver Bream *Blicca bjoerkna* and Ruffe *Gymnocephalus cernuus*, in addition to the Roach, Pike and Perch mentioned earlier. Common Carp *Cyprinus carpio* are present in small numbers though rarely seen, these are thought to be fish that have moved out of stillwater fisheries during times of extreme flooding.

In late autumn and winter there are marked changes in fish distribution with particularly the smaller species, such as Roach, Dace and Bleak, heading for overwintering areas. Typically these are in deep, quiet water or in sheltered urban reaches such as Bewdley and Stourport town centres. This is thought to be in response to the need for the fish to conserve energy and reduce the risk of predation. Only Chub and some Barbel remain in the faster flowing reaches in winter, and even some of those will move into relatively sheltered slacks and deeper pools, especially in times of flood.

Most of the species resident in the middle Severn spawn in spring after they have moved out of overwintering areas. Pike and Dace are the first to spawn in March, followed by Perch in late April and the other species from May until early July. The careful observer can sometimes see fish spawning taking place: the easiest to spot are the larger gravel-spawners such as Chub and Barbel in shallow, swift-flowing, water over gravel shoals. Specifically Barbel spawning can be sometimes seen from the A456 Bewdley bypass bridge over the river, typically in late May. Species that lay their eggs on plants (phytophilous species) such as Roach, Perch and Bream are harder to spot, simply because of the sheer availability of potential spawning substrate such as tree roots and marginal vegetation in the Forest.

The tributaries
Dowles and Gladder Brooks support some of the fish species found in the main river but also some that are more or less confined to the tributaries. Brown Trout *Salmo trutta* are present in both brooks in small

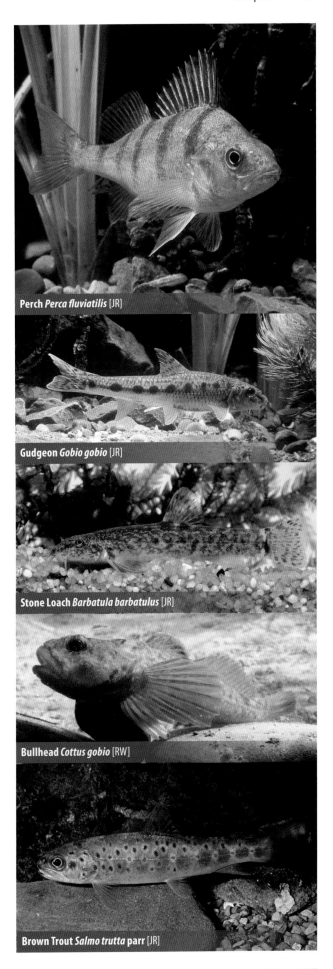

Perch *Perca fluviatilis* [JR]

Gudgeon *Gobio gobio* [JR]

Stone Loach *Barbatula barbatulus* [JR]

Bullhead *Cottus gobio* [RW]

Brown Trout *Salmo trutta* parr [JR]

numbers and can be seen from footbridges. Shortage of good spawning gravel (large sections of Dowles Brook consist of bedrock) and high input of sediment, especially during winter, restrict spawning success, and the various impoundments restrict migration, but the Brown Trout persists in the Forest streams. (This species can adopt a migratory life history and move to the sea to feed and grow before returning as mature adult Sea Trout to spawn in freshwater (Davies *et al.* 2004), but there is no evidence that this happens in the Wyre.)

Brook Lamprey *Lampetra planeri* have been recorded as adults and ammocoetes in Dowles Brook (Westwood 2013) and are probably present in other Forest streams. They can sometimes be observed spawning in the spring in very shallow gravel riffles. Unlike the River and Sea Lampreys, which migrate to the sea and become parasitic, the Brook Lamprey remains in freshwater. It feeds on detritus and small invertebrates in the silt beds where it spends most of its life as an ammocoete, and the adult, pre-spawning, phase is a mere six months (Phillips & Rix 1985).

Bullhead and Stone Loach are found in shallow riffle areas and glides in the main river but also thrive in the tributaries. They can easily be found there by searching likely areas with a dip-net. Stone Loach prefer slightly steadier areas of the stream where there is a little more silt. Bullhead like the faster water where there are cobbles, boulders and woody debris.

The downstream parts of the tributaries, upstream of the confluence with the main river, unsurprisingly support species more usually associated with the main river, such as Chub, Dace, Eel and Salmon parr, which are there in small numbers. In times of flood the lower reaches of these brooks are deep and relatively still, as the flow is held back by the main river. They are a magnet for river species seeking shelter, especially juvenile Roach, Dace, Chub and Bleak, as well as attendant predators such as Pike.

Stillwaters

Most of the stillwaters are artificial, and, since they are usually formed by damming small watercourses, they are generally inaccessible to fish from downstream. This restricts natural colonisation to small numbers of fish that may live upstream of the impoundment. Such fish—Bullhead and Brown Trout—are generally not well suited to ponds; probably only the Three-spined Stickleback, *Gasterosteus aculeatus* would naturally occur in these situations without further human intervention. Hence the fish communities in these lakes are essentially a result of introduction by man, though some species may form self-sustaining populations long after the initial introduction.

A number of such waters in Wyre are operated as commercial recreational angling lakes. In these both the species of fish and their abundance are heavily manipulated and so the conservation/biodiversity value of such waters is limited. These lakes usually contain large numbers of Carp, with Roach, Perch, Bream, some Tench *Tinca tinca*, Rudd *Scardinius erythopthalmus* and Crucian Carp *Carassius carassius* as accompanying species.

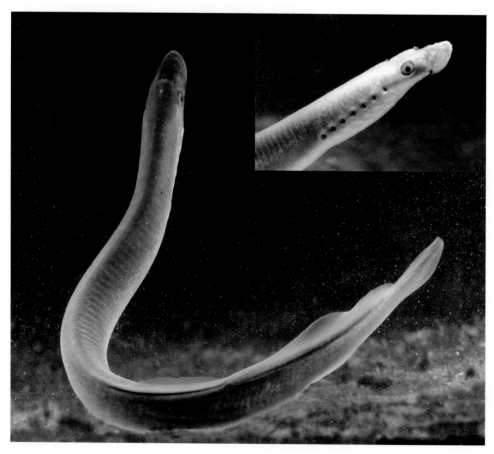

The Brook Lamprey *Lampetra planeri* lives for several years as a blind larval form known as an ammocoete. In its final adult phase shown here, the eyes and sucker mouth become apparent, though it does not feed in this stage.
[Both JB]

'Wild' carp?

Uncllys Reservoir in the south-east of the main Forest is no longer used for organised angling and is reputed to contain some specimens of the original, wild strain, of Carp. This was brought to Britain in the Middle Ages for early fish culture and food for monasteries (Everard 2013). In contrast, the Carp seen in recreational fisheries are derivatives of fast-growing strains bred in continental Europe for the table, and look quite different from the slow-growing, elongated wild strain. The true origin of the Uncllys Carp is not known and it has not yet been possible to verify if they are the historic wild strain and thus of special biodiversity value.

Other species known to be present in Uncllys are Roach, Perch and Gudgeon. A seine-netting survey in April 2011 produced seven Gudgeon, 24 Perch and 564 Roach (Peirson 2011). All were small, and analysis of scale samples revealed that all three species had slow growth rates. They are probably also present in other unmanaged pools in the area, where they can form self-sustaining populations not dependent on further stocking. Other species, such as European Eel and Three-spined Stickleback are likely to be present but were not observed.

Future conservation of Wyre fish

None of the fish species found in Wyre waters are unique to the Forest, or even to this part of the UK. Brook and River Lamprey, Bullhead, Atlantic Salmon and European Eel however are species listed under the Habitats Directive and all those species are listed under Annexe II. This covers animal and plant species of community interest whose conservation requires the designation of Special Areas of Conservation (SACs). River Lamprey, Brook Lamprey and Atlantic Salmon are also listed under Appendix III of the Bern Convention (1982) which controls exploitation of certain species. River Lamprey and Atlantic Salmon are listed under the UK Biodiversity Action Plan (1994). Under all this legislation we are required to develop plans to promote both the conservation of the species themselves and their habitats.

Wyre's water bodies are not considered as particularly important refuges for any of these species at national level. Nevertheless it is in the general interest of conservation of these species, and more common co-existing species, to improve the environment in which they live. This can be done by protecting their habitats from negative impacts and maintaining ecosystem functionality. Specifically this means continuing to work to reduce the incidence and severity of acute pollution, such as agricultural or industrial spillages and run-off, removing man-made barriers to fish migration wherever possible, and better managing diffuse pollution such as road run-off and poor agricultural waste management. Management of the Forest itself has an important part to play, especially for the Forest streams which are vulnerable to large inputs of sediment from logging activity during wet winter conditions.

Wyre Forest Study Group members searching for Brook Lamprey ammocoetes near the mouth of Dowles Brook, north of Bewdley. The young lampreys live in burrows in silt banks for up to five years, filtering diotoms and other microscopic life. [RW]

Chapter **12**

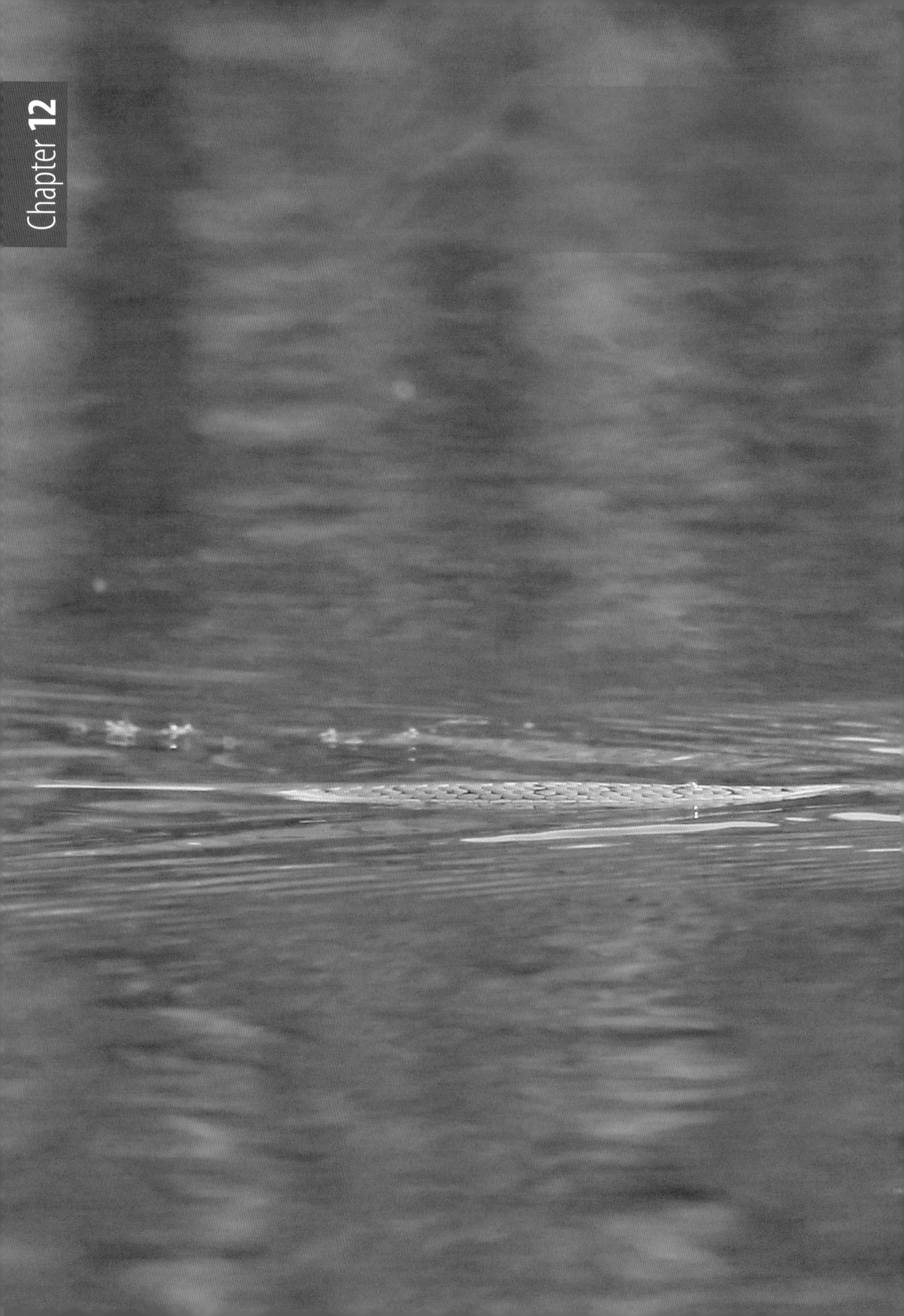

Amphibians and Reptiles

Wyre's five species of amphibians and four species of reptiles are typical of many areas of lowland England, but the Forest shelters important populations of Adders *Vipera berus* and Common Lizards *Zootoca vivipara* which are now becoming increasingly rare and localised in the surrounding countryside. The sparse road network combined with large blocks of woodland may also be beneficial to amphibians such as Common Toads *Bufo bufo* and the three species of newts which breed here. Outside the breeding season many of these reptiles and amphibians are hard to find, but new trapping and monitoring techniques are uncovering more information about them and helping to guide conservation measures.

Amphibians
Common Frog

The amphibians which occur in Wyre usually stay well hidden. But if you pick a mild day in late February or early March, you may hear what sounds like the rumble of a distant motorcycle rally coming from a small woodland pool. This low purring sound reverberating in the stillness of the woods is a chorus of male Common Frogs *Rana temporaria* competing for their mates. Although they have not fed for months, food is the last thing on their minds. After overwintering in the mud at the bottom of ponds, or in damp places under soil or rocks, the males are keen to establish their paternity. They do this by croaking loudly and exposing their white throats to signal their presence to the females. A single male will claim his mate by climbing onto her back and holding himself in position with special pads on his front legs in a clasp reflex. He is said to be in amplexus, and from here he is ready to fertilise the female's eggs as they are laid (Smith 1951). To speed the growth of their eggs, common frogs spawn in the shallow, sunny reaches of a pool; often the same area is used year after year.

Frogspawn clump counts have been made annually at most pools in Wyre since 1988 (Winnall 2003). Numbers vary at individual pools from year to year, but totals across the Forest have been more or less consistent during that time. St George's Pool, Mandarin Pool near Lodge Hill Farm, Drymill Pond, the brick-built pool in Rock Coppice, and wetland at Furnace Mill, all have over 100 clumps of spawn recorded in most years and often many more than that. Frogs also spawn in ditches alongside Forest tracks and sometimes in wet marshy areas, although the spawn and tadpoles here are especially vulnerable to drying out in dry weather. Few urban ponds in Bewdley are without their resident frogs. Although predation of spawn by ducks and newts cause large losses annually, frogs continue to do well in Wyre; they have not yet suffered from the major diseases such as chytridiomycosis which have reduced populations elsewhere in the British Isles.

A study of breeding frogs in a garden pool in Bliss Gate showed that each frog has unique body markings (Winnall 2004) and from these it is possible to check which frogs pair in the breeding season, whether they return in subsequent years, and how far they move when found away from the pond during the summer. Even shed skin retains this distinctive patterning.

Strange records of frogspawn have been made during the winter months when clumps of jelly, looking rather like slime mould, and separate groups of black eggs, have occasionally been found on land. It is presumed that a female frog has been predated, and she has either jettisoned her immature spawn or the predator has left this behind because it is in some way distasteful. Several different predators will take adult frogs, including Grass Snake *Natrix natrix*, Fox *Vulpes vulpes*, Otter *Lutra lutra*, Hedgehog *Erinaceus europaeus*, and Grey Heron *Ardea cinerea*. In Wyre, Neville Wilde photographed adult Tawny Owls *Strix aluco* bringing in frogs as well as fish for their nestlings in a nest close to Dowles Brook (Wilde 2002).

Common Frog *Rana temporaria*

Male frog croaking, showing white throat [RW]

Male frog holding female in amplexus [RW]

Adult male Common Frog showing distinctive body markings [RW]

Common Frogs clustering around spawning area in a garden pond [RW]

Common Toad

In most years Common Toads *Bufo bufo* arrive at their breeding pools in late February or March when the water has reached 7°C (Hand *et al.* 2006) and soon after the frogs have finished spawning. The toads have generally trekked long distances from hibernation sites within the Forest and this mass migration is impressive to watch as dozens of toads advance from all directions, clambering over obstacles, climbing up steep banks and over logs and rocks with steadfast determination. Males often waylay females *en route* to the ponds and hitch a ride, holding them in amplexus to guard them against rivals. There are generally more males than females in the breeding pool and 'mating balls' can sometimes be seen involving several males with amorous intent surrounding a single female. Females may drown on these occasions (Hand *et al.* 2006).

There are several established spawning sites in Wyre where you can hear the soft piping chorus of male toads by day and night. The reservoir above Uncllys Farm is a typical breeding location and although it has a large population of Roach *Rutilus rutilus* and other fish which can eat frog tadpoles, toad tadpoles survive here because the toxins in their skins make them unpalatable to fish. Toads choose deeper pools than frogs, usually where there are underwater plants to which their long spawn strings (up to 2.5 m long) can be anchored (Frazier 1983). Toads also breed in ponds that flood occasionally like the pool near the River Severn alongside Northwood Lane just north of Bewdley, where spawn twisted around vegetation will presumably survive short periods in deeper water.

During spawning the male in amplexus uses his back legs to push off rivals, and squeezes the female's abdomen whilst using his back feet to tease out the spawn. It takes a female up to two days to lay her strands of around 1,500 eggs, a little at a time, during which the pair is effectively attached to the vegetation and cannot swim away. The animals are particularly vulnerable to predation at this time, but the toxic warts of their skins act as a deterrent. Occasionally a female is seen with one male on her back and a second male gripping her tightly from underneath.

By midsummer, the Forest paths near breeding ponds swarm with toadlets though the vast majority are unlikely to survive their first winter. No bigger than a bluebottle, these tiny creatures feed avidly on small invertebrates and will sometimes climb up to a metre in the grooves of tree trunks. They will not return to water until they are mature, males between two and three years old, and females between three and four years old (Hand *et al.* 2006). Adult Common Toads are widespread and can survive in much drier places than frogs. They feed at night along Forest tracks and paths, plodding slowly or sitting and waiting for insects, slugs, beetles, woodlice, and other invertebrates to come past. They hibernate under leaf litter, in dry banks, small mammal burrows and in log piles.

Many gardens around Wyre have toads that spend the summer in the greenhouse or in favourite daytime retreats, overwintering in rockeries, under dense humus or corrugated sheets. Tomes stated in 1901 that: "The toad is easily tamed with gentle treatment, and will follow the hand to take flies from the fingers. Gardeners like to introduce the toad into the cucumber and melon frame, where it consumes a great quantity of insects and sometimes attains a great size." However, no modern records of this particular type of pest control have been received.

Common Toad *Bufo bufo*

Adult Common Toad [RW]

Common Toads in amplexus with strands of spawn [RW]

Male Palmate Newt *Lissotriton helveticus* [JR]

Overwintering Palmate Newts [RW]

Newts

Wyre is home to all three native newt species, Palmate Newt *Lissotriton helveticus*, Smooth Newt *L. vulgaris* and Great Crested Newt *Triturus cristatus*. They are not always easy to find, but a walk around a Forest pond after dark on a warm evening in late spring is the best time to search for them. Torchlight reveals their slender shapes floating below the surface or shimmying to each other in ritualistic display. Although they breed in water, for the rest of the year they roam the Forest and overwinter in hibernacula on land. When feeding they come out at night to search for their prey of worms, insects, springtails and aquatic crustaceans. During winter it is possible to find two or three overwintering newts lying together under the same log or stone. Their skin at this time of the year has a velvety texture.

To the inexperienced eye a newt on land may look very like a Common Lizard, a reptile which is well-distributed in Wyre. Lizards have bead-like scales on their skin and sharp claws, both of which newts do not possess, and a tail that is round in cross-section (Inns 2009). The tails of newts look narrow from above and are smooth and flattened.

In Wyre the most common species is the Palmate Newt, our smallest British newt. This species was recorded in 1894 by Jannion Steele-Elliott as follows: "Palmated Newt in Worcestershire and Shropshire. During the height of the present breeding season (middle of March), I have found this species abundant in the many small pools and water-holes of the Wyre Forest. They are common on both sides of the Dowles Brook, which runs through the Forest, forming the boundary line between Worcestershire and Shropshire. Newts in general are known as "asgulls" in this locality. To the best of my knowledge this species has not been recorded before for either of these two counties." (Steele-Elliott 1894a.)

Palmate Newts prefer to breed in neutral or slightly acidic pools and are more frequent in the west of Britain. They are remarkably adaptable in Wyre and occur in larger water bodies such as the lower reservoir at Trimpley as well as smaller pools. Palmate Newts also breed in very shallow spring-fed ditches at the edge of some forest tracks, sometimes no more than a few centimetres deep. Young newts looking like tiny fish,

dart across puddles in deeper vehicle tracks in summer. Ideally the female newts prefer waters with submerged vegetation on which their eggs can be laid. Here, if the water is neutral, they often occur with Smooth Newts that avoid the more acidic ponds (Hand *et al.* 2006). In the breeding season male Palmate Newts have webbed back feet, a dark line through their eyes and a small projecting filament at the end of their tails. Both sexes have a vertical white mark above their back legs. Males of the slightly larger Smooth Newt develop a wavy crest along the length of their backs in the breeding season. Like the females their underbellies are pale with dark spots. He also has a central orange stripe, whereas the female has an orange line along the bottom edge of her tail and tubercles on her back feet. It is often difficult to separate female Palmate and Smooth Newts unless you examine the skin under their chins. Smooth Newts have spotty throats: Palmate Newts have pale unspotted throats. (Hand *et al.* 2006).

Although Smooth and Palmate Newts occur together frequently in the British Isles, hybrids are extremely rare. However John Robinson found and

Male Smooth Newt *Lissotriton vulgaris* [JR]

Male Smooth × Palmate Newt hybrid [JR]

photographed a male hybrid Smooth × Palmate Newt in one of his garden ponds at Lodge Hill in March 2011 (Robinson 2011).

Courtship is an elaborate affair in both species as the males quiver their tails and arch their bodies prior to the transfer of sperm and egg laying. The female lays several hundred eggs, using her hind legs to fold each one inside a leaf. Despite this care many are eaten, especially by water beetles, and only about 20% of eggs are thought to survive to hatching (Hand *et al.* 2006).

The third Wyre species is the Great Crested Newt which sometimes occurs in the same ponds as other newt species. In Wyre they are distinctly local and prefer weedier, fish-free, nutrient-rich pools. Observing them for the first time is quite an experience as these colourful dragons loom up from the deep, twice the size of the other newt species (up to 17 cm) and resplendent in their breeding finery. Spring males sport impressive crests along their backs and tails, and have

a conspicuous silvery white flash along their tail-sides. The females, like the males, are warty and blackish. They have no crest, but show a yellow-orange flash that is present all year along the base of the tail. Each female lays about 250 eggs per season (Langton *et al.* 2001), carefully folding each in turn in an underwater leaf, using her back feet. Their tadpoles can be separated from those of the smaller newts by black blotches on their bodies, tails and crests, and by the presence of tail filaments.

Great Crested Newts have been found in several pools within Wyre, and occasionally on land under reptile refugia, plastic sheeting and logs. Ponds along the southern edge of the Forest in Callow Hill, Bliss Gate and Heightington have provided records, and these newts seem to readily colonise new pools. At one of these pools a Heron was observed taking four Great Crested Newts on 29 May 2007. Without predation they can be long-lived, surviving seven or eight years on average, and can travel considerable distances over land where they feed on slugs, snails, insects and earthworms (Hand *et al.* 2006).

The current newt studies that are being undertaken in Wyre (see box opposite) will eventually tell us much more about these intriguing creatures (Lambourne 2011).

Habitat management for amphibians

To flourish amphibians need good aquatic and terrestrial habitats. Breeding ponds should be at least partly sunlit and contain submerged plants for egg laying. They should also have both shallow and deeper water, and a variety of suitable poolside vegetation for feeding within, and for refuge. Good water quality

is crucial if the pond is to support high biodiversity (Baker *et al.* 2011). Maintenance is vital to prevent ponds from silting up, becoming scrubbed over and drying out, a fate which befell the Experimental Pool at the southern end of Longdon.

All amphibians spend most of their lives on land, although they are rarely seen as they only appear at night or after heavy rain (Tomes 1901a). They can travel some distance in search of food, so it is important to manage the Forest between the pools with amphibians in mind. Young amphibians may not return to the water for two to three years, and adults will shuttle between water and land on a seasonal basis (Baker *et al.* 2011). They require damp resting places and habitats that support the creatures on which they feed. Hibernation sites include tree stumps, stone walls, log piles, rockeries, and mammal burrows, and these should not be disturbed during the winter months.

All the larger pools within the forested area have been created within the last 200 years, and these must have substantially benefitted amphibians by providing extra breeding sites. Many of the pools on smallholdings on the south edge of the Forest are much older and some of these have good amphibian populations. The importance of well-managed garden ponds with adjacent areas of rough grass and log piles cannot be underestimated, but moving amphibians or spawn between ponds is no longer recommended as this can spread disease.

Greater Wyre remains an important area for all five species of amphibians, and with sensitive countryside management it is hoped that the Wyre Forest will remain a special refuge for a long time to come.

The male Great Crested Newt *Triturus cristatus* is impressive in breeding splendour with distinctive crests, a silver stripe along the tail and unique orange and black markings beneath. [JR]

Newt surveys

Since 2011 newt surveys have been carried out in the larger ponds in Wyre by Phil Rudlin and Val Lambourne during May and June each year. Thirteen ponds have been surveyed using between one and four Dewsbury Boxes per pond according to its size and leaving the box traps *in situ* for 24 hours. A Dewsbury Box is a converted sandwich-box with a hole cut in the side to which a plastic gauze funnel is attached allowing newts to enter but not to leave (see diagram below). A plastic bag is attached to the box with elastic string, and a float with an air hole is secured in the far end of the bag. The trap is placed on the pond bottom and the float takes the bag up to the surface. If there is overnight rain and the pond level rises, the float takes the bag higher in the water, so that the air hole remains above the water. This allows the newts to continue to reach the water surface to breathe, even though the water in the pond has risen.

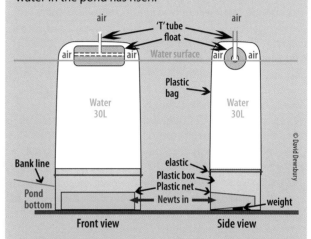

The average catch per year using this method is eight Great Crested Newts, 15 Smooth Newts and 225 Palmate Newts. No newts have yet been recorded in Uncllys Reservoir, Park Pool and Hitterhill Pool, all of which contain fish. Two pools have been found to contain all three species at the same time, namely the pond in Longdon below the deer hide, and Mandarin Pool south of Lodge Hill Farm. This survey continues and from 2014 a photographic record is being made of the unique patterning on the underside of each Great Crested Newt, so that individuals can be recognised, and their movements recorded in the future (see photographs below [all PR]).

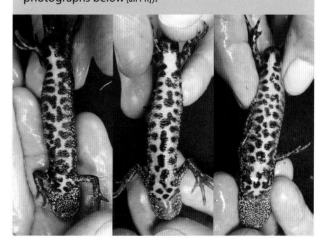

Reptiles

A glimpse of a scaly tail disappearing into a bramble clump, or the skittering of lizards' claws across a sunlit log, are typical fleeting signs of reptiles in Wyre. There are four species in the Forest: Adder *Vipera berus*, Grass Snake *Natrix natrix*, Common Lizard *Zootoca vivipara* and Slow-worm *Anguis fragilis*. All are local and usually very unobtrusive.

Adder

Adders are the subject of a detailed survey by Sylvia Sheldon and Chris Bradley whose observations have shed new light on the behaviour of this fascinating snake. This long-running study of Adders in the Wyre Forest allows identification of individual snakes and, sadly, charts the decline of this once common reptile over several decades. As our only venomous snake, Adders have been persecuted by Forest workers and local people, who often referred to them as "ethers" (E. George, pers. comm.) and the common assumption was that there were 'thousands' in the Forest. Sadly that is not the case today and, although killing Adders deliberately is forbidden by law, past and current pressures have reduced their numbers dramatically. Annual surveys undertaken from 1988 to 2014 (Sheldon *et al.* 2000–2014) indicate there may be now fewer than 100 mature individuals in Wyre.

Some persecution once took place in the name of science. Between 1854 and 1889 the Rev. Josiah T. Lea was vicar of Far Forest. During his residence at Far Forest Vicarage he published a booklet entitled *Personal Observations of the Natural History of the Wyre Forest* (Lea 1889) which included a discourse on Adders and his endeavours to determine whether "the dark grey and copper-coloured Adder were male and female or a distinct species". In order to solve this problem he dissected about 50 specimens in 1888 alone, and mentions examining a further 500 dead Adders to ascertain their average length, which was 56 cm: the longest was 77.5 cm. Despite this persecution Norman Hickin, in *The Natural History of an English Forest*, (Hickin 1971), mentions the Adder as "being abundant".

Simon Fletcher, in his book, *Wyre Forest Diary* (Fletcher 1981) states that "country people have traditionally killed Adders and I know of one man,

who lives near the Hop Pole (Inn), whose personal record was twenty four before breakfast". The legacy of this persecution and, more recently, disturbance and habitat destruction, is that Adder numbers and their sites have greatly reduced, and continue to fall even with legal protection and greater public awareness.

In 1977 Sylvia Sheldon started photographing Adders at several sites in spring. Although these snakes are extremely timid creatures, always retreating into cover when disturbed, they are faithful to basking sites and hibernacula and return annually to these spots.

Sylvia Sheldon and Chris Bradley found 208 mature Adders in 42 sites in 1988 with the help of information from Forestry Commission Wildlife Ranger Edwin George, forest workers and local people. Table 9 shows sites surveyed between 1990 and 2014, sites with Adders present, and the total numbers of mature males

Table 9 Adder numbers recorded during Adder surveys in Wyre				
Year	Sites surveyed	Sites with Adders	Mature males	Mature females	Total
1990	56	50	185	55	240
1991	76	61	211	56	267
1992	78	55	159	33	192
1993	80	59	186	70	256
1994	76	50	153	29	182
1995	76	44	103	14	117
1996	80	41	112	32	144
1997	84	44	102	31	133
1998	85	42	103	34	137
1999	67	35	100	20	120
2000	87	24	69	13	82
2001	Data incomplete due to Foot and Mouth Disease				
2002	20	13	36	17	53
2003	20	9	26	10	36
2004	47	20	40	19	59
2005	54	25	40/65*	16/38*	56/103*
2006	38	21	74	26	100
2007	28	19	67	24	91
2008	51	24	120	35	155
2009	55	22	96	30	126
2010	55	24	83	23	106
2011	44	20	59	27	86
2012	27	14	56	19	75
2013	26	12	35	22	57
2014	26	15	43	16	59
*The total with the three new sites added					

Adder head markings

By 1981 Sylvia Sheldon was aware that the markings on the back of each snake's head (pictured right [SS]) varied and were different on each snake. The apex of the zigzag, the inverted V, the eye lines and even the zigzag itself allowed individuals to be identified. They could also be identified from their sloughed skins. By keeping drawings of head patterns alongside photographs of each snake, together with location notes and dates, she could recognise individuals. This allowed her to identify favourite basking sites, their movements, and the interactions and hierarchy among males at mating time. In 1984 Chris Bradley also became proficient in recognising individuals and during the following five years both he and Sylvia Sheldon showed that no two Adders had identical head patterns. In December 1989 their paper *Identification of individual Adders (Vipera berus) by their head markings* was published (Sheldon & Bradley 1989). Sylvia Sheldon's grandson, Alonza Garbett, also contributed a great deal to the surveys and the preparation of the annual reports (Garbett 2011).

Adder *Vipera berus* is well camouflaged whilst basking amongst bracken litter in spring sunshine [SS]

Several female Adders intertwined on a favourite sunny bank [SS]**. The tiny baby Adder (below** [SS]**) basking in the open is vulnerable to predation.**

and females recorded. The highest count of 267 mature individuals was in 1991, though mature, non-breeding females are rarely seen in the spring census, giving a potential further 60 females in that year. The table shows the continuing decline of Adders in the Wyre Forest.

During the spring surveys there seemed to be a shortage of female Adders. Sylvia Sheldon monitored ten females over an 11-year period (1984–1994) and found that most of them bred only three times, sometimes with two, or even three years, between breeding. Females were sedentary when pregnant and easy to locate in their chosen summer areas. Often they joined other pregnant females to bask whilst their embryos developed to full term, usually not until September, and they did not feed until birth had taken place. In 1988 however, during a spring survey, dissection of a freshly killed female revealed three unborn baby Adders. In March 1999 a female seen regularly during the previous spring and summer emerged from hibernation looking very fat. By late April she was exceptionally thin with a newborn baby nearby. These observations indicate that both females had carried young through winter hibernation and therefore not fed for 18 months.

Several births seen over the past 30 years were all in September. Three females each produced seven babies; another had six babies and two others only three. Each youngster began to slough its skin within 15 minutes of birth and began exploring the following day. Only

three young Adders out of six were observed for over three days. None were seen afterwards and presumably entered hibernation. Very few youngsters are seen the following spring, probably because many do not survive hibernation, though at only 15 cm long, they are easy to overlook.

Adult Adders return to their hibernation areas during late August and September and exceptionally will bask in November, or even early December, in warm sunny weather. Most retire in September and October and are very faithful to their chosen hibernacula, returning annually. They need to hibernate at least 30 cm below ground (Appleby 1971) where an even temperature is maintained free from frost. They use existing holes, often small mammal burrows.

In Wyre male Adders start emerging from hibernation during February and are first observed in the middle of the day basking at the base of old, south-facing, tree stumps. They bask for only an hour or two in the winter sun when ground temperatures reach approximately 10°C or above. As temperatures rise Adders bask regularly, allowing their new skin to develop until the old one is ready to slough. The first females to emerge are those in breeding condition, usually in mid-March, following a spell of warm weather. Later in March and April non-breeding females and juveniles emerge to bask for a few days before dispersing to feed. Females in breeding condition stay in the hibernation areas and wait for males who locate them by scent.

Male Adders combat close to a female Adder in breeding condition. They rise up as each tries to dominate the other in this display of strength. This 'dance' can last for up to 20 minutes after which the winner earns the right to mate. [Both SS]

On a warm spring day the males slough their skins by wriggling through stems of vegetation, revealing their vivid refreshed markings. They are then ready for the spring combat dance which is a wonderful sight, especially as they are now at their brightest. Now the males are alert and excitable, and move around in pursuit of breeding females who give off pheromones to advertise their condition. When males meet, they raise the forepart of their bodies off the ground and press against each other, heads and necks arching to slap their rival down. This combat dance is a contest of strength, with no attempt to bite or injure the opponent, and can last a few seconds or up to 20 minutes until one male escapes with an amazing turn of speed. All males near a female will wrestle with each other to establish their position in the pecking order. When the dominant male locates a receptive female he moves over her in jerking sensuous movements, his tongue flicking over her body, trying to encourage her to uncoil and mate. When he has left, the next male in the pecking order will court and mate with the female, and Sylvia Sheldon has observed five males copulating

Abnormal behaviour

During a 30-year study only one Adder was seen to exhibit what one might term hermaphrodite behaviour. A female, first identified in April 1984 when she was approximately nine years old, was named 'Dotty', due to three darkly pigmented scales on the top of her head. She was seen regularly throughout April and May 1985, but although in fine condition, no males showed any interest in her. On 22 May 1986 Dotty was seen scenting feverishly and moving over a plump female, 'Goldie', in the manner of a courting male. This activity was brief and quickly abated. In 1987 she was seen on many occasions, again in prime condition. In early May it was noted that a male did approach her, but showed little interest and moved on. On 4 May 1988 she was seen in copulation with a male. Dotty was observed through the summer months basking in the manner of a pregnant female, although her body did not swell with young as is typical in these cases. She was seen on 25 October, with no change in her appearance. She looked plump and healthy through 1989, 1990 and 1991 during which she was largely ignored by males. In 1992, she emerged from hibernation on 3 March and thereafter travelled rather erratically from one site to another, until she sloughed her skin on 6 May, unusually early for a female. Following this her behaviour changed completely and when next seen on 11 May, she was courting another female, as if she was a dominant male. On several occasions she was seen, to rise in combat with intruding males. This situation continued for four days after which both females disappeared. The saga finally ended later that same year, when Dotty was killed whilst crossing the old railway line on 10 October, presumably by a motor vehicle. She was 65 cm long. What caused Dotty to exhibit such strange behaviour is open to question, possibly a hormonal imbalance, but this is mere speculation.

with the same female in a single day. However some research indicates that after a successful mating the female can develop a vaginal plug to prevent further sperm entering, giving single paternity to her brood (Andrén & Nilson 1987). The mating period can extend for 3–4 weeks, but the majority of mating activity occurs over 7–10 days, weather permitting, and usually tails off during the first week of May.

Wyre Adders can live to a great age. One female, still breeding in 2009, was first identified in August 1984 when she was pregnant and basking with four other gravid females. If she was then in her first breeding year, and therefore at least six years old, she was born in 1978, and consequently 31 years old in 2009. Prior to this another female and a male were both estimated to be 28 years old when last seen. There are currently several Adders seen annually on the main study site, male and female, in their 'teens'. The biggest female recorded during 30 years of study was Olive, so named because of her prominent olive-grey appearance. Her sloughed skin measured 91 cm, and her body length was estimated at 79 cm. She may have been over 30 years of age when last seen in 1989.

The future for Adders

In Wyre Adders are associated with heathland: Heather *Calluna vulgaris*, gorse, bramble, bracken, scrub and rough grassland, although open heathland is no longer favoured because of public disturbance. Young conifer plantations can support viable populations, having a plentiful food supply of voles, mice and lizards. Unfortunately young conifer plantations soon become dense thickets shading out basking spots and forcing the snakes into failed conifer glades and ride edges. Following harvesting with heavy machinery on known Adder sites, it was noted that no Adders emerged from hibernation there in the following spring. Liaison with Forest managers and contractors is needed before harvesting such sites to manage them sensitively.

Radio-telemetry tracking

Due to increasing concern over the declining Adder population a radio telemetry project with herpetologist Nigel Hand was initiated in 2010 to discover more about the habits of these enigmatic creatures (Hand 2010). This original research was carried out here in Wyre with funding from the Grow with Wyre Project used to purchase the necessary equipment: 11 tiny transmitters, an aerial receiver and a Global Positioning Service handset. The principal aim was to ascertain how far a male Adder might travel in the course of mate-searching and feeding, and also the habitat used. The transmitter was attached to the upper body of snakes using special surgical tape, well clear of the cloaca and leaving the underside free to allow full movement. The transmitters had a battery life of approximately eight weeks, and it was hoped they would remain in place until the old skin was sloughed.

Two sites were chosen, one predominantly heathland planted with Corsican Pine *Pinus sylvestris* ssp. *laricio*, and the other, south of Dowles Brook, a much more open habitat dominated by bracken beds, heather clumps and scrubby Silver Birch *Betula pendula*. By late April transmitters had been attached to four males, five females (three in breeding condition) and two juvenile females.

Adders have eyes with an elliptical pupil, unlike the circular pupil of the Grass Snake (see page 226) [RW]

Nigel Hand (seated) is with Sylvia Sheldon, Chris Bradley (behind) and Alonza Garbett during the telemetry project in the Wyre Forest. [RW]

As expected the initial results confirmed that females were rather more sedentary than males, at least during the spring. Of males one travelled at least a kilometre through habitat that was primarily high oak forest to find a female in breeding condition. He returned two weeks later to his original position around his main hibernacula. The other ten individuals appeared to wander rather haphazardly although within a clearly defined home range. The juveniles did not move far from point of capture during the life of the transmitters. Similarly non-breeding females, having emerged from winter hibernation in April, did not immediately move off to feed, perhaps awaiting more settled and somewhat warmer weather to aid their digestion. This indicates that on occasion, feeding might be delayed until June or even July.

It was also discovered that some males remain within their main core area, but spend much of the time below ground, especially in hot weather, occupying vole and mouse runs, where they ambush the unwary rodents.

Radiotelemetry was undertaken again in 2011 and 2012. In 2012 more emphasis was placed on tracking pregnant females. Unfortunately bad weather caused major problems with wet vegetation and ground humus severely undermining the bond of the adhesive tape holding the tiny transmitters in place, and during the course of the active season several Adders lost their 'tags'.

There were success stories. One breeding female, who was re-tagged in July after sloughing her skin, retained her tag thereafter and was seen on every visit to the main site. She was fully expected to give birth sometime during early September but the days and weeks passed by with little sign that this event might be imminent. On 27 September three of the four tagged females were located and all found to be gravid. Later, the remaining female known

as 'Rosie', was also tracked down having moved some 70 m from her previous position, a favourite basking spot. On this occasion she was seen to be very thin, a positive diagnosis of a recent birth. Upon searching the immediate vicinity, six tiny Adders were soon discovered and their unique head markings photographed for later identification. A heavy shower then interrupted proceedings. Observers returned to the very same spot about one hour later, to find that the young snakes had barely moved and were still basking close to a main ride. However, there was no sign of the female in this area, but a strong signal via the radio receiver revealed that Rosie had already left her babies, and moved back to her previous basking spot, about 70 m away. The youngsters would have to fend for themselves, natural behaviour for most reptile species, and hopefully find a safe place to hibernate before the first winter frosts. The other three tagged females were monitored daily, or whenever the fickle weather permitted, and were still swollen with young when last observed on 21 October. This perhaps indicating that they would enter hibernation carrying their young and hopefully give birth the following spring.

Telemetry has provided valuable information about Adder behaviour but there is still much to learn before it is too late. Wyre now has only four areas with viable Adder populations and their survival here hangs in the balance. Many factors affect their future survival. Housing and industrial development on the Forest margins, forest operations, and track and pipeline maintenance continue to give concern. Predation, especially of young Adders by Buzzards *Buteo buteo* and Pheasants *Phasianus colchicus*, continues to be a threat in the Forest, as does disturbance through increasing public access. We do not know what effect climate change will have. The remaining Adder sites must be protected and future management undertaken with extreme care and sensitivity.

Grass Snake

Grass Snakes are elusive and not nearly as predictable in their habits as Adders. Once disturbed they are not inclined to return to the same basking spot. They are rarely found on a daily basis in Wyre except for short spells when they are digesting a recent meal or approaching skin slough: otherwise they are mostly nomadic. Grass Snakes recorded during the annual Wyre reptile census are found mostly in March and April, often in Adder sites, and occasionally found basking with Adders and Slow-worms when there is apparently no antagonism between the species. These snakes are known to frequent damp sites and swim readily. An adult has been observed swimming across the River Severn from east to west south of Arley (Winnall pers. comm.).

A hibernaculum has been noted amongst gorse on a bank above Gladder Brook at Bliss Gate. Up to six Grass Snakes were seen basking in the early spring and again in the autumn close to the scrub (Winnall pers. comm.). Grass Snakes mate much earlier in the year than Adders and this activity was observed at Bliss Gate on 19 April 2005. They do not participate in lengthy courtship rituals or combat and rivalry between males for possession of a female has never been observed in Wyre. Males search for females as soon as there is a spell of warm weather in late March or early April.

The development of eggs within a female's body is controlled by the ambient temperature. A few weeks after mating the female will search for a suitable place to lay her eggs, often returning to the same site annually. She chooses a pile of decaying vegetation, or perhaps a compost heap in a neighbouring garden, to provide the right temperature and humidity necessary to incubate the leathery eggs. The number of eggs laid by one female varies between 15 and 20. After laying the female takes no further interest in her clutch which, if undisturbed, will hatch several weeks later. The average length of a newly hatched Grass Snake is 17.2 cm. Compost heaps in gardens or rotting hayricks are important for Grass Snakes, and should be left undisturbed in late summer if possible.

There have been several reports of enormous Grass Snakes in Wyre. The late Edwin George, Forestry Commission Wildlife Ranger in Wyre for many years, once told of an encounter he had with a huge Grass Snake in Fastings Coppice in about 1970. It was curled up in the middle of a bulldozed track, and he could see it was of exceptional girth but was astonished at its length as it moved across the track into the cover of vegetation. He thought it to be over 153 cm long. Edwin had seen many Grass Snakes in his lifetime but never one as big as this (E. George pers. comm.).

The late Neville Wilde, a Wyre naturalist, also recalled seeing a very large Grass Snake at Longdon Wood on 22 June 1975. He was entering the Forest via a track from Button Oak when the Grass Snake in question came out of a meadow on his left and crossed the track ahead before disappearing into woodland vegetation. He estimated it to be about 168 cm long, thick in girth and the biggest he had ever seen in Wyre (N. Wilde pers. comm.). To reach such a length these snakes must have been over 30 years of age. No modern Grass Snakes compare with these giants, though Sylvia Sheldon recorded specimens of around 122 cm long in the 1980s and 1990s.

The Grass Snake's *Natrix natrix* forked tongue is used to pick up chemical particles in the air and on the ground, providing it with extra information about its environment. [AG]

Slow-worm *Anguis fragilis* [PCI]

Mating Slow-worms, the male holding the head of the female [SS]

Female Common Lizard *Zootoca vivipara* [RW]

Male Common Lizard [RW]

Slow-worm

Slow-worms, despite their snake-like appearance, are legless lizards. Fully grown adults are normally 30–41 cm long, but longer specimens have occasionally been found. They give birth to live young, 7–10 cm in length, usually during July, August and September. A female found under a refugium in Rock Coppice had just given birth to live young on 9 September 1997 (R. Winnall pers. comm.) Slow-worms can be extremely long-lived, one individual surviving in captivity for 54 years (Arnold, Ovenden & Corbet 1979). They are secretive reptiles, preferring to stay under cover rather than to bask in the open, a habit which can further be encouraged by putting out refugia. They readily take shelter beneath corrugated metal sheets, rubber-backed carpet underlay, or roofing felt, but can also be found in covered compost heaps.

At Knowles Mill, on 10 May 1993, a large grey male Slow-worm had the head of a yearling Slow-worm firmly clamped in his jaws. Whilst it is known that males will subdue females in this manner prior to mating, this juvenile was far too young to mate, and hence it was decided to release it. The tiny head was pitted by pressure marks from the jaws of the big male. On 14 and 15 May the juvenile was rescued again, and on the 18 May it was found dead. The big male was nearby, although no attempt had been made to eat the dead juvenile.

At Bliss Gate a basking gravid Slow-worm was taken by a Magpie that flew with it to some open ground where it proceeded to peck it to death and eat most of it (R. Winnall pers. comm.).

Common Lizard

Many heathy areas have good populations of Common Lizards. Young conifer plantations, in particular Larch *Larix* spp. and Corsican Pine, can provide excellent habitat with lots of sunny glades for basking, and heather, bramble and bracken cover for the lizards to retreat into at the first hint of danger. Mature specimens reach 13–15 cm in length, although nearly two-thirds of this is tail which they can shed in a predator's mouth and regrow again within a few months.

Courtship and mating commences a few weeks after emergence from winter hibernation, and reaches a peak in April or early May. Females give birth to an average of seven young, usually in July or August, although in cold summers this event can be delayed until early September. At birth the tiny blackish young lizards are approximately 4 cm in length and they spend much time basking on fallen logs in sunny spots and chasing small invertebrates. Life expectancy is four or five years.

Glade creation, conifer felling and ride-widening have all provided more open habitat in Wyre where Common Lizards are now either more numerous or more noticeable than they were in the shadier woods of the 1970s and 1980s.

The reptiles of Wyre Forest are worth protecting, not least because they are scarce or absent in much of the surrounding intensively farmed countryside. Their conservation will require more public education, along with positive measures to create and protect their forest and heathland habitats.

Chapter **13**

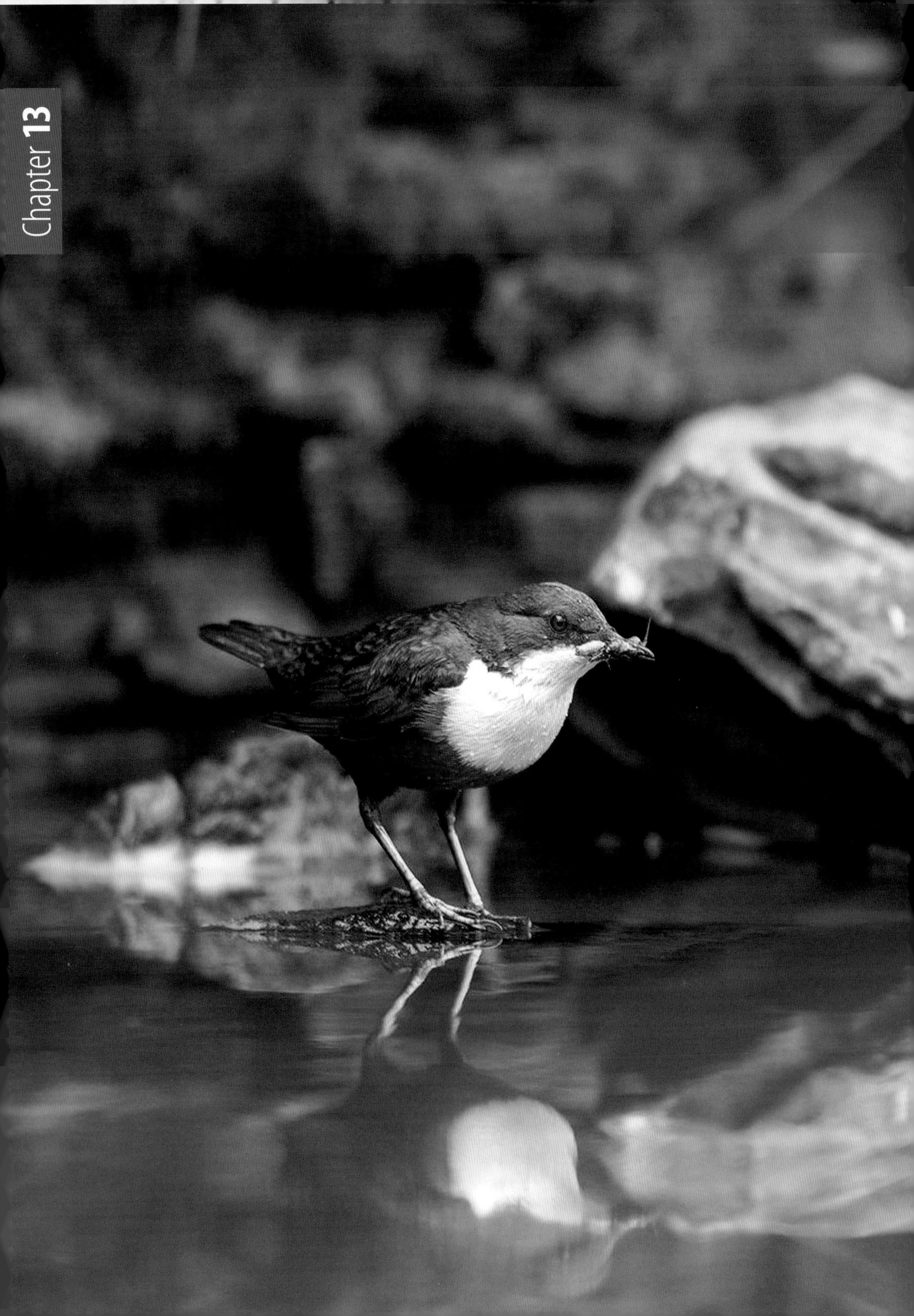

Birds

Wyre Forest lies within 25 miles of the centre of Birmingham and yet its rich and varied landscape contains birds of woods, heaths, rivers, mountain streams, orchard, field and hedgerow. There are Wood Warblers *Phylloscopus sibilatrix*, Pied Flycatchers *Ficedula hypoleuca*, Dippers *Cinclus cinclus* and Grey Wagtails *Motacilla cinerea*—a flavour of the wooded mountain stream valleys of Wales—and all the tits, warblers and woodpeckers found in the best ancient woodlands. Common Crossbills *Loxia curvirostra* and Siskins *Spinus spinus* feed and breed in the conifer plantations, Tree Pipits *Anthus trivialis* add a heathland element and scrub-loving Yellowhammers *Emberiza citrinella* are more typical of open spaces. Exotic Mandarin Ducks *Aix galericulata* nest in tree holes, saw-toothed Goosanders *Mergus merganser* swirl on the River Severn currents, and on spring and summer evenings roding Woodcock *Scolopax rusticola* lumber over the darkening forest. Ravens *Corvus corax* gronk above the canopy where, for lucky observers, the spring skyline may be enlivened by displaying Goshawks *Accipiter gentilis*. This account of the birds of Wyre is greatly enhanced by records and observations collected over 40 years by John Robinson while he lived and worked in the Forest. His notes have been invaluable.

Past glories

Wyre is still rich in birdlife, but once there were even more species, many of them unimaginable now. Around 1900 Jannion Steele-Elliott, who lived at Dowles Manor, found a few Cirl Buntings *Emberiza cirlus* nesting at the Forest edges (Steele-Elliott 1904). Breeding Wrynecks *Jynx torquilla* (Steele Elliott 1908) and Red-backed Shrikes *Lanius collurio* were abundant (Steele-Elliott 1905), but all three species are now nationally rare. In the 1800s Blackcock lekked in Wyre Forest and in 1911 Steele-Elliott noted that *Berrows Worcester Journal* 14 August 1817 carried an advertisement for the sale of 1,100 acres of Bewdley forest "abounding with Grouse and Pheasants". From this he deduced that Black Grouse were once common. In 1888 he reckoned he saw about a score and his last records were a hen on 10 June 1883 and a cock on 11 March 1894. Interestingly an account of a visit to Wyre by the Herefordshire Woolhope Club on 25 August 1904 reported seeing Red Grouse which seems improbable although Hastings (1834) writes "The Red Grouse *Lagopus scoticus* and the Black Grouse *Tetrao tetrix*, inhabit the Wyre Forest, near Bewdley and the latter is found on the Clee Hills, and in the woods upon the banks of the Teme at Eastham".

Pied Flycatcher *Ficedula hypoleuca* [ML]

Edgar Chance (centre) entering a cuckoo-watching hide made from heather branches on Pound Green Common. The background clearly shows the open nature of the Common suitable for nesting Meadow Pipits *Anthus pratensis*, the Cuckoo's main host at that time.
[Photographer unknown, from HG]

Nowadays Black Grouse are mainly restricted to small areas of northern England, north Wales and the Scottish highlands and none remain in Wyre. They are birds of thinly wooded uplands with a mix of scrub and tall grasses and usually plenty of tall Heather *Calluna vulgaris*. The males gather and display, or lek, in an endeavour to attract a mate. Imagine a group of male Blackcock gathering on a grassy patch amongst heather on a misty spring morning in Wyre Forest, strutting their stuff and uttering strange purring calls. Their historical presence in Wyre suggests a very different landscape to that of today, when parts of the Forest would have been much more open with heathery shrubland alongside dense woodland.

Such habitats would also have attracted Stonechats *Saxicola rubicola*, Whinchats *S. rubetra* and possibly Wheatears *Oenanthe oenanthe* as breeding birds. However Blackcock require large areas of undisturbed open forest and, as popular game birds, were soon driven from Wyre and many other places by increasing human activity.

The openness of parts of the Forest in the past is also apparent from Edgar Chance's famous studies of Cuckoos *Cuculus canorus* at Pound Green Common on the northern edge of Wyre. (Chance 1922 and 1940; Wilde 2001). The photographs in Chance's books show an open heathery place and his observation hides were wickerwork camouflaged with heather

Edgar Percival Chance (1881–1955)

Edgar Chance was a British businessman (Director of the family glass-making business in Smethwick), ornithologist and a passionate egg-collector. His collection of 25,000 wild birds' eggs is now in the Natural History Museum at Tring. He is renowned for his detailed studies of Cuckoos at Pound Green Common in Wyre Forest between 1918 and 1925 which showed for the first time exactly how a female cuckoo laid her eggs in a host's nest. The cuckoo watches host nests (they were usually Meadow Pipits at Pound Green) and during the period when a host is laying a clutch she flies to the nest, removes an egg holding it in her bill, turns round and lays her egg, all at great speed, then flies to a perch and swallows the host's egg. By removing clutches and inducing the hosts to re-lay Chance found that one cuckoo could lay an egg every two days and he collected a sequence of 25 eggs in one season from his famous Cuckoo A. Modern studies show this can occur naturally as a female cuckoo deliberately destroys host clutches at the 'wrong' stage to induce re-laying.

Chance arranged for the laying sequence to be photographed and filmed, first by E. Hawkins and then, in 1922, by pioneer wildlife photographer Oliver Pike. A website dedicated to Oliver Pike **www.olivergpike.info/cuckoo.html** includes a slide show of his cuckoo pictures and gives web links to the film.

Illegal egg collecting led to Edgar Chance being prosecuted and fined and he became unpopular with later ornithologists. Despite his pioneer study of Cuckoos he was expelled from the British Ornithologists' Union (the premier British society concerning birds) and his obituary in *British Birds* journal is brief and attributed simply to "G.C." (*British Birds* 1956 volume 49 page 215). His studies have been beautifully summarised by Nick Davies in *Cuckoo: Cheating by Nature* (2015) and his 1922 and 1940 books are readily available on the second-hand market.

Cuckoo *Cuculus canorus* [JR]

branches. He was the first to describe in detail, and with photographs, how cuckoos select their hosts and lay their eggs, and how many eggs a single female can lay. The Cuckoos' host in his studies was most often the Meadow Pipit *Anthus pratensis*, very much a bird of open country, heather moors and open hillside grasslands. He describes Pound Green Common as "comparatively open ... about a mile round its irregular shape. For the most part bordered by forest ... and orchards ... with occasional trees placed, as if on purpose, as observation posts for cuckoos. Best of all, it was an isolated breeding ground for Meadow Pipits, there being no other birds of this species within two to three miles".

In his descriptions of individual Cuckoos' activities he mentions dense Heather, Bracken *Pteridium aquilinum* and young gorse and also ground "clothed for the most part with short gorse and bracken" so the Common must have been a quite varied open space. He notes Linnets *Linaria cannabina*, Skylarks *Alauda arvensis*, and Tree Pipits, all birds of open habitats. Chance also watched Cuckoos parasitising Yellowhammers at a common called Sturt Fields two to three miles away from Pound Green and described as "covered with dense heather". From these hints it seems that in the past Wyre Forest contained scattered patches of similar habitat supporting a wide range of birds from Blackcock to Nightjars *Caprimulgus europaeus*. Nowadays the edges of open spaces can develop into similar open heather heath with scattered bushes and trees.

Norman Hickin (1971) writes "for me the principal bird of the dusk is the churring nightjar": sadly there has been little or no churring in Wyre for many years now although in 1998 one churred for four days in May (Harrison & Harrison 2005) and in 2015. Hickin also notes that in the 1930s Steele-Elliott estimated one pair per hundred acres in Wyre. A further indication of past abundance is a note by Steele-Elliott that on the 19 May

1901 he watched hundreds of Noctule Bats *Nyctalus noctula* and Swifts *Apus apus* hawking emerging mayflies over the Severn north of Bewdley. Eventually they were joined by two Nightjars and the spectacle continued until it was too dark to see: a vision of a lost countryside.

The national population of Nightjars halved between 1972 (estimated at between 3,000 and 6,000 males) and 1981 (estimated at 2,100 males) and certainly contracted in range, probably due to habitat loss, especially heathland destruction and a general loss of big areas of open shrubby habitats. The most recent national survey, in 2004, shows a further decline in population and range in north Wales, north-west England and Scotland, although overall the population had increased by 36% since the previous survey in 1992. The survey revealed that Nightjars were almost always associated with either heathland or young conifer forestry plantations, often after clear-felling and replanting of large areas. In South Wales Jenks *et al.* (2014) found most birds in plantations between clear-felling and five years later, although plantations up to 15 years old were used. Nightjars are now probably dependent on conservation restoration of heathland, and clear-felling and replanting of conifer plantations (Conway *et al.* 2007). They need large areas of suitable habitat exceeding 5 ha and both habitat types need to supply sufficient large dusk-flying insects (moths, beetles and others) on which Nightjars feed. A return to Wyre will require habitat creation on a suitable scale. In recent years, conifer felling has provided more open space than seen for many years so the chances of recolonisation have improved despite the national decline.

Eighty years ago Nightingales *Luscinia megarynchos* sang in the Forest. Nightingales are birds of scrub, thickets, overgrown hedges and woodland understorey. In England they reach the edge of their European range and that edge cuts through Worcestershire. Harthan (1946), quoting Tomes, noted that Nightingales were plentiful in the valleys of the Severn, Avon and Teme in 1900. At that time they probably reached their most extensive range in Britain, nesting regularly here, in parts of Shropshire, and even further north. Thereafter they declined but enjoyed a resurgence in the 1930s, followed by a steady decline continuing to the present day. In 1948 Harthan heard 14 singing males at Great Witley but only one in Wyre a few miles to the north (Harthan 1961). Since then the national range has shrunk towards south-eastern England with a handful of pairs in south Worcestershire; a singing Nightingale in Wyre today would attract many listeners.

These historic reports of Cuckoos, Nightjars and Nightingales all indicate that Wyre Forest was a wooded area encompassing many open spaces, with heath and scrub between the blocks of woodland. Such areas are scarcer nowadays, although they have increased in recent years as a result of special management. Where this takes place, birds of scrub and open country often follow.

Borderland birds

Even without these former breeding species, modern Wyre is rich in birds, partly because of its variety of habitats and partly because of its location. A glance at national distribution maps (British Trust for Ornithology (BTO) Atlas 2013) shows that Wyre is a borderland where birds with breeding distributions mainly to the north and west nest alongside many species which are quite common throughout most of the British Isles, especially England. These include Pied Flycatchers, Redstarts *Phoenicurus phoenicurus* and Wood Warblers which are typically birds of western and northern oak woods, and Siskins, birds of northern and western pine woods, which are colonising maturing conifer plantations in the south. Dippers are birds of fast-flowing streams in the north and west: the Dowles Brook and its main tributaries provide similar habitat.

Birds and woods

Wyre is ancient woodland which has never been completely cleared, although it has been used by people for woodland products and patchy cultivation for perhaps 2,000 years. There have been, and still are, many variations of internal structure ranging from large open areas to extensive forest cover. Open areas are created when mature trees are felled, in areas cut for coppice, or where heather heathland predominates on poorer soils. Some heathy spaces persist for a long time and are only slowly invaded by shrubs and trees, whereas clear-felled or coppiced areas are rapidly filled by regrowth.

Large areas of Wyre were planted with conifers in the first part of the 20th century and after World War Two, converting broadleaved deciduous woodland and heathland to dense evergreen woods. These activities resulted in structural variation and provided a variety of niches for many different birds, as first reported by W.B. Yapp (1962) in his book *Birds & Woods*. Although in the 1930s and 40s, and earlier in the 20th century, some efforts had been made to understand woodland bird communities elsewhere, Yapp applied rigorous transect-based methods to assess populations and their distributions. He walked the transect lines at a steady speed counting bird contacts as he went along. He then applied statistical methods to interpret his results. A paper in *Bird Study* (Yapp 1956) contained his mathematical formulae and at the time caused uproar in parts of the ornithological community more used to natural history, observations and simple reportage. Nowadays a paper on bird populations without statistics would be surprising. Yapp's studies and other early investigations showed that birds were unevenly distributed in woodland, both in the breeding season and in winter. Since then there have been many studies aimed at understanding the causes (summaries for example in Fuller 1995, Fuller *et al.* 2012, Newton 2013).

Well-grown fairly young oak woodland with adjacent open space is often used by nesting Tree Pipits *Anthus trivialis.* [PC]

Part of Yapp's project aimed to understand changes in bird populations during development of forest after clear-fell by estimating bird numbers in woodland at different stages of growth. He studied a variety of woods throughout Britain. In Wyre Forest he surveyed three areas in 1950–53 and again in 1954–59. The first area (6.5 ha) had been clear-felled about 12 years previously and had regenerated to mainly birch *Betula* spp. about two to three metres tall at the time of his survey. The second plot (67 ha) was formerly oak coppice last cut about 20 years previously. At the time of the survey it consisted of oak and birch about 8 m tall with an understorey of bracken and bramble. The third area (87 ha) was well-grown oak about 12 m tall under-planted with Beech *Fagus sylvatica* about 12 years previously. The low ground cover was mostly Bilberry *Vaccinium myrtillus* and Heather, small beech about 30 cm high, and taller beech thickets in places. Overall his simple conclusion was that on the whole many species increased from one sample period to the next as woodland grew and developed. However these broad-brush conclusions from quite big areas did not take small habitat differences within them into account, or the uneven distribution of birds.

In his later paper (1969) Yapp reported further on the oak and beech, and oak and birch plots in Wyre, summarising the density of several species averaged in five year blocks running from 1950 to 1967. He showed that Chaffinches *Fringilla coelebs* first increased as the trees grew, declining as the canopy closed and the planted beech understorey thickened, whereas Blackbird *Turdus merula* and Robin *Erithacus rubecula* densities increased with tree growth to a steady level and remained there for the second half of the survey. For Tree Pipits, a more open woodland edge species, density proved variable in the oak-beech and was related to open patches caused by forestry work,

whereas in the more open birch-oak they increased quickly and then rapidly declined as scrub and then woodland became dense. These seminal observations first made in Wyre are now recognised as familiar patterns, usually based on mapping the territories of breeding birds. This technique is much better at revealing breeding bird density in relation to small variations in habitat. Additionally more precise ways of measuring woodland and scrub density have been devised.

Clearly structural details in woodland are the key to understanding local bird distributions, reflecting the 'ecological niche' which suits a species' needs. This is most obvious during the breeding season when most species, certainly most small song birds, establish a territory of a structure and size to provide nest sites and ample food. This they defend from others of the same species by song, display and, if necessary, battle. In woodland a territory can be likened to a bubble, and when the habitat is good over a large area with many adjacent territories, to a mass of bubbles—a foam of territories. The bubbles vary in size and shape depending on habitat quality and pressure from neighbours. Disputes between adjacent bubble-holders alter the boundaries. Wood Warbler bubbles extend from the forest floor to the treetops: the birds nest on or near the ground, they sing from the lower branches of trees, and hunt for insect food in the canopy, but occur only where there is open space beneath the trees with few shrubs. In contrast Wren *Troglodytes troglodytes* bubbles are usually near ground level, only a few metres high and are situated where there are dense patches of brambles, shrubs or fallen tree branches within which the birds forage and nest. Each species establishes its own characteristic territory bubble. For some, like the Wood Warbler, the requirements are special. Generalists like Blackbirds use a wide range

The Wren *Troglodytes troglodytes* usually nests low down in scrub, cavities in trees, bramble tangles or any place where the domed nest can be fitted. It is a bird with a nesting territory near the ground. [PC]

of habitat structures from mature forest to bramble-bracken tangles with very few trees or shrubs.

It follows that bird populations change from year to year as woodland grows or develops an understorey or is felled and regenerates, or is replanted (Fuller *et al.* 2012). Local changes may also reflect national population trends.

The use of woodland by birds also changes through the year. Breeding birds require nesting territories: they include summer visitors such as warblers and flycatchers as well as residents such as thrushes and woodpeckers. In winter the need is primarily for food and sheltered roosting sites. Besides the resident species (for example Blackbirds and Wrens) winter visitors arrive (for example Fieldfares *Turdus pilaris*, Redwings *T. iliacus*, and Bramblings *Fringilla montifringilla*) from overseas. Resident species move about, perhaps entering the woods from the neighbouring countryside or leaving to forage elsewhere.

Wyre Forest is naturally broadleaved woodland with conifer plantations thrust upon it, although this situation is now changing as large areas of conifers are being removed. The initial clearance of broadleaved trees and heath in the 20th century, followed by extensive planting of conifers, immediately resulted in rapid growth of broadleaved shrubs and young trees, especially birch, alongside the young conifers. This produces a shrubby habitat suitable for Stonechats, Whinchats, Yellowhammers and Grasshopper Warblers *Locustella naevia* soon followed by Long-tailed Tits *Aegithalos caudatus*, Greenfinches *Chloris chloris*, Bullfinches *Pyrrhula pyrrhula*, Linnets and Goldfinches *Carduelis carduelis*. Developing young birch scrub is rapidly colonised by Willow Warblers *Phylloscopus trochilus*, Whitethroats *Sylvia communis* and common woodland birds such as Blackbirds, Robins and Dunnocks *Prunella modularis*.

What happens next depends on forestry operations. Vigorous removal of regenerating scrub encourages growth of another wave of shrubs and the process continues until the conifers grow and shade out competition. If the broadleaved scrub colonises and becomes dense, Garden Warblers *Sylvia borin* move in. As the scrub ages and thins out beneath taller broadleaved trees, Blackcaps *S. atricapilla* arrive. Across Wyre there have been many variations in the timing of forestry operations which have created a mosaic of changing shrubby habitats with shifting bird communities. When conifers mature they can form a closed canopy which shades out most or all ground flora and shrubs. The remaining breeding birds are generally conifer specialists such as Goldcrests *Regulus regulus*, Coal Tits *Periparus ater* and perhaps Crossbills and Firecrests *Regulus ignicapilla*.

Many of the birds mentioned so far are associated with open areas, shrubby growth and edges between open habitats and woodland. In the past, before conifers were planted, the Forest was either of large mature trees or tall oak grown as coppice on long rotations, or shrubs and trees regrowing after felling operations. Shrubs or brambles would have grown beneath the oaks if sufficient light reached the Forest floor, forming an understorey suiting many common breeding birds including Blackbirds, Robins, Dunnocks, Song Thrushes *Turdus philomelos*, Jays *Garrulus glandarius*, Woodpigeons *Columba palumbus* and Blackcaps. If the tree canopy closed, obscuring light, the Forest floor would have been relatively clear and open. The main habitat for birds in forest or old coppice with a closed canopy is the trees themselves which provide both nesting sites and food. Nesting birds closely associated with mature trees in Wyre include woodpeckers, Nuthatch *Sitta europaea*, Treecreepers *Certhia familiaris*, Blue Tits *Cyanistes caeruleus*, Great Tits *Parus major*, Coal Tits, Marsh

The Bullfinch's *Pyrrhula pyrrhula* soft and mournful contact calls can often be heard before it is seen. The male (as seen here) is more brightly coloured than the female. These birds frequent hedgerows, orchards and woodland edges. [JR]

Tits *Poecile palustris*, Pied Flycatchers, Redstarts, Stock Doves *Columba oenas*, Jackdaws *Corvus monedula*, Tawny Owls *Strix aluco* and Mandarin Ducks, all nesting in holes in trees. Birds nesting within the canopy include Hawfinches *Coccothraustes coccothraustes*, Mistle Thrushes *Turdus viscivorus*, Woodpigeons, Sparrowhawks *Accipiter nisus* and Carrion Crows *Corvus corone*.

Many of the tree-nesting birds are locally distributed, depending in part on the availability of nest holes. Holes in young trees are scarce, but increase after about 30 years. Early on, a few holes are formed when branches break off or following storm damage. Other hole nesters benefit from woodpecker excavations and small cavities caused by fungal decay. The supply of holes varies as trees mature, decay and fall over and this change, along with the type of hole available, may limit the numbers of each bird species. Tits use small holes whereas Tawny Owls and Jackdaws require large cavities. Treecreepers usually nest behind loose bark or big ivy stems, whilst Nuthatches plaster their hole entrances with mud to reduce them to a satisfactory size. Willow Tits *Poecile montana* excavate or enlarge a hole in soft decaying wood.

Woodland feeding—the tits

Walk anywhere in Wyre's woodland and you will see the ubiquitous tits, which are mainly insect eaters. They produce large broods whose success is linked to a spring superabundance of defoliating moth caterpillars. To rear their broods successfully the parent birds need to time egg laying and incubation so that the young are in the nest when tree-feeding caterpillars are most abundant. Because of climatic changes winter and spring weather now tends to be warmer than in the past. Some insect populations have responded to this change, peaking earlier in the year. Many resident birds have tracked this change, but at a slower rate, and now nest about three weeks earlier than 40 years ago. Nevertheless annual variation in spring weather may disrupt the timing of nesting and insect abundance resulting in small or failed broods. Often there is more food than the birds can eat and

so breeding density is determined by the number of nesting holes and a minimal territory size.

Outside the breeding season tits forage in every part of the tree from topmost twigs to the bole. Each tree is parcelled out by different species. Generally Blue Tits search high in the branches, Great Tits lower down, and Marsh Tits still lower, though there are large overlaps. These divisions break down in spring when all the tits and many other species feed in the tree canopy on the caterpillar crop. Coal Tits tend to prefer conifers, their fine bills well-adapted to probing needles for invertebrates. Between late summer and early spring tits often flock together, and in Wyre it is a common experience to be standing in silent woodland that is suddenly engulfed by calling birds which sweep through the branches on a feeding circuit, taking the more obvious food items and moving on.

Marsh Tits are declining in parts of the British Isles, but in Wyre they are still widespread though local. Studies of the birds in other woods (Broughton *et al.* 2006, 2014) give insight into their needs. In the study area, nesting territories were quite small: 2.3–4.6 ha in a mature oak wood, 1.5–2.2 ha in a mixed wood. This is larger than territories held by Great and Blue Tits. It may be influenced by year-round occupation by Marsh Tits and their habit of making food stores which they defend. Other tits tend to move further afield in winter. Marsh Tit territories contain mature trees with a low canopy and well-developed understorey of shrubs rather than young trees. Nests are constructed in rot holes in mature trees, generally quite near the ground, and lower than those used by Great and Blue Tits.

Although Marsh Tits are year-round residents and do not move far, they occupy a large winter range averaging around 39 ha around the core nesting territory in the woodland studied. Within this there is a tendency for the birds to use oak trees more often than other trees or shrubs possibly because they carry more food. Marsh Tits take many invertebrates, including their eggs and larvae, from tree branches, twigs and hanging dead leaves, and also oak gall tissues in winter. Yapp (1962) comments "Marsh Tits can be heard in the tree tops in winter tearing oak buds apart".

Coal Tit *Periparus ater* [JR]

Marsh Tit *Poecile palustris* [JR]

Wood Warbler *Phylloscopus sibilatrix* [JR]

Woodland migrants

Summer visitors fall into two groups, young growth and mature tree species (Fuller *et al.* 2012). Young growth species are those associated with shrubs and small trees: Willow Warbler, Nightingale, Garden Warbler, Blackcap and Chiffchaff *Phylloscopus collybita*. Old tree species are Redstart, Pied Flycatcher and Wood Warbler. The first two are hole nesters which often respond to provision of nest boxes.

Pied Flycatchers winter in West Africa south of the Sahara and arrive in Wyre in April. The males are attractive black and white birds; the females are browner. Reports over the last 200 years indicate that small numbers of Pied Flycatchers have nested in Worcestershire for a long time, including the Wyre

Forest. They were probably encouraged by many nest boxes erected near Dowles Manor by Jannion Steele-Elliott in the years around 1900 (Hickin 1971). John Robinson knew of around 12 nesting pairs between Lodge Farm and Knowles Mill in the 1970s and territories were often near Dowles Brook, the birds catching emerging aquatic insects to feed nestlings. One pair fed its brood on emerging mayflies. Nationally however their main breeding areas are oak woodlands in western and northern Britain.

Early BTO Atlases (see Mapstore on the BTO website) show a small expansion in range between 1968–72 and 1988–91 and also a considerable increase in numbers, perhaps partly encouraged by provision of nest boxes in suitable woodlands. Since 1994 numbers

Garden Warbler *Sylvia borin* [JR]

Male Blackcap *Sylvia atricapilla* [JR]

Male Pied Flycatchers *Ficedula hypoleuca* arrive in April ahead of the females [JR]

have declined by around 50% throughout the British range, accompanied by a moderate European decline. The national changes are clearly reflected in Wyre. For many years small numbers nested along the Dowles valley in both woodland and orchards. Norman Hickin was very pleased when they started using his nest boxes at The Newalls in 1965. Thereafter, following the success of similar schemes elsewhere, many nestboxes were erected in Wyre woodlands and orchards, often by licensed bird ringers collecting information on nesting success and migrations. These were soon occupied by Great Tits, Blue Tits, and Pied Flycatchers, and occasionally by Redstarts. Tits were often prevented from using nestboxes by plugging entrance holes and unplugging them when Pied Flycatchers arrived and the tits were already nesting in other boxes. This micromanagement is not always possible.

Pied Flycatchers are in conflict with tits as they often try to use the same boxes and territories, perhaps because the presence of nesting tits indicates best quality sites. Tits usually win the battle between the species and Pied Flycatchers entering boxes occupied by tits may be killed (Kern *et al.* 2014). The overall result could be to lower the number of young birds produced. Since the mid-1990s numbers have fallen and by 2014 the Wyre Forest population had dwindled to a handful of pairs. A nest box study showed that in 2006 431 nest boxes produced 20 broods; in 2009 only four broods were raised (Spencer 2009). Since then the decline in Wyre has continued.

The reasons for the national and European decline appear to be linked directly or indirectly to changing habitat and weather patterns in the African wintering zone and the timing of movement north after the birds arrive in southern Europe. Also, in a similar way to tits, Pied Flycatchers rear their nestlings when insect food is most abundant in the tree canopy, and fewer young are produced if there is a mismatch in timing between the two. Some long distance migrants now arrive in Britain earlier than in the past so nesting time shows a better match with the abundance of invertebrate food. However the picture is not clear for Pied Flycatchers. Arrival times now appear to be earlier in Britain by about ten days with a better, but not perfect match to caterpillar abundance; in the Netherlands the mismatch has become greater. In the Czech Republic the match between the timing of caterpillar abundance and nesting by Collared Flycatchers *Ficedula albicollis* and Great Tits have advanced together.

Compensatory genetic change may lurk in the shadows perhaps linking birds which hatched at an earlier date with a timely return to their breeding territory. Of all British breeding birds most long distance African migrants that nest in woods are declining, probably because of mismatch between food supply and nesting time. Migrants breeding in marshland where food is available over a much longer period are doing well (Both 2007; 2012). Two of Wyre's summer migrants that winter south of the Sahara and nest in 'young growth' of small trees and shrubs

are Garden Warbler and Willow Warbler. Two other woodland warblers, Blackcap and Chiffchaff, are short range migrants wintering in southern Europe or North Africa.

Garden Warbler numbers vary from year to year in a similar way to the other long distance migrants and these variations may be due to changes in wintering areas. However, Garden Warblers have extended their distribution in the British Isles in recent years and now nest in more northerly parts of Scotland and Ireland (BTO Mapstore) although actual numbers may have declined. Overall Garden Warblers have disappeared from some southern English woods and colonised woods further north, probably as a reaction to climate warming. The picture is blurred because Garden Warblers require dense scrub growth between 0.5 and 2 m tall beneath woodland trees, a habitat in short supply. Most woodlands are becoming high forest with little growth beneath the trees because of lack of coppicing, the shade created by tree canopy closure and heavy deer browsing which prevents regrowth (Mustin *et al.* 2014).

In contrast Blackcaps have steadily increased in numbers and distribution in the last 40 years and are now found throughout the British Isles and Ireland wherever there is suitable habitat (BTO Mapstore). They use a wider range of shrubby habitats than Garden Warblers and often occupy less dense scrub beneath trees. In coppice Garden Warblers generally depart around ten years after cutting, while Blackcaps may remain for 15–20 years if sufficient low bushy nesting cover remains (Fuller *et al.* 2012). It follows that in Wyre the numbers and distribution of both species vary depending on forestry activity both in big stands of trees and along tracks. John Robinson notes for both species "Populations go up and down from year to year but remain about the same generally". Current forest management in Wyre of coppice and wide tracks with scrubby edges benefits both species.

For many years before the late 1980s the lilting song of newly arrived Willow Warblers was a prominent feature of early spring. Although it is still one of the April pleasures of walking along open rides in the Forest, over the last 20 years or so surveys of breeding birds have shown a severe national decline of around 55% in southern England. Conversely, in northern England and Scotland numbers have rallied slightly from a lesser fall. Willow Warblers nest near the ground amongst vegetation on the edge of, or amongst, young tree growth. The main characteristic of a Willow Warbler territory is a dense growth of young trees all with trunk diameters between 5–10 cm: areas with smaller or thicker trunks tend to be avoided. Willow Warblers forage for insects on trunks, twigs and leaves of such trees, so structure and area of foraging potential, combined with shelter, seems to be important.

Willow Warblers might be better named 'Birch Warblers' since they are often associated with dense thickets of the young trees, but will also use similar stands of alder and willow: structure is a better

The colourful male Redstart's *Phoenicurus phoenicurus* tuneful song may be heard from the tree tops [JR]

prediction of territory than tree species. It could be that loss of woodland of this structure is contributing to Willow Warbler decline and may reflect the growth of continuous cover forestry rather than clear-fell, coppice management and encouragement of tree regeneration (Stostad & Menéndez 2014). Because southern breeding Willow Warblers winter nearer the Sahel zone, which has experienced huge human population growth and habitat changes, the birds may also be affected by changes on their African wintering grounds (Wernham *et al.* 2002; Zwarts *et al.* 2009).

Wood Warblers are one of Wyre's ornithological attractions, moss-green and yellow migrants which bring a taste of the Welsh valley woodlands to within a few kilometres of the Midland conurbation. They are mainly birds of woods with tall trees and few shrubs with generally open ground conditions. Larger than Willow Warblers, with snow-white underparts, they have two strikingly different songs: a shivering trill which has been compared with a spinning coin on a marble surface, and an ascending series of plaintive notes delivered from high in the canopy or from the lower branches of trees. The nest, built on the ground amongst low vegetation, is vulnerable to predators, especially Jays (Mallord *et al.* 2012).

Historically Wood Warblers have bred mainly in the south and west of Britain but, since the early 1990s, their range has contracted and birds have forsaken many apparently suitable woods in southern England. This, together with a sharp drop in numbers, has led to Red-listing as a species of conservation concern. The reasons for the fall in numbers are unclear, but may be connected with changes in woodland structure and management, though in Wyre the habitat has not noticeably altered during the period of decline. It is possible that changes in Wood Warbler winter habitats in the Congo Basin in Africa are also implicated.

Harthan (1946) notes that in Worcestershire Wood Warblers occurred in many woods, especially in the zone between the southern Malvern Hills and Wyre Forest. In Wyre numbers vary widely from year to year and occupied territories are usually on steeper ground along the brooks. Some birds may sing for only a few days before mating, making them difficult to census, whereas males singing persistently in late May or early June are often still in search of a mate.

From early April, the sweet rattle of Redstarts resounds from treetops near forest rides and clearings, though the singer is often hard to locate. Harthan (1946) writes "the Redstart is common on the Malvern and Lickey Hills ... also plentiful in the high country from Wyre Forest to Tenbury". The birds still breed in small numbers throughout woodland and in old orchards where nest boxes are a popular substitute for natural tree holes. Redstarts also nest in walls or buildings, including the old mills along Dowles Brook valley, and have successfully raised young in Knowles Mill. They are birds of open woodland rather than dense cover and may benefit from modern forest clearance if populations remain buoyant.

Female Redstart [JR]

Nationally Redstart numbers declined sharply in the late 1960s, along with several other species, notably Common Whitethroats, because of severe drought conditions in their wintering area in the African Sahel region on the south side of the Sahara: each bird remains in a small area all winter. Numbers started to recover in the mid-1980s and an upward trend has continued. The national distribution has contracted though and Redstarts are now mainly birds of west England, Wales and Scotland. Since the 1960s crash, many lowland parts of south-east England (and also south-east Worcestershire) have lost Redstarts.

Woodpeckers, Nuthatches and Treecreepers

All three British woodpeckers breed in Wyre: Great Spotted *Dendrocopos major*, Lesser Spotted *D. minor* and Green *Picus viridis*. As Hickin (1971) pointed out one cannot walk far in the Forest without hearing or seeing a woodpecker, although they are less common in conifer plantations. The commonest are Great Spotted and Green Woodpeckers. Lesser Spotted Woodpeckers were commoner in the past, but are now scarce. All are closely associated with dead and decaying wood; the invertebrates it contains are an important food resource, especially for the first two species outside the breeding season. Great Spotted Woodpeckers forage in rotting timber, mainly on the lower parts of trees including stumps and branches lying on the ground. They reach insects by pecking holes or stripping away bark. Breeding Great Spotted Woodpeckers will glean invertebrates, especially moth caterpillars, from leaves in spring.

Lesser Spotted Woodpeckers tend to forage on smaller decaying branches in the higher parts of trees. Green Woodpeckers feed mainly on ants and the view

A male Green Woodpecker *Picus viridis* searching a low anthill in old grassland for ants which are a staple item in their diet. [JR]

of one probing the mounds made by Yellow Meadow Ants *Lasius flavus* is one of the characteristic sights of Wyre, as they forage in unimproved pastures, woodland rides and orchards. They even brave the formic acid showers of Southern Wood Ants *Formica rufa* whose huge nests are sometimes attacked, usually in the winter when the ants are inactive. Near anthills, it is common to find Green Woodpecker droppings, which resemble discarded cigarette ends and are crammed with chitinous ant remains.

Woodpeckers excavate nest holes in both living and dead wood. Over half of those excavated by Green and Great Spotted Woodpeckers are in living rather than dead wood (rot holes are occasionally used) whereas three-quarters of the smaller and weaker-billed Lesser Spotted Woodpecker nests are in decaying wood. The amount of dead wood on a living tree increases with tree age and size so big mature trees provide the greatest resources both for foraging woodpeckers and for potential nest sites. Oaks are usually more than 30 cm in diameter at chest height before Great Spotted Woodpeckers excavate nest holes in them. Short-lived birches rarely supply woodpecker resources until aged about 30 years; nest holes are excavated when the trees reach about 20 cm in diameter. Oak trees are afflicted by a range of diseases and recently bacterial Acute Oak Decline has become a particular concern. The main symptom is dark sticky fluid oozing from splits in the bark from damage beneath. This disease kills oak trees but some birds may benefit from the potential increase in decaying wood (Denman & Webber 2009; Denman *et al.* 2010).

Green Woodpeckers usually nest near open ground in broadleaved forest trees and also in old apple orchards. Apple trees rarely live for longer than 100 years and start to decay at a relatively young age compared with forest trees. Great Spotted Woodpeckers are more strictly woodland birds but will use orchards adjoining woodland (for a review see Fuller *et al.* 2012).

The national distribution of Lesser Spotted Woodpeckers is restricted to Wales and England, extending north to Lancashire in the west and Northumberland in the east (BTO Atlas 2013). Numbers peaked in 1979 following the severe outbreak of Dutch Elm Disease in the 1960s which provided vast amounts of decaying wood laden with invertebrate food. By 1999 the population had declined by half and the fall has continued. The birds are now so scarce that it is impossible to include the species in national monitoring schemes. The BTO Atlas also shows that, within the national range, only about 70% of previously occupied 10 × 10 km squares are now occupied compared with earlier surveys, and the species is scarce where it does occur.

Wyre Forest supports a small, but nationally important, population of Lesser Spotted Woodpeckers. Detailed research in the Forest and elsewhere shows they are usually associated with open woodland, oaks containing plenty of dead wood, and with extensive well-wooded landscapes. They may nest in old orchards but usually return to woodland to forage. Rosemary Winnall (2001) studied the woodpeckers of Rock Coppice in Wyre, a woodland of 65 ha, over four years 1987–1990. It usually contained eight pairs of Great Spotted, two pairs of Lesser Spotted and one pair of Green Woodpeckers. Average territory size was 8 ha for Great Spotted and 32 ha for Lesser Spotted Woodpeckers.

European studies of Lesser Spotted Woodpeckers at different places, cited by Charman *et al.* 2010, gave average breeding territory sizes as 27 ha and 43 ha. All three species require large breeding territories and much larger home ranges are used in winter averaging

Female Great Spotted Woodpecker *Dendrocopos major* [JR]

Lesser Spotted Woodpecker *Dendrocopos minor*, **male (right), female (left)** [JR]

211 ha and 742 ha in the same studies. The reasons for these large winter ranges are not known but they may be associated with protection from predators, or the amount of decaying wood and its invertebrates required for winter feeding. Bigger areas may contain conifers where Lesser Spotted Woodpeckers may feed in winter, and be less visible to predators, but the European studies were in mixed woodlands. In winter Lesser Spotted Woodpeckers mainly eat insect larvae extracted from small-diameter decaying wood.

As an important reservoir for Lesser Spotteds, Wyre Forest was one of three English study areas used in a recent attempt to understand the decline of this species. One of the survey's findings was that survival of young birds in the nest has been poor in recent years with many chicks starving (Smith & Charman 2012). The nestlings are fed on invertebrates gleaned from the uppers parts of trees, especially leaves, and include moth caterpillars, aphids and a wide range of small insects. Possibly this food supply is less readily available than in the past because of vagaries in weather patterns which, as with warblers and tits, have created a mismatch between the timing of invertebrate numbers and woodpecker nesting.

Typically the male undertakes most of the brooding at night and provides the majority of the food for the nestlings, but if one of the pair disappears the remaining parent can rarely supply enough food to enable the young to fledge. Females often move on and in European studies the male increases his feeding rate to compensate. The British research indicates that, here at least, lone males rarely succeed in rearing a brood, which suggests the national decline; there is now about a thousand pairs (Charman & Dodds 2011; Charman Smith & Dodd *et al.* 2012; Charman Smith & Dillon *et al.* 2012; Smith & Charman 2012). Fortunately in Wyre there are still places where you can hear their ringing "pee-pee-pee" call from a treetop and, with luck, see the wing-waving display of ardent males.

Two other species closely associated with trees are Nuthatch and Treecreeper. Nuthatches are associated with big, often over-mature, deciduous trees with at least some wood decay. Their loud wolf-whistles in the treetops are familiar sounds in Wyre. Nuthatches occasionally forage on the ground so may tend to prefer woodland without dense shrub and ground flora layers beneath trees (Cramp & Perrins 1993). An association with hazel nuts was more frequent in the past before the rise of Grey Squirrels and their plundering of the nut crop.

Nuthatches nest in both natural and old woodpecker nest holes in trees, and are well known for their habit of collecting mud pellets to reduce the size of the nest entrance hole. Neville Wilde (1973) describes watching a pair at a Wyre nest hole where a male adopted a motionless camouflage posture near the base of a tree to escape predation by a Sparrowhawk. Nuthatches have increased in both range and abundance in Britain since the 1970s and the trend appears to be continuing, driven by higher

Nuthatch *Sitta europaea* launching into flight. With large powerful feet Nuthatches can climb tree trunks and large branches in all directions and also move about clinging to small branches. [JR]

Treecreeper *Certhia familiaris* [ML]

productivity for each pair. In common with many other birds, they are now laying their first eggs about 14 days earlier than in 1970, the influence of climate change.

Nuthatches feed largely on invertebrates in spring and summer and mainly on seeds in the winter. Matthysen (1989) recorded that Nuthatch bills become longer and deeper in spring and summer and shorter and thinner in winter. This may reflect a change in diet, the longer bills more efficient at collecting the prolific spring invertebrates and ferrying them to hungry nestlings, and the shorter and blunter winter bills better for dealing with nuts and seeds. Tough insects and nuts are wedged into cracks in trees and hammered open with the bill, hence the old name 'Nut-hack'. In Wyre, opened nuts and seeds can often be found wedged in rough bark.

Treecreepers are virtually confined to trees, using practically any species that has more or less vertical trunks covered in bark. They extract hidden invertebrates from crevices in the bark with their thin, slightly down-curved, bill. Treecreepers always climb upwards clinging on with large feet and supported by a long stiff tail, compared to Nuthatches that can move in any direction. Although fairly common throughout Wyre, Treecreepers are easily overlooked as they prefer closed woodland rather than edges and tracks. They have very high pitched calls; a walk through the Forest in late winter or spring will almost certainly

be enlivened by their sibilant song with its terminal flourish. Treecreepers nest behind detached bark or ivy, or similar sites, and will use specially designed nest boxes (Lowe 2014): John Robinson notes Treecreepers using such boxes in Wyre. Treecreepers are vulnerable in very cold winters when numbers fall dramatically, but recover well and the population currently seems to be steady. Like Nuthatches, first egg dates are now about 14 days earlier than in the 1970s.

Hawfinches

Hawfinches are birds which lure many hopeful enthusiasts to the woods. John Robinson writes: "I remember 1985 very well indeed. I had been warden at Wyre Forest National Nature Reserve for some time, and had a pretty good idea where most species of plants and animals were to be found in the Forest ... and it was during these times that I first became acquainted with Hawfinches. I had seen them in the past at my previous reserve, Castorhanglands near Peterborough. The ones in Wyre though, afforded me much better views and we would see them regularly singing at first light from the tops of 80-foot high Douglas Firs. I also remember that year well because I found several Hawfinch nests and they were nothing like the ones on the 'fag cards' I had collected as a boy. Hawfinches were always supposed to nest on some pretty fruit tree branch festooned with blossom. It wasn't like that at all. One was in a sapling young beech festooned with Honeysuckle and another was in the same climber in a Birch sapling. The end of a long horizontal branch of a Rowan was the site of another, and the last was in an oak tree, 50 feet from the ground." (Robinson 2007).

In the early 1800s Hawfinches were rarely seen in Worcestershire and probably did not breed in Britain. Several winter flocks appeared in 1833, 1854 and 1869 and by the end of the 19th century they were nesting in most counties in England and Wales. The spread and increase may have been assisted by widespread planting of cherry orchards. Although Hawfinches eat the seeds of many trees, they are able to crack open cherry stones to eat the kernels, using powerful cheek muscles calculated to exert a force of 12 kg per square centimetre. In Worcestershire numbers seem to have increased to be 'not infrequent' until the 1920s (Harthan 1946; Hastings 1834; Holloway 1996). Thereafter populations fell and, in the last half of the 20th century, small numbers probably nested in many west Worcestershire woods including Wyre, peaking in the 1980s. Since then, numbers and distribution of breeding birds have declined locally and nationally. The reasons for the decline are obscure especially as the species is still common across the Channel in France and elsewhere in Europe.

Hawfinches often nest in small colonies. The nestlings are fed on invertebrates collected from the canopy of trees, especially moth larvae, a food source important for many woodland birds. The Hawfinch increase in Victorian times coincided with reports

of large numbers of defoliating larvae of Green Oak Tortrix moth *Tortrix viridana*. Nowadays moth larvae populations appear to be smaller than in the past. At other times Hawfinches are dependent on fruits with kernels. Extensive woodland coppicing was also in full swing, encouraging the growth of many berry and seed bearing shrubs—Hazel *Corylus avellana*, Field Maple *Acer campestre*, Yew *Taxus baccata*, Wych Elm *Ulmus glabra*, Hornbeam *Carpinus betulus*—providing ample food for winter colonies of Hawfinches. Loss of coppice and changes in woodland management producing shadier conditions, may have led to a reduced food supply so contributing to the decline. Hawfinch nests also suffer high predation rates from Sparrowhawks, Carrion Crows, Magpies *Pica pica*, Jays and Grey Squirrels. Colonial nesting helps protect against predators so a habitat capable of supporting enough Hawfinches to form a colony is important. Nests in colonies also produce more young than solitary nests (Mountford 1956).

In the history of Hawfinches in Worcestershire (and nationally) the winter of 2005–2006 is memorable. Flocks appeared, often in churchyards, feeding by cracking open the seeds in fallen yew berries (Green 2007; Warr 2007). These birds were probably winter visitors from northern Europe as Hawfinches breeding in Britain appear to be sedentary (Mountford 1956). On the forest fringes of Wyre, in winter, Hawfinches occasionally appear in churchyard yews and these may be locally breeding birds.

Hawfinch *Coccothraustes coccothraustes* [JR]

The woodland wader

Visit Wyre at dusk on a still spring evening and, as light fades, dark shapes lumber over the trees, grunting and whistling: Woodcocks on their territorial patrols. The Woodcock is unique in the British Isles; a wading bird adapted for life in woodlands. Harthan (1946) estimated that Wyre contained a pair every 200 acres. John Robinson believes there are around 30 territories in the Forest today, probably equivalent to Harthan's estimate. In the report on the national 1934–1935 census Alexander notes that the first record for Worcestershire was of young seen in Bewdley Park in 1801. He concludes there were at least 60 pairs in Worcestershire and notes "apparent general decrease in Wyre Forest in recent years attributed to forestry activities" without describing the "activities" which could relate to the first conifer planting (Alexander 1945).

The BTO Common Bird Census from 1966 to 2002 suggests a national decline in nesting Woodcock since about 1980, but this may not be fully correct as the plots surveyed did not include conifers and had a marked bias to south-east England. However subsequent work has shown a considerable contraction of range with many woods being deserted throughout the British Isles, noticeably in Worcestershire, although the Wyre population appears to be stable. Recreational disturbance, drying out of natural woodlands, overgrazing by deer, declining woodland management, and the maturing of conifer plantations are possible causes of the Woodcock's decline (BTO Trends website).

Woodcock chicks [RW]

Most recent survey work was based on counts of the males' crepuscular territorial flights. This activity is called roding, a display during which the birds repeatedly fly low along the same route making a croaking sound immediately followed by a higher pitched "twissick". A BTO survey in 2003 used a method based on roding males. Jim Martin and others surveyed at seven points in Wyre at dusk with negative results at six sites. Birds were recorded near Earnwood and it was estimated that at least 20% of the 1 × 1 km squares in Wyre contained breeding Woodcock (Martin 2003).

Woodcock *Scolopax rusticola* [JR]

Woodcock nest on the ground, usually in fairly open places under trees with abundant fallen oak leaves. The pictures taken in Wyre in Rosemary Winnall's 2007 note show this typical habitat. Neville Wilde (2004) observed and photographed at a Wyre nest in similar habitat. Territories generally contain wet ground with soft mud which the birds probe for earthworms and invertebrate larvae. In winter, when up to a million birds are present in the British Isles, Woodcock are more widespread in Wyre, especially under Bracken and Bramble in open woodland or, in hard weather, along sheltered stream valleys.

In recent years Woodcock migrations have been studied by fitting them with either geolocators or tags that can be tracked by satellite telemetry. In the first instance the bird has to be re-caught to download information; in the second the bird can be tracked in real-time. In Britain geolocators have shown that some birds return to breeding grounds in Scandinavia, the Baltic countries and farther away still: a bird wintering in Cornwall travelled 4,800 km into Russia. These studies also showed that a woodcock can fly non-stop at an average speed of 40 km an hour for up to 24 hours, usually followed by a break of 11–17 days. The break is probably needed to build up body fat for the energy necessary for the next part of the journey. Various studies suggest that winter populations in the British Isles comprise about 17% British breeders, 51% from Russia and the Baltic states and 32% from Scandinavia and Finland (**www. gwct.org.uk/research/species/birds/woodcock/**).

Birds of conifers

In Wyre all conifers apart from Yew are introduced, most planted for commercial forestry. The principal species are Douglas Fir *Pseudotsuga menziesii*, Scots Pine *Pinus sylvestris*, Corsican Pine *P. nigra* subsp. *laricio*, Western Hemlock-spruce *Tsuga heterophylla*, and European Larch *Larix decidua*, hybrid Larch, with smaller stands of Lawson's Cypress *Chamaecyparis lawsoniana* and, very locally, Western Red Cedar *Thuja plicata* and Weymouth Pine *P. strobus*.

Although conifer plantations are unpopular with many naturalists, mature stands of evergreens have their own characteristic suite of birds, notably Goldcrests, Coal Tits and the rarer crossbills and Goshawk. They are also well used by generalist birds such as Song Thrushes and Chaffinches and, in even the darkest woods, the pulsing song of Wrens is a year-round accompaniment. Mature conifers have very few holes, and little decay, because any wounds are sealed with resin. This prevents fungi reaching the heartwood and so there are very few opportunities for hole-nesting birds. Coal Tits, which are one of the commonest birds closely associated with conifers, nest in holes in the ground: indeed Yapp (1962) goes so far as to suggest that Coal Tits are ground nesters, but need trees to supply food. However, in western oak woods they may outnumber Great and Blue Tits, perhaps because these woods are often in hilly countryside with many holes in the ground readily available.

Coal Tits are a little smaller than Blue Tits, with finer bills adapted to searching among needles for very small insects and spiders. They also eat seeds extracted from open cones. In oak woods their nestlings are fed on moth caterpillars collected from the canopy, but in conifers caterpillars are less abundant and they eat more spiders. Coal Tits regularly store or cache food amongst needles, and in crevices in trees or on the ground.

Crossbills are the birds most often associated with conifers and use their crossed bill-tips to shear open cones, prising the seeds out from between the bracts. In Wyre they must have been scarce birds in the days before the conifer plantations started to produce cones, although eruptive movements into Worcestershire are noted by Harthan (1946). He later (1961) stated they were seen every year between the two reports, often in flocks of around 50, and young birds were seen in the Lickey Woods in 1959 after a big invasion in 1958. John Robinson notes that they have been seen in Wyre every year for the last 40 years.

In volume two for 1829 the *Magazine of Natural History* (edited by J.C. Loudon) correspondent J.W. notes "In the autumn of 1821, being at Cothoridge, [near Worcester] I was aroused early one morning by the information that a large flock of crossbills

Pine trees, Dowles valley (Wimperhill) [RW]

The Common Crossbill *Loxia curvirostra* (male seen here) has a distinctive bill crossed at the tips which it uses for extracting seeds from the cones of conifers. [PW]

was feeding in a grove of firs near the house. After watching them for some time, with a gun I procured fifteen specimens, out of which only two were in full feather, the breasts and backs of the others being nearly bare. After this they used to visit the same spot pretty regularly twice a day. The males varied very much in colour, some being of a deeper red, and others inclining rather more to yellow, particularly on the tail coverts, and being a little mottled with yellow upon the breast and back". This is an interesting reminder of the likely fate of rare birds in those days.

Crossbills breed widely throughout boreal conifer forests in northern Europe and Russia. They are famed for periodic eruptive movements of birds leaving the breeding zone and appearing in large numbers in more southerly parts of Europe and Britain. Their annual cycle is linked to the crop of spruce cones. This is well described by Newton (2006). Paraphrased: "Over much of Europe, Common Crossbills feed primarily on seeds of Norway Spruce *Picea abies*. ... The annual cycles ... can best be understood ... [from the] fruiting patterns of Norway Spruce. ... new cones ... provide food from about June into the winter, and particularly from January on, when the cones begin to open. By late May, most cones have fallen ... Crossbills then switch to alternative foods and eventually to the new Norway Spruce crop. Crossbill breeding in Norway Spruce areas occurs January–April when seeds are readily available, but may begin as early as November in years of exceptionally good crops. In many regions ... other conifers also provide food. Scots Pine *Pinus sylvestris* cones open later than Spruce, providing food into July, bridging the gap between successive spruce crops, and sometimes allowing Common Crossbills to breed into May or June."

In some years the spruce cone crop may be good over a very large area. In other years it may be patchy and in those years Common Crossbills move into the productive areas. When there is widespread failure

of the spruce cone crop and a high population of Common Crossbills eruptive movements occur, mainly in a south-westerly direction away from the breeding area. These birds arrive in Britain anytime between May and October but mostly in June and July, and they may remain to breed in places with a good food supply. Ringing has shown that at least some of these birds return to boreal nesting areas, but not in the same year as the outward movement.

The BTO 2007–11 Atlas (BTO 2013) shows a great expansion of distribution and numbers of Common Crossbills in the British Isles in both winter and summer, in line with maturing of conifer plantations. In Wyre they are often attracted to plantations of Larch and Scots Pine and small numbers can now be seen throughout the year. Larger flocks occur in eruption years and flocks of 60 to 100 have occurred recently. Although some of the birds are probably residents, and streaky immature birds are seen in 'good' crossbill years, others may arrive from Europe and act as 'carriers' for other immigrant species. Between November 2013 and April 2014, three Two-barred Crossbills *Loxia leucoptera* fed in Larches on the Shropshire side of Wyre, occasionally making sorties into Worcestershire. They were part of an exceptional influx which brought over a hundred birds to the British Isles, probably from Finland or Russia. They were feeding from pine and larch cones and their trumpeting calls, once heard, were enough to locate them along with a flock of Common Crossbills, Siskins and Lesser Redpolls *Acanthis cabaret* (Farmer 2013). A video of these birds extracting seeds from a pine cone on 8 December 2013 appeared at **www.youtube.com/ watch?v=F4v_x-Fu3Y0**.

Amongst the many crossbills seen in Wyre during the 2013–2014 winter there were unconfirmed reports of a Parrot Crossbill *Loxia pytyopsittacus*. On 18 February 2014 Craig Reed (Reed 2014) saw a female of this species and, through photographs, his record was accepted by the Shropshire Rare Birds Committee. To see all three crossbill species near to each other in the same winter in the UK is unusual. A few Parrot Crossbills nest in Scotland and other parts of the UK. Winter visitors during a crossbill invasion year are probably from northern Europe or north-west Asia.

Harthan (1946) described Siskins as irregular winter visitors in Worcestershire upgrading them slightly to "regular winter visitors" (Harthan 1961). For most of the 19th century Siskins bred mainly in Scotland with occasional nesting in southern England and north Wales. They invaded Ireland about the middle of the 19th century and spread across that country as conifer plantations matured. Similarly numbers increased in England in the early 20th century. However, extensive conifer felling during the First World War brought breeding populations to a low ebb for some years (Holloway 1996). Numbers increased as conifers planted between the wars and after World War Two matured. The first recorded breeding Siskins in Wyre were in the early 1970s (Harrison & Harrison 2005) and John Robinson saw birds carrying nesting material in 1978. Now their twanging calls are heard all year round in the Forest. Nesting Siskins are remarkably inconspicuous and evidence of nesting may only come when juveniles and adults visit garden feeding stations.

Siskins nest in spruce and pine forests and, like crossbills, are affected by the biennial or geographically variable production of seed cones. They are less dependent than crossbills on these and switch to other plants and invertebrates when necessary. Interestingly Shaw (1990) found that in winters when the cone crop in forests was poor, increasing numbers of both Siskins and Coal Tits visited garden feeding stations. Siskins nested two months earlier when cones that had developed in the previous summer were abundant, which explains the surprising appearance of small flocks in July and August in some years. In the year following a poor cone crop, the start of breeding was delayed until May as the birds waited for other seeds to become available (Mckenzie *et al.* 2007).

In winter many of the Siskins that nest in Scotland move south into England and winter visitors arrive from northern Europe, especially from Scandinavia and western Russia. These wintering birds are less dependent on pine cone seeds and their distribution often mirrors the availability of alder or birch seed. In Wyre flocks of up to 200 sometimes gather in the remaining larch plantations, often with Lesser Redpolls and Goldfinches.

Whilst Lesser Redpolls and Siskins often flock together in winter, in the breeding season their needs are different. Redpolls are associated with conifers but they are also scrub birds, often breeding in young conifer plantations where there is lot of young birch. In the breeding season they mainly eat a wide range of invertebrates, usually collected from trees. In winter they eat seeds, particularly from birch and alder, moving to seed fallen to the ground or on herbs later in winter. At this time they forage more widely with other finches in seed-rich habitats and often visit garden feeders.

Harthan (1946) notes Lesser Redpolls as regular winter visitors with a few nesting in summer. That had probably been the situation for many years until numbers were very severely reduced by hard winters in the 1960s. Between 1970 and 1975 there was a huge recovery nationally and Redpolls probably nested in many more parts of the Midlands than ever before, including Wyre. Over the next 20 years there was a steady decline until numbers stabilised at a low level. At the same time their national distribution contracted (BTO Mapstore). John Robinson notes that in Wyre Redpolls occasionally visit pools in summer so may breed rarely, probably in young conifer plantations. In the last few years there has possibly been a slight upward trend in breeding numbers here. In the late 1980s Rosemary Winnall found a nest in a garden adjoining Rock Coppice.

The redpolls are a complex group of species. The one breeding in Wyre is the Lesser Redpoll. In winter other species may turn up. John Robinson notes that Common, also called Mealy, Redpolls *Acanthis*

Male Siskin *Spinus spinus* [JR]

Male Lesser Redpoll *Acanthis cabaret* [JR]

Goldcrest *Regulus regulus* [JR]

flammea are recorded in Wyre from time to time and that an Arctic Redpoll *A. hornemanni* turned up in the 1980s along the disused railway line, indirectly causing massive traffic jams as bird-watching twitchers came to see it. Four were also seen there in 1996.

Goldcrests occur throughout the British Isles in both winter and summer. Breeding birds are joined by numerous winter visitors moving in from northern Europe, though not all observers believed that the diminutive birds were capable of braving the North Sea crossing unassisted. In places, Goldcrests were known as 'woodcock pilots' because they were thought to travel on the backs of migrating Woodcock. In Worcestershire Hastings (1834) states "it is not uncommon in our shrubberies, approaching close to towns in the winter season, braving the severest weather". They were probably visiting towns in bad weather foraging for food, especially on conifers. Goldcrest numbers were severely reduced by the cold winters of 1963 and 1964, but soon recovered. Since then they have tended to fluctuate, reflecting sensitivity to cold winter weather and an ability to produce many young. Their small bodies (about 6 g) lose heat very quickly on cold nights and icing-up on trees prevents them reaching prey, the small invertebrates found between conifer needles. As conifer plantations have matured breeding numbers have increased: this is apparent in Wyre where they are widespread and common in all stands. Conifers are the preferred habitat, especially for nesting, although they also use mature deciduous woodland.

They also nest in conifers in gardens around the Forest edge.

The much rarer Firecrest is a gem of a bird with a neat black and white eyestripe and golden shoulder patch. For many years Firecrests only occurred as occasional winter visitors or passing migrants. The first British breeding pair was found in the New Forest in 1962. Since then their numbers have steadily increased, mainly in south-east England with a few elsewhere, usually in conifer plantations, but also in oak and beech woods. In Wyre, Firecrests are still very local, but probably overlooked. They have bred in Douglas Firs at Sturt and there are several winter and spring records from the Ribbesford, Trimpley and Arley areas (B. Westwood pers. comm.).

The two 'crests' are similar in many ways but there are differences in feeding behaviour and morphology. Both use their very fine bills to pick up small invertebrates from conifer needles and twigs, but Goldcrests' thinner bills are better adapted for searching between needles. Firecrests have broader-based bills and take slightly larger prey. In addition they have developed larger bristles at the base of the bill to protect their eyes from these larger items. Faced with the choice between searching spruce and Beech in experimental conditions Goldcrests prefer the conifers, but Firecrests show no preference. Goldcrests' toes have more ridges and papillae than Firecrests, and are more efficient at gripping conifer needles (Leisler & Thaler 1982). In winter Firecrests often forage in holly or ivy clumps where they seek out tiny invertebrates.

Birds of scrub and clearings

A flock of Long-tailed Tits moving through scrub, hedges or trees is a familiar sight especially outside the nesting period. During the breeding season they are more of a scrub or woodland edge bird, since the nest is usually constructed in Bramble or other low bushes. The nest is an extraordinary ball, about ten centimetres in diameter, of moss fragments, many feathers and spiders' webs covered with lichen fragments. The feathers are mostly collected from dead birds and provide good insulation. John Robinson notes these birds are common in Wyre, especially in scrubby areas, and he has seen nests in Gorse, Bramble, Broom *Cytisus scoparius*, Blackthorn *Prunus spinosa*, Heather, and even in a garden conifer, and that 80–90% of early nests are predated. The disused nests are sometimes occupied by Hazel Dormice in summer.

For most of the year Long-tailed Tits live in small flocks that continually move round a home range foraging for small invertebrates on twigs and branches, at times visiting garden feeders. In February and March the flocks break up and some individuals (mainly females) move to other groups before a flock reforms. Pairs form and then gradually separate from the flock and start nesting. Many nests are lost to predators and after about the second week in May pairs do not rebuild, but help to feed the young at other nests within the group's home range. Nests with helpers do well and the helped pairs' young survive better that those without help.

Long-tailed Tits are tiny birds weighing a gramme or two more than Goldcrests and easily lose heat during cold winter nights, although they may roost huddled together to conserve warmth. Populations crash after very cold winters but soon bounce back. Over the last 25 years numbers have risen steadily. Research over 19 years near Sheffield showed that warm springs and autumns increase annual survival unless the weather is wet. Cold wet weather in spring demands more energy and nest building thereafter leaves adults in poorer condition to face the autumn. Adults in poorer condition die in cold wet autumns while those in good condition survive, and also survive cold winters reasonably well (Gullett *et al.* 2014). Nevertheless climatic change to warmer, albeit wetter, springs and autumns is probably driving the steady increase in numbers.

Even on the hottest summer days, Tree Pipits perform their distinctive song flights in clearings, often parachuting down to isolated trees in open scrubby places and on ride edges. They nest on or near the ground amongst low scrub, such as Bilberry and Heather, or in grassy places. They are not infrequently parasitised by Cuckoos. Since the late 1980s Tree Pipits have declined severely in England, especially in the south and Midlands while holding up in Wales and Scotland. This is probably due to loss of habitat, especially in woodlands without open places, and the lack of new plantations. John Robinson notes they are fairly common in Wyre, increasing in recent years as

Long-tailed Tit *Aegithalos caudatus* [JR]

forestry has created more coppice plots and clearings. Here and elsewhere young conifer plantations and areas of conifer clear-fell are often used. Tree Pipits winter in Africa somewhere south of the Sahara, and there is a possibility that changes there are affecting European breeding populations. John Robinson once saw an Adder curled up in a nest with eggs. The eggs hatched and the young fledged so the snake was probably basking in a sunny spot rather than lurking in predatory mode.

The soporific crooning of Turtle Doves *Streptopelia turtur* was once common in Wyre. These summer visitors to Europe colonised the British Isles around the first half of the 19th century and gradually spread through lowland England. By 1900 they nested in most English and Welsh counties south of a line from the Humber to North Wales, with a few further north (Holloway 1996). Tomes in 1901 (quoted by Harthan 1946) regarded them as a common summer visitor throughout Worcestershire and noted that Hastings (1834) did not mention the species. This is not strictly true as he does list it, with arrival dates of other migratory birds, as appearing 26 April to 1 May. Harthan (1946) notes them as common throughout Worcestershire, nesting in tall hedges and the fringes of woodland. The first BTO Atlas 1968–1972 (BTO Mapstore) showed a distribution very similar to the one described by Holloway in the late 1800s. A few years later, in 1975, however a decline started which has continued since with an overall loss of at least 90% in numbers and a steady shrinkage of distribution towards south-east England.

Very few now nest in Worcestershire or Shropshire and nationally the species faces extinction. In Wyre Turtle Doves were once found wherever there was scrubby open habitat and John Robinson notes they often nested in 10–15 year old plantations. In Wyre they will also use older conifers for nesting, and in the early 1980s up to four birds sang in mature Norway Spruce in Eymore Wood (B. Westwood pers. comm.). Neville Wilde (2002) spent many nights recording Tawny Owls in Wyre and writes "On the 10 June 1988 the dawn chorus was notable for the number of Turtle

Doves and Cuckoos present". Now they are very scarce, if not extinct.

Turtle Doves require tall bushes for nesting and places with low-growing plants for feeding—big hedges by weedy arable fields are ideal. Nowadays both these features are in short supply in intensively farmed land. Turtle Doves take more grain now than in the past and this is only available for a short period as modern harvesting is rapid and spillage of grain minimal: this shortage has shortened the nesting season. Second broods were once common, but are now rare and so the birds do not produce enough young to maintain previous population levels (Browne & Aebischer 2005). Pressures on the wintering grounds in the Sahel and along migration routes are also likely to affect populations adversely.

Waterbirds in Wyre

Wyre Forest and its surroundings are quite rich in wetland birds. The River Severn and Trimpley Reservoir attract small numbers of ducks and gulls, and Cormorants *Phalacrocorax carbo* regularly commute along the valley. Because the reservoir is on the Severn flyway it attracts occasional rarities such as the storm-wrecked Leach's Petrel *Oceanodroma leucorhoa* seen fluttering over nearby oaks in December 1989. A Storm Petrel *Hydrobates pelagicus* over the Severn at Bewdley in July 1968 must have been an equally incongruous sight. Other unusual birds at Trimpley have included Shag *P. aristotelis*, Shelduck *Tadorna tadorna*, Red-throated Diver *Gavia stellata*, Whooper Swan *Cygnus cygnus* and Yellow-legged Gull *Larus michahellis*. Ospreys *Pandion haliaetus* are occasionally seen, especially in late summer or autumn

when they have been seen plunging for fish among the weekend sailing boats. Wigeon *Anas penelope* are rare birds here, but have managed to hybridise with Mallard *A. platyrhynchos*, producing male and female 'Willards' which graced the reservoir for several years between 2010 and 2012. Although nesting sites are scarce, at least one pair of Great Crested Grebe *Podiceps cristatus* breeds and larger numbers occur in winter.

Well-used footpaths bordering both banks of the Severn cause disturbance, limiting its value for water birds. However, since the 1980s Goosanders *Mergus merganser* have increased in line with the national trend, and up to 80 have been counted between Bewdley and Arley in cold winters. In one ice-bound January they were joined on the Severn by a Redhead Smew *Mergellus albellus*. Goosanders are remarkably confiding and often consort with Mallards in the centre of Bewdley. Goosander breeding has been confirmed recently along the Severn; young chicks were seen in 2014 and 2015 (R. Winnall; C. Reed pers. comm.).

An outstanding wetland feature of the Forest is the Dowles Brook and its tributaries which bring a flavour of Welsh mountain streams. The name Dowles is derived from the Welsh 'dulas', meaning dark, and its cold waters flow over stony beds in the heart of the Forest through oakwoods clinging to steep slopes in places. Along the Dowles are breeding Dippers, Grey Wagtails, and Kingfishers *Alcedo atthis*, which streak like sapphire flares through tunnels of overhanging Hazel. In recent years an equally colourful bird, the tree-nesting Mandarin Duck has colonised the brook and nearby ponds. Some records are completely unexpected, such as the Black Stork *Ciconia nigra* flushed from the banks of the brook in May 1956

Mandarin Duck *Aix galericulata*, male (right), female (left) [JR]

The Dipper *Cinclus cinclus* breeds early in the year along the Dowles Brook [JR]

(Bradney 1957) and the immature Gannet *Morus bassanus* found in July 2008 by Alan Beamish (2008). After recuperation at a wildlife rescue centre, this was later released successfully on the north Devon coast.

The fortunes of the Dowles Brook birds have been followed by two BTO annual surveys: the Water Birds Survey (WBS) 1991–2006 and the subsequent Water Birds Breeding Survey (WBBS) from 2002 to the present day. Both cover about 4.5 km of the brook upstream from the confluence with the Severn. Michael Harrison undertook these surveys until 2007 when Steve Davies took over. Michael has written a general account of both up to 2006 (Harrison 2006), along with a fuller account on surveying the Dippers (Harrison 2007).

The WBS is based on mapping birds associated with water on eight to ten visits, from early March to early July, and then determining the likely number of territories using species maps plotted from the fieldwork. WBBS is basically a transect survey similar to the Breeding Birds Survey (BBS) when all the birds encountered on the transect walk along the watercourse bank are recorded. Both BBS and WBBS are part of national BTO monitoring schemes based on annual standardised recording. The earlier WBS is similar to the original Common Birds Census used for a similar purpose and based on mapping territories.

Dippers are well known for their close association with rocky streams, their habit of bobbing as if on hinges on midstream boulders, their sweet rambling song and their ability to walk under water in search of prey. This includes caddisfly and stonefly larvae and small fish. The Dowles surveys revealed three to five Dipper territories in this 4.5 km stretch, varying little from year to year. Nests are often sited at or near to the same site for many years, sometimes failing through flooding, bank collapse, disturbance or predation. Dippers appear to have been scarce in Worcestershire in the 19th century, but slowly increased until all suitable streams supported pairs. Harthan (1946)

estimated 30 pairs in the county and quoted Steele-Elliott's estimate of ten pairs along Dowles Brook. Hickin (1971) doubted that ten pairs remained although Harrison (2007) estimated five to eight pairs and John Robinson, from observations made over 40 years, considers that the Wyre population has remained at eight or nine pairs.

Nationally Dipper populations have fluctuated over the last 30 years with an overall downward trend starting in the 1970s. They are sensitive to acidification and water-borne pollution which reduce aquatic invertebrate prey, giving rise to lower breeding densities and poorer productivity on acidic than on more neutral streams. Dippers have long been birds of western England, Wales, Scotland and Ireland, and the most recent 2007–2011 BTO Atlas shows a retraction in range and also of abundance (BTO Mapstore). Although Dippers are normally found along Dowles Brook, they will move out onto the Severn in times of low flow when one or two may be seen foraging on exposed river shingle. In cold winters when the brooks are frozen they can be seen feeding in river riffles from ice-bound boulders and tree roots. They often sing in autumn and as they are establishing territories in winter. They have even been heard singing beneath the Bewdley bypass road bridge.

Grey Wagtails are mainly birds of fast-flowing shallow rocky streams bordered with broadleaved trees and they often live alongside Dippers, even using the same midstream boulders as perches. Unlike Dippers they also occur more widely on bigger rivers, usually near locks, weirs or waterside buildings. They are less susceptible to acidification, feeding on a wider range of insects. In Wyre there are around seven pairs along Dowles Brook and its smaller tributaries and by the Severn. Although most Grey Wagtails nest close to water this is not always so, as noted in Wyre by Steele-Elliott (1919–20): "It is seldom that the Grey Wagtail (*Motacilla cinerea*) nests out of sight, or any distance away from a stream … although I have known a nest

Grey Wagtail *Motacilla cinerea* [JR]

Kingfisher *Alcedo atthis* [ML]

in the rock face of the railway cutting through the Wyre Forest, some 250 yards from water. This year a pair chose to nest in a hole in the back wall of my stable, some fifty yards from the stream and on the opposite side of the building. This nesting site had been previously occupied by a pair of Blackbirds, whose nest the Grey Wagtails adapted to their own requirements by merely re-lining it". Grey Wagtails are found more widely in lowland England than Dippers but are more susceptible to cold winters, when they will move into town centres.

A flash of cobalt blue and a sharp whistle over the water tell you that a Kingfisher has gone by almost before you have seen it properly. Kingfishers are birds of linear waterways such as streams, rivers and canals where they create in the bank an upward-sloping nesting tunnel which can be a metre long. At the end is the foul-smelling nest-chamber which can hold up to six chicks along with their droppings and piles of fish offal. The flash floods which are a feature of Dowles Brook may create earthy banks as nest sites, but can also wash out nesting kingfishers. There are other dangers too. For a bird so dependent on open water it is not surprising that freezing conditions kill many: those that survive find shallow open water or move to the coast. They have a great capacity to bounce back and can, if the weather is suitable, rear three broods in a single summer. Despite this ability Kingfishers are of moderate conservation concern (amber warning) because of a general decline throughout Europe. About four pairs nest along the Dowles Brook every year and

they are also a feature of Bewdley town when birds often fish from the quays where water levels are low.

Mallards are a common duck along Dowles Brook and almost everywhere else that has water. They nest on the ground amongst tall plants or under Brambles and sometimes in the crown of a pollarded willow or similar. In winter they gather on the Severn with flocks of Canada Geese *Branta canadensis*, Moorhens *Gallinula chloropus* and the occasional Tufted Ducks *Aythya fuligula*. In November 2012 they were joined for a few days south of Bewdley by a Red-throated Diver.

Mandarin Ducks also swim with Mallards on the Severn in winter. Nesting was first recorded by Dowles Brook in Wyre in 1983 (Harrison & Harrison 2005). A pair used a nest box in Wyre 1988, and John Robinson notes that in 2007 a pair nested in the orchard at Lodge Hill Farm and fledged nine chicks. Another pair was seen to emerge from a disused chimney at the same site. Nests are now found regularly in holes in orchard apple trees, including one at Uncllys Farm in 2008, and other natural sites usually not far from water. Since 2005 there has been an 'explosion' of numbers, and winter flocks along the Severn and at Trimpley Reservoir can contain over 100 birds (192 on 10 December 2009; C. Reed pers. comm.). A pure white individual was seen in a flock of 120 on the Severn near Trimpley on 6 December 2010 (Westwood 2010).

Male Mandarins in full breeding plumage are exotic birds and bring an Oriental touch to this English forest. They are natives to China and other far-eastern countries and were introduced into England before 1745. Since then, through various introductions and escapes into the wild, they have slowly spread throughout England, increasing more rapidly since 2000. BTO Mapstore shows a spread from a small area west of London (1968–72 Atlas) to occupy much of southern and central England south of a line from the Humber to the Mersey. There are scattered records further north and into Scotland. A foothold has been established in Ireland (2007–2011 Atlas, BTO Mapstore).

In Wyre, as elsewhere, Mandarin Ducks have slipped into a vacant niche in the British Isles as wetland birds that perch on trees and nest in large tree-holes (Lever 2013). They are also agile fliers and may be seen on small streams and pools throughout the Forest: when disturbed they can take off vertically, twisting through and over branches with ease. In places there is some competition for large tree holes from Jackdaws, Stock Doves, Kestrels *Falco tinnunculus*, Tawny Owls and even Grey Squirrels *Sciurus carolinensis*. The drabber female incubates the eggs and accompanies her ducklings on the perilous journey to open water soon after hatching. In late spring and summer, when the females are busy nesting, the males form bachelor parties on the Severn, moulting into a drab eclipse plumage while their flight feathers are replaced. In winter both sexes loaf by day and feed at night on the Forest floor on beech mast and acorns, grass seed and invertebrates.

Forest raptors

Wyre probably has more species of breeding raptors now than at any time in the last 200 years. Reduced persecution is the main factor, but the growth of conifers and changing attitudes have also played their part. Kestrels, Sparrowhawks, Buzzards *Buteo buteo* and Goshawks all nest, and Peregrine Falcons *Falco peregrinus* are frequent visitors from local breeding sites in Shropshire and north Worcestershire. Red Kites *Milvus milvus* are recorded annually and may be natural colonists from the central Welsh population which has increased its range to include Ludlow and the surrounding Shropshire countryside: breeding must surely be imminent. Ospreys, as noted earlier, drift down the Severn valley, probably annually and there is always the exciting possibility that the growing British Honey-buzzard *Pernis apivorus* population will colonise Wyre … we can dream.

Kestrels are most often seen hovering and hunting for mice, voles and young birds over fields and open spaces in and around the Forest, and especially in grasslands along the Severn such as Ribbesford churchyard or near Trimpley Reservoir. They nest in tree holes, old crows' nests or buildings such as church towers.

Sparrowhawks are smash and grab hunters of small birds, often visiting garden feeding stations around the Forest or patrolling woodland rides. They have recovered dramatically since the banning of organochlorine pesticides in the 1960s and 70s, and are now a common sight, especially in spring when females perform their remarkable slow-flapping displays. Although Sparrowhawks are smaller and more slender, brief or distant views lead to misidentification as Goshawks. Their large and untidy nests are often constructed in conifers or in broadleaved ivy-clad trees. Sparrowhawks time their breeding to coincide with the fledging of small birds such as tits, but will take a wide range of woodland birds and species of open country. They are masters of manoeuvre and weave expertly between tree-trunks in pursuit of prey, sometimes passing silently and unnervingly close to the observer. In summer the keening cries of young birds are among the few sounds in the conifer woods.

Goshawks first bred in Wyre in 1973 when a female carrying jesses bred for several years: she and her mate were probably escaped birds. The population increased slowly and John Robinson knew of eight different nest sites. Several pairs still nest in the Forest, perhaps fewer than in the 1980s, though the British population is increasing. Nationally the BTO 1968–72 Atlas (BTO Mapstore) showed a few nesting areas throughout Britain. Since then numbers and distribution have increased throughout the country and nesting has

Kestrel *Falco tinnunculus* [JR]

Sparrowhawk *Accipiter nisus* [JR]

Goshawk *Accipiter gentilis* [PW]

started in Ireland. Currently the national population is about 400 pairs. Most occur in well-wooded parts of England, throughout Wales and in lowland Scotland. Goshawks are elusive woodland birds and fleeting glimpses make them prone to misidentification as Sparrowhawks and *vice versa*. Nevertheless they are now scattered through Worcestershire. They eat mammals and birds and can catch prey weighing up to 5 kg, such as a full-grown hare. John Robinson has seen

birds catching Grey Squirrels and Pheasants *Phasianus colchicus*. On clear days in late winter and early spring, the switch-backing display of Goshawks is one of Wyre's most spectacular ornithological events.

Two of the most remarkable changes in numbers and distribution of British birds during the last 40 years have been those of Buzzards and Ravens. Buzzards led the way: Harthan (1946) notes an increase during World War One, and in the 1920s and 1930s, when gamekeepers were mainly absent and Rabbits *Oryctolagus cuniculus* swarmed over the countryside. This was repeated during and after World War Two, and he tells of a nest found by a member of the Women's Land Army in 1944. Eventually Buzzards received legal protection and nowadays they are common throughout much of England, having reached the east coast during the last few years. This change in distribution is well documented by the BTO Atlases which record dramatic differences between 1968–72 surveys and 2007–11. John Robinson's first record in Wyre was in 1980, but the birds now nest throughout the Forest and surrounding countryside. In spring groups of up to ten can be seen soaring overhead. Parties of up to 30 have been seen near Wyre, walking around recently ploughed fields seeking earthworms; they also take reptiles and amphibians and carrion, but Rabbits are their staple diet. They are often seen very early in the morning before it is properly light, presumably to take Rabbits unawares as they feed.

Ravens are following a similar pattern of change and extending their range eastwards. In the 1950s they were mainly restricted to hill country throughout western Britain. Around 40 years ago there may have been a couple of pairs nesting in Worcestershire and

Buzzard *Buteo buteo* [JR]

Shropshire but now they are common in both counties. Their hollow croaks are a feature of modern Wyre where several pairs nest, usually in tall conifers. Ravens bred throughout Britain at the beginning of the 19th century (Holloway 1996), though Hastings (1834) notes that they had become rare. Harthan (1946) regarded Ravens as winter visitors and states that a pair nesting at Park End, Bewdley in 1859 were the last pair to nest in the County. The 1968–72 BTO Atlas (BTO Mapstore) shows them to be on the western fringes of Worcestershire.

The original decline is usually attributed to better farming practices and fewer dead farm animals providing carrion on which Ravens feed, though persecution by gamekeepers and farmers was a factor. "The Raven has an extremely varied bill of fare" (Ratcliffe 1997) and is both scavenger and predator. The Middle Ages were high times for Ravens when people discarded food of all sorts in towns and there was an abundance of dead animals. In later times sheep farming probably provided most carrion and sustained Ravens, especially in areas where sheep died on the hills through poor quality shepherding. Doubtless Ravens find carrion in Wyre and, armed with powerful sharp-edged bills, they are quite capable of killing any animals up to the size of a Rabbit, including small mammals, birds, reptiles and insects. They also probe into the ground for earthworms and other invertebrates and have been seen riding on the backs of sheep, probably looking for ticks.

Little Owls *Athene noctua*, Tawny Owls, Barn Owls *Tyto alba* and possibly Long-eared Owls *Asio otus* occur in Wyre. Little Owls were introduced into England at the end of the 19th century and gradually spread throughout southern England, reaching Worcestershire about 1911. By the 1930s they were common breeding birds, especially in hollow trees in old apple orchards and in pollarded willows (Harthan 1946). Hickin (1971) observed them in Wyre in the 1960s and 1970s. A few remain around Wyre, but since 1985 their national distribution and numbers have declined. Little Owls prey on small birds and mammals, earthworms and large insects, especially beetles. The decline may be related to agricultural changes with the disappearance of invertebrate-rich permanent grassland and the loss of many old orchards with nest holes.

Tawny Owls are common woodland owls and occur throughout the Forest. They are nocturnal hunters, mainly of small mammals, but they have a varied diet which includes frogs, slugs and earthworms. Rosemary Winnall found a dormouse skull in a pellet from Rock Coppice—unusual prey for a Tawny Owl. Once they have established a woodland territory Tawny Owls become sedentary and dependent on knowledge of their area for survival. They usually nest in hollow trees and also in owl boxes in hedgerow trees around the Forest edges. On nocturnal visits to the Forest the familiar hoot of the males or sharp 'ke-wick' call of the females is a regular accompaniment. In early summer the owlets leave the nest and can be seen branching, sitting around while calling hoarsely for food which their parents bring to them for many weeks after they have fledged. Tawny Owls are almost wholly nocturnal and during the day usually roost in dense tree cover, though birds are sometimes heard calling by day. Steele-Elliott (1936–37) wrote of an unusual instance of daylight hunting: "When walking along a ride of

Tawny Owl *Strix aluco* [NW]

Male Tawny Owl [RW]

Tawny Owl chick recently fledged from nest [RW]

my woodland in Wyre Forest, Shropshire, at 4.45 p.m. on April 27th, 1936—a bright summer afternoon—I flushed a Tawny Owl from the undergrowth. It rose heavily but soon settled again on the lower branch of an oak tree and I was then able to make a close approach and saw that it held a small rabbit in its talons.". Harthan (1946) notes: "Common in woods and even in town gardens where there are trees... very bold in defence of its young and can be quite dangerous unless the nest is approached with care".

A Tawny Owl became famous for attacking photographer Eric Hosking in 1937 with unfortunate consequences. Returning to a Tawny Owl hide late at night, he was struck in the face by the owl, and its claw penetrated his left eye. Undaunted, he became a leading bird photographer. Interestingly Jannion Steele-Elliott (1912) described his observations at a Tawny Owl nest in his orchard near Dowles Manor where a pair nesting in a hollow apple tree nearly caused a similar incident. On 11 May he wrote: "At 10.35 p.m. whilst standing on a short ladder to feel into the nest, the entrance of which is some eight feet from the ground, and the hollow eighteen inches deep, I was struck a severe blow on the back of the neck by the male bird; being taken unawares (although I have experienced a similar attack before when climbing up a tree to replace a young one that had fallen from the nesting-hole) I jumped to the ground and pulled my coat over my head just in time to ward off a second attack. Lighting a candle prevented my being further molested, and I was then able to satisfy myself that the hen bird was still with the young." On 20 May he wrote: "I was under the impression I was keeping a sharp look-out, when, without any warning, I felt a terrific blow on the side of my face, and I was partly dazed for the moment. The Owl had torn my ear and side of my face with her talons, and my hearing was affected for a day or so as the result of the blow. From the vicious swoop made I came to the conclusion that it was the female that had now attacked me, and I made a note at the time, wondering how the bird escaped injuring herself by the contact. The impetus with which the swoop is made is sufficient to knock the life out of a rat or similar prey."

Long-eared Owls are a mystery in Wyre and one of the most elusive British breeding birds. They are strictly nocturnal and very hard to find by day, when they roost in thickets or amongst dense conifers. Harthan (1946) states they were nesting in Wyre in the 1890s. Norman Hickin (1971) found one nest in Wyre in "a dusty space between the roots of spruce". They are usually associated with woodland or scrub when nesting and are specialist mouse hunters in fairly open habitats. In winter migrants arrive in the British Isles from Fennoscandia and occasionally from western Russia, these birds settling in open habitats and even hunting in daylight. Although moth-ers regularly run traps in the Forest in summer, there have been no reports of the owlets' 'unoiled gate' calls, but the Forest is large and there is always hope.

Barn Owl *Tyto alba* [MB]

The sight of a Barn Owl hunting low on fanning wings at dusk, over an old meadow or along a country lane, is a rare one in Wyre, but a few pairs do nest, usually in surrounding farmland or in the Severn Valley. Numbers fluctuate depending on the supply of small mammals and weather conditions. Cold, wet springs are damaging and in some seasons pairs may not breed. They tend to occupy favourite holes in trees or buildings for many generations. Those in use may be identified by splashings of white droppings and pellets beneath the entrances. In Wyre analysis of regurgitated pellets at nest sites and roost holes has revealed the extent of their dependence on small mammals, including, unusually, Water Shrews *Neomys fodiens* (Winnall 2013).

Winter birds

At the end of the breeding season great changes take place in bird populations. August and September are usually quiet months for bird song as many birds moult into a new set of feathers at that time, becoming silent and 'disappearing' into cover to avoid predators. They need a good food supply at that time for good feather growth. Some birds change their habits; for example summer visitors Wood Warblers and Pied Flycatchers become tree canopy feeders and are rarely seen. They and other summer migrants depart in August and September and winter visitors arrive. Pairs of resident birds often separate and may disperse. Some locally

Robin *Erithacus rubecula* [PC]

resident species leave the woods to forage in the surrounding countryside, whilst others remain among the trees.

Robin pairs break up and each sex occupies and defends a separate winter territory. Tits tend to gather into loose flocks and forage through the trees together. These flocks move quite quickly through the trees, probably taking the most easily found food before moving on. They may be accompanied by Goldcrests and Nuthatches. Long-tailed Tits form bands of several families and tend to follow a daily circuit of several miles through scrub, understorey and woodland.

Many birds arrive from northern or central Europe and either remain for the winter or move on to Ireland or western Europe. The familiar flocks of Scandinavian breeding Fieldfares and Redwings arrive in October, and in some years there are many

Bramblings, Chaffinches and Blackbirds from similar origins or central Europe. Bramblings are regular winter visitors to Wyre in variable numbers. John Robinson notes they used to be seen feeding on beech mast below trees planted as part of an earlier forestry scheme, many now felled in recent forestry operations. In the 2004–05 winter Britain received a remarkable invasion of Waxwings *Bombycilla garrulus*, when flocks descended on berry-bearing trees in town and country. From January to March flocks of up to 66 birds were seen in Bewdley, in Wyre itself and in a garden at Bliss Gate (Winnall 2005). Waxwings breed in northern Fennoscandia and such irruptive movements follow good breeding seasons and a subsequent shortage of berries.

How many bird species are found in Wyre during the breeding season?

The main system used for monitoring British bird populations is the BTO's Breeding Bird Survey (BBS). This is based on annually repeated transect surveys within randomly selected 1 × 1 km squares of the Ordnance Survey national grid. Two visits are made to each square, one between the beginning of April and mid-May, the other between mid-May and the end of June. All birds are recorded during two roughly parallel transect walks each 1 km long. In some respects the BBS is a development of Yapp's original work. The fieldwork is undertaken almost entirely by volunteers, and the data are analysed by BTO scientific staff. About 4,000 1 × 1 km squares are surveyed every year. The overall aim of the BBS is to obtain an accurate assessment of national trends in species' populations over many years. BBS follows on from data

Waxwings *Bombycilla garrulus* [BK]

collected by the earlier Common Bird Census (CBC) a method based on smaller sites surveyed by painstaking territory mapping of all bird species. The two surveys have been integrated giving population trends over about 40 years. Six BBSs are currently running in the Wyre area with the longest set of results covering 21 years. The survey squares cover a wide range of habitats: woodland, fields, hedgerow, a stretch of the River Severn and Trimpley Reservoir. From a local point of view they provide a list of species breeding in the Wyre area and give some hints of changes. Jim Martin (2000) gave some results from two CBC type censuses in Wyre and, in 2002, preliminary results from three BBS squares

Changes in bird numbers observed over the years in these local squares need to be considered in relation to national results to see if they match real trends or are responses to local changes in habitat (perhaps forestry management) or minor variation in census results (perhaps a change of surveyor). Such effects tend to be ironed out in the large national data set which then shows actual trends. However, taken together, the six squares show that the Wyre area is rich in birds with 98 species recorded in the breeding season over a period of 21 years. Not all are breeding birds: some are passage migrants, others are passing overhead or non-breeders using the Severn or the reservoir (Table 10).

In Wyre square SO7475 is the only BBS square almost entirely within woodland and so contains fewer species than the other five squares because they contain a wide mixture of habitats suitable for more species. The SO7475 transects include plantation Beech, plantation conifers, mature oak woodland, and some patches of regenerating scrub following clear-felling. Fifty-nine species were recorded and of these 16 were recorded every year (Pheasant, Woodpigeon, Great Spotted Woodpecker, Carrion Crow, Goldcrest, Blue Tit, Great Tit, Coal Tit, Chiffchaff, Willow Warbler, Blackcap, Wren, Blackbird, Song Thrush, Robin, Chaffinch). In addition species seen in 19 and 20 years of the 21 were Cuckoo, Garden Warbler, Mistle Thrush, Tree Pipit and Nuthatch. Less frequent were Wood Warblers 14 years, Jays 17 years, Treecreepers 15 years, Bullfinches 11 years, Long-tailed Tits 10 years and Redstarts only in six years. A summary of the birds recorded in each BBS square and the main habitats are listed in Table 11.

Table 10 Summary of number of species recorded during Breeding Bird Surveys in six 1 × 1-km squares

1 × 1 km square	No. of years surveyed	Total no. species recorded	Average no. species each year	Habitat
SO7074	19	80	40	Part woodland, part open
SO7374	21	66	39	Half woodland, half open
SO7472	19	65	37	Mixed countryside
SO7475	21	59	29.5	All woodland
SO7674	15	69	42	Mixed countryside
SO7778	14	87	47	Woodland, reservoir, river, mixed countryside

Table 11 Alphabetical list of birds recorded in all six 1 × 1-km squares surveyed during the Breeding Birds Survey categorised according to their favoured habitat

Woodland and shrubby habitats
Total 56 species
Blackbird *Turdus merula*
Blackcap *Sylvia atricapilla*
Blue Tit *Cyanistes caeruleus*
Bullfinch *Pyrrhula pyrrhula*
Buzzard *Buteo buteo*
Carrion Crow *Corvus corone*
Chaffinch *Fringilla coelebs*
Chiffchaff *Phylloscopus collybita*
Coal Tit *Periparus ater*
Common Crossbill *Loxia curvirostra*
Cuckoo *Cuculus canorus*
Dunnock *Prunella modularis*
Garden Warbler *Sylvia borin*
Goldcrest *Regulus regulus*
Goldfinch *Carduelis carduelis*
Goshawk *Accipiter gentilis*
Great Spotted Woodpecker
    Dendrocopos major
Great Tit *Parus major*
Green Woodpecker *Picus viridis*
Greenfinch *Chloris chloris*
Jackdaw *Corvus monedula*
Jay *Garrulus glandarius*
Kestrel *Falco tinnunculus*
Lesser Redpoll *Acanthis cabaret*
Lesser Spotted Woodpecker
    Dendrocopos minor
Lesser Whitethroat *Sylvia curruca*
Linnet *Linaria cannabina*
Little Owl *Athene noctua*
Long-tailed Tit *Aegithalos caudatus*
Magpie *Pica pica*
Marsh Tit *Poecile palustris*
Mistle Thrush *Turdus viscivorus*
Nuthatch *Sitta europaea*
Pheasant *Phasianus colchicus*
Pied Flycatcher *Ficedula hypoleuca*
Raven *Corvus corax*
Redstart *Phoenicurus phoenicurus*
Robin *Erithacus rubecula*
Siskin *Spinus spinus*
Song Thrush *Turdus philomelos*
Sparrowhawk *Accipiter nisus*
Spotted Flycatcher *Muscicapa striata*
Starling *Sturnus vulgaris*
Stock Dove *Columba oenas*
Tawny Owl *Strix aluco*
Tree Pipit *Anthus trivialis*
Treecreeper *Certhia familiaris*
Turtle Dove *Streptopelia turtur*
Whitethroat *Sylvia communis*
Willow Tit *Poecile montana*
Willow Warbler *Phylloscopus trochilus*
Woodcock *Scolopax rusticola*
Wood Warbler *Phylloscopus sibilatrix*
Woodpigeon *Columba palumbus*
Wren *Troglodytes troglodytes*
Yellowhammer *Emberiza citrinella*

Wetland habitats
Total 27 species
Black-headed Gull
    Chroicocephalus ridibundus
Canada Goose *Branta canadensis*
Coot *Fulica atra*
Cormorant *Phalacrocorax carbo*
Curlew *Numenius arquata*
Goosander *Mergus merganser*
Great Crested Grebe *Podiceps cristatus*
Great Black-backed Gull *Larus marinus*
Grey Heron *Ardea cinerea*
Grey Wagtail *Motacilla cinerea*
Greylag Goose *Anser anser*
Herring Gull *Larus argentatus*
Kingfisher *Alcedo atthis*
Lapwing *Vanellus vanellus*
Lesser Black-backed Gull *Larus fuscus*
Little Grebe *Tachybaptus ruficollis*
Mallard *Anas platyrhynchos*
Mandarin Duck *Aix galericulata*
Moorhen *Gallinula chloropus*
Mute Swan *Cygnus olor*
Pied/White Wagtail *Motacilla alba*
Reed Bunting *Emberiza schoeniclus*
Reed Warbler *Acrocephalus scirpaceus*
Sedge Warbler
    Acrocephalus schoenobaenus
Shelduck *Tadorna tadorna*
Shoveler *Anas clypeata*
Tufted Duck *Aythya fuligula*

Human habitations
Total 7 species
Collared Dove *Streptopelia decaocto*
Feral Pigeon *Columba livia domestica*
House Martin *Delichon urbicum*
House Sparrow *Passer domesticus*
Indian Peafowl *Pavo cristatus*
Swallow *Hirundo rustica*
Swift *Apus apus*

Open country
Total 4 species
Meadow Pipit *Anthus pratensis*
Red-legged Partridge *Alectoris rufa*
Rook *Corvus frugilegus*
Skylark *Alauda arvensis*

Passage migrants
Total 4 species
Common Sandpiper *Actitis hypoleucos*
Fieldfare *Turdus pilaris*
Redwing *Turdus iliacus*
Wheatear *Oenanthe oenanthe*

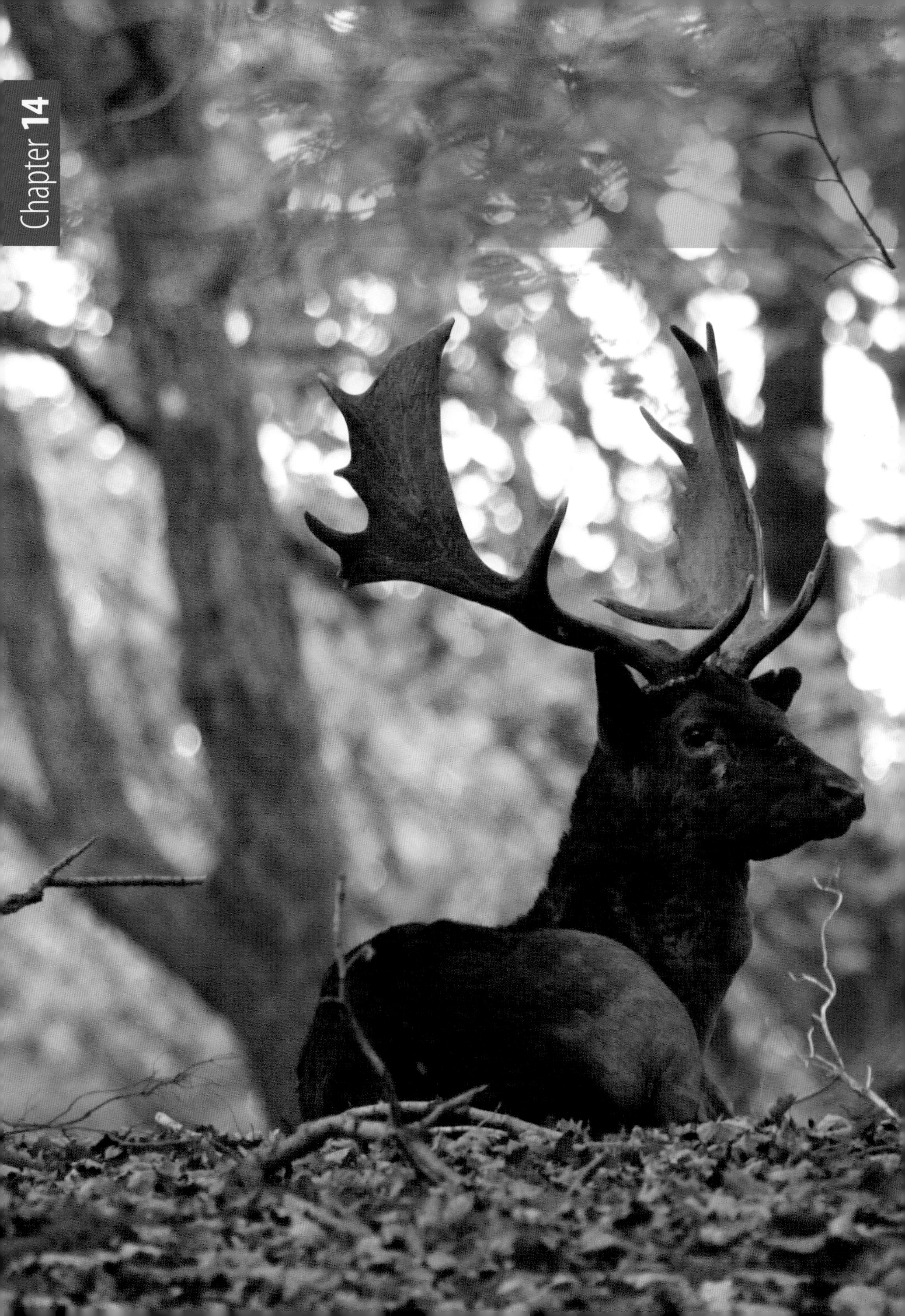

Chapter 14

Mammals

A rustle in the undergrowth, a footprint in the mud, a nibbled hazel nut, a dropping on a mound, or small bones protruding from an owl pellet: all provide clues to the mammals that live in the Wyre Forest. Just a handful are regularly seen alive. Fallow Deer *Dama dama*, Grey Squirrel *Sciurus carolinensis* and Rabbit *Oryctolagus cuniculus*, all introduced species, are the most obvious, but many are reclusive and can only be detected by the signs they leave. Although they can be difficult to survey and monitor, recent use of remote cameras has revealed more about their lives.

Wyre was once a richer place for mammals. Wild Cat *Felis silvestris* and Pine Marten *Martes martes* have long gone, though we should not rule out the latter's return with the discovery of one in a west Shropshire wood in 2015. The last record of the Red Squirrel *Sciurus vulgaris* was as recently as 1963. Other species are coming back. The Otter *Lutra lutra* and Polecat *Mustela putorius* were exterminated during the last hundred years, but with the decline in pollution and persecution, they have recolonised old haunts. Two other introduced mammals, the Grey Squirrel and American Mink *Neovison vison* have settled in Wyre within living memory. Long-term studies into the distribution and behaviour of Wyre's bats have revealed new species, while work on Hazel Dormice *Muscardinus avellanarius* and deer has considerably improved our knowledge of their conservation needs.

Bats

On a summer evening walk along the woodland rides of Wyre Forest you will often see the flickering silhouettes of bats as they flit past hawking for insects in the failing light. This shadowy presence is not only a matter of what we can or cannot see; bats are emerging from the scientific gloom too and our perception of them is changing as technology reveals their world anew. Unless indicated otherwise the sources of information on topics mentioned here are from either Dietz *et al.* 2009 or Harris & Yalden 2008.

Although many naturalists have studied the Wyre area, bats (Chiroptera) have generally been under-recorded mainly because they are nocturnal, mobile and hard to detect at roosts. Without specialist equipment such as ultrasonic bat detectors, it is very difficult to identify bats with certainty, and some cryptic species can only be identified in the hand. In the past most identifications were of individuals found in bat or dormouse boxes, roosting in buildings, or of dead specimens. Only in the last 20 years or so have technology and survey techniques been developed to successfully record these elusive mammals. We now know that of the 18 species of bat currently known in the UK (Bat Conservation Trust) ten have been recorded in Wyre.

Bats are a remarkably diverse group with over 1,110 species worldwide (Altringham 2011) and are the only mammals capable of sustained flight. All bat species in the UK are nocturnal, exclusively insectivorous, and forage, navigate and communicate using ultrasonic calls (Altringham 2003). They are highly adapted to their environment and have evolved a sonar system called 'echolocation' which allows them to build up a sound image of their environment. Bats create this sound image by producing a series of high-pitched ultrasonic calls, inaudible to the human ear, and then rapidly analysing the returning echoes. So highly developed is this system that it allows them to navigate, and to locate, catch and devour their prey in total darkness. Using ultrasonic detectors these calls are used to identify bats to their genus, and some to species level. As well as echolocation, bats have evolved highly sensitive hearing and, contrary to popular myth, excellent low light vision, so much so that some can successfully forage without echolocating.

One of the most exciting things about studying bats is the potential for new discoveries. As recently as 1997 the most familiar UK bat, the Common Pipistrelle *Pipistrellus pipistrellus*, was split into two separate species: Common Pipistrelle and Soprano Pipistrelle *P. pygmaeus* They are distinguished by minute physical differences, and also by the sound frequency of their echolocating and social calls. Both have been recorded in the Forest where they are considered common and widespread.

The Common Pipistrelle is very flexible in its choice of foraging habitat and will feed around street lamps, in places cluttered with vegetation and in the open, adjusting its echolocation calls to suit each particular habitat. In Wyre they are often seen when on their multiple feeding circuits along the edges of woods and in scrub, coppice, dense undergrowth or the tree canopy. The Soprano Pipistrelle is also a flexible forager but more closely associated with wetland and wooded riparian habitats. Both species are often found hunting together in a range of habitats, and are frequently recorded during bat detector surveys, bat box inspections and mist-netting/harp-trapping surveys.

After the two pipistrelles, the Brown Long-eared Bat *Plecotus auritus* is probably the next most common bat in Wyre, and has been recorded throughout the Forest (Hickin 1971; Worcestershire Biological Records Centre). These easily recognisable woodland bats are frequently recorded foraging in broadleaved woodlands and conifer stands. They can glean their prey from vegetation or take it in flight, returning to feeding perches to consume larger items (Altringham 2003). The Brown Long-eared Bats' diet consists largely of moths, but includes flies, beetles, bugs, spiders and harvestmen. They have very quiet echolocation calls and highly sensitive hearing and often locate their prey by the sounds it makes as it flies or moves on vegetation.

Brown Long-eared Bats roost in a variety of structures and locations, including buildings, bat boxes at Lodge Hill and Longdon, and in dormouse boxes in Ribbesford Wood, Wimperhill, Longdon and New Parks (Worcestershire Biological Records Centre). In Wyre there are more records for this species in dormouse boxes than in bat boxes, which may suggest

A Pipistrelle *Pipistrellus* sp., a small bat, fast and jerky in flight, catches small insects in flight [JR]

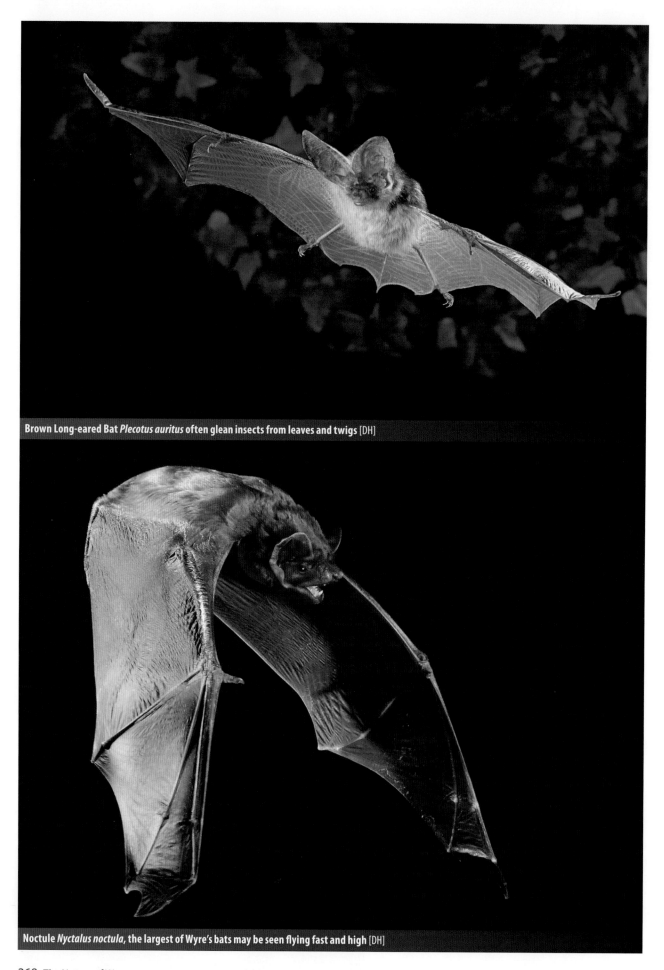

Brown Long-eared Bat *Plecotus auritus* often glean insects from leaves and twigs [DH]

Noctule *Nyctalus noctula*, the largest of Wyre's bats may be seen flying fast and high [DH]

that roost selection and bat box design are not always compatible. Despite being frequently recorded on static detectors, and during walking bat detector surveys, this species has only once been caught during mist-netting and harp-trapping surveys.

The Noctule *Nyctalus noctula* is widespread throughout the Forest, and hawks its prey from dusk onwards high above the tree canopy. It is both the largest and loudest of our UK bat species, and its characteristic 'chip-chop' echolocation call, sounding like bubbling oil in a fryer, is commonly heard during surveys. Noctules are opportunistic and feed on a broad range of prey, including moths, flies and beetles. They hunt over water in the Severn valley, over broadleaved and conifer stands, above meadows and heath, and in open woodland and wood pasture. They have been caught during mist-netting surveys in both Withybed Wood and Town Coppice but not yet recorded in the bat boxes.

Four species of *Myotis*, often known as 'whispering bats' are recorded from Wyre: Daubenton's Bat *Myotis daubentonii*, Natterer's Bat *M. nattereri*, Brandt's Bat *M. brandtii* and Whiskered Bat *M. mystacinus*. The genus is relatively easy to distinguish from other species by bat detector, but it is challenging and often impossible to identify them to species level by their calls alone. Some of the more cryptic *Myotis* species (Alcathoe Bat *M. alcathoe*, Brandt's Bat and Whiskered Bat) can only be identified in the hand by experienced experts (see box, page 270).

On spring and summer evenings small bats flicker at dusk over the River Severn and Trimpley Reservoir, skimming the surface with their wingtips. These are Daubenton's Bats, a species closely associated with rivers and open water. They are widespread, but localised in Wyre. Although usually recorded close to water, they also forage in woodland. Their staple diet is non-biting midges, but they also take other flies, mayflies, aphids, lacewings, moths and bugs from large and small waters including the pools in Hitterhill, Symond's Stool and Town Coppices. Daubenton's Bats are also frequent visitors to the Lodge Hill bat box scheme, and have been caught in mist net surveys along Dowles Brook and at the pool in Symonds Stool Coppice.

Records of Natterer's Bat are few and mostly from the last five years, though this elusive species is probably under-recorded rather than rare. They feed in various habitats including parkland, orchards, over open water, along river corridors, and in coniferous forests and broadleaved woodlands. They are highly agile bats, which can hover around vegetation when foraging, and glean insects from leaves and twigs. In the air they regularly use their tail membranes as a basket to enfold prey. In Wyre bat detector surveys located them foraging along forest rides and woodland edges, although low numbers make their habitat preferences difficult to gauge. They have been recorded in the Forest on static detectors along the old railway line near Shelf Held Coppice, Lodge Hill and along Dowles Brook and also during mist netting surveys along Park Brook

in Shelf Held Coppice. Natterer's Bat is an occasional visitor to the bat box scheme at Lodge Hill.

Brandt's Bat is primarily a woodland bat and probably rare here: the first record was confirmed during mist netting in Shelf Held Coppice in 2013. It prefers to feed in cluttered vegetation in well-structured woodland and woodland edge habitat, especially in damp areas or close to water. In Wyre it has only been found in broadleaved woodland, but elsewhere it feeds in coniferous and mixed woodland.

A Whiskered or Brandt's Bat was also discovered using Lodge Hill bat boxes on two occasions, during the winter of 2013, though fear of disturbing the hibernating bats prevented full identification. Bats are very vulnerable when hibernating and unnecessary disturbance can lower their energy reserves and thus their chances of successfully surviving harsh winters.

Like its fellow *Myotis* species, the Whiskered Bat is considered uncommon in the Forest, but is probably under-recorded. Unlike Brandt's Bat, it has a more varied range of foraging habitats and is not so restricted to woodlands, feeding in open places such as orchards, and meadows (Harris & Yalden 2008). In the Forest it has so far only been located during mist netting and harp-trapping surveys in closed canopy woodland. In 2013 six individuals were recorded during these surveys in three different locations in Symonds's Stool, Lord's Yard and Shelf Held Coppices. As well as a possible individual in the bat boxes at Lodge Hill (see above) there are also a number of historical records of Whiskered Bat roosting in houses in the Forest. In the mid-1980s one was found roosting in the tractor shed at Lodge Hill Farm, and in 1985 an adult is mentioned as having been "shot and buried" somewhere in Far Forest (Worcestershire Biological Records Centre).

The Gothic-looking Barbastelle Bat *Barbastella barbastellus* is a woodland bat that was once thought of as very rare in the English Midlands, but has been revealed by increased monitoring and more sophisticated technology as much more widespread. It is still an uncommon and localised bat, but does occur sparingly in Wyre. It is a moth specialist that forages in the tree canopy and along woodland edges, but it will also feed in the open and along hedgerows, rivers and other linear features (Dietz *et al.* 2009; Harris & Yalden 2008; Russ 2012). Barbastelles can have large foraging territories, and are known to travel as far as 18 km each night. They like to roost in tree crevices, split limbs and under loose bark, but occasionally roost in buildings. In Wyre Barbastelles have been recorded widely but infrequently, for instance along the Dowles Brook, at Beacastle, Bell Coppice and, in 2014, during a mist-netting survey in Town Coppice.

One of oldest bat records in Wyre is of a Lesser Horseshoe Bat *Rhinolophus hipposideros* from Dowles Manor in 1904 (Worcestershire Biological Records Centre). These bats are rare in the UK (Bat Conservation Trust) though locally common in the south west, including parts of Worcestershire and Shropshire. In the Forest there have been no further records, and they have not been found during bat detector, mist-netting or harp-trapping surveys in recent years. However, an individual filmed in late summer 2014, roosting in a workshop next to Ribbesford Wood, proves that they are still present in the area. Other nearby records include one roosting at the old vinegar factory site in Stourport-on-Severn, and another hibernating in a sandstone cave next to Wilden Marsh on the outskirts of Kidderminster.

Although mainly a species of broadleaved woodland Lesser Horseshoe Bats also forage in meadows, along hedgerows, treelines and by riparian vegetation hawking prey in the air or gleaning from vegetation. Prey too large to eat on the wing is taken to a feeding perch to be consumed. It includes moths, flies and lacewings (Altringham 2003; Csorba & Thomas 2003; Russ 2012). The echolocation call of this species converted for human ears by a bat detector is quite beautiful, and has a haunting, warbling quality, reminiscent of the 'Clangers' in the popular children's TV show. It is a high frequency call and easy to miss on a bat survey if the bat detector is tuned too low.

Lesser Horseshoe Bats illustrate the elusiveness of bats generally and in Wyre there are other suspects lurking in the shadows, including two large species, the Serotine *Eptesicus serotinus* and Leisler's Bat *Nyctalus leisleri*. Both have probably been recorded during bat detector surveys in recent years, but not yet confirmed, thus providing a challenge to future naturalists.

There are three other possible resident bats in Wyre: Bechstein's Bat *Myotis bechsteinii*, Nathusius's Pipistrelle *Pipistrellus nathusii* and Alcathoe Bat. Their presence is less likely, however, as Wyre is on the edge of their natural range, and there is a shortage of suitable habitat.

Bats are highly specialised mammals and the management of the Forest and surrounding landscape has a very significant influence on their populations and distribution. The historic management of Wyre would undoubtedly have had a massive impact on them and today, in spite of the mosaic of habitats and the variety of bats present, large areas of the Forest are less than ideal either for foraging, roosting or hibernation. Substantial areas of woodland are poorly structured, with a very limited understorey and shrub layer, an even-aged closed canopy, and with relatively few plant species in the oak and conifer stands. This is largely the result of selected felling in the past, browsing by deer and planting of non-native trees.

In spite of this, the future for bats in Wyre looks good and modern surveys are revealing more about the bat fauna in different parts of the Forest. There are plans, already in progress, to restore Wyre's ancient woodland, remove many conifers and increase the diversity of woodland structure. Together with effective deer control, and the creation of new habitats such as wood pasture, species-rich grassland, lowland heath and orchard, these changes could bring benefits for bats, as well as many other creatures and it will be fascinating to monitor the response of the bat communities.

As naturalists study Wyre, this large block of semi-natural woodland, orchard and meadow, will allow them to observe how bats respond at a landscape scale to land-use change, and to monitor the potential impacts of climate change. There will also be opportunities to find out how important the Forest is, both locally and regionally, for hibernating bats and their movement through the landscape in spring and summer. The monitoring of this elusive group of mammals is still in its infancy and many parts of the Forest remain unsurveyed, but in conjunction with the continuing positive management, bat conservation in Wyre has a very encouraging future.

Bat survey and recording techniques

Survey effort in the Forest has increased significantly in the last decade. Multiple techniques are being used to gain a better understanding of which bat species are here (Barbastelle Bat *Barbastella barbastellus* pictured right [FF]), the size of their populations, and their distribution. Survey techniques include: static automated bat detectors, walked transects with manual bat detectors, bat box monitoring, and, most recently from 2012, harp-trapping/mist-netting surveys (see below). Each method has its strengths and weaknesses, such as accuracy, cost, and degree of invasiveness. Together these survey techniques are being used to gather data to inform habitat management and restoration in the Forest where this has the potential to significantly benefit bats.

Mist netting tends to be used on more open survey sites, such as rides and glades, to survey edge habitats. The nets are very fine, barely visible when erected and similar to those used by bird ringers. They are quick to erect and using a pulley system can be stacked three or more high to capture bats foraging in the canopy. Harp traps are used in more cluttered environments such as scrub, coppice or areas of dense understorey where the use of mist nets is not practical. They are devices that allow bats to be caught without having to disentangle them from a net. They are essentially a rectangle metal frame with two or more banks of vertically strung fishing lines. Bats fly into the traps, unable to detect the lines, and drop into a catch bag attached below. The bats can then be collected from the catch bag unharmed and are examined before being released.

In the case of the cryptic *Myostis* species a positive identification to species level requires multiple body measurements to be taken into account, many of which overlap in their ranges. These include tragus shape and length; thumb claw length; forearm length; penis shape; nostril shape and dentition. Sometimes DNA analysis of bat droppings is also used.

Hazel Dormouse

Until recently the honey-coloured Hazel Dormouse *Muscardinus avellanarius* has been associated with ancient semi-natural woodland maintained by traditional coppicing (Bright *et al.* 2006). This secretive mammal has a reputation for being vulnerable to dramatic changes in land management and most research projects have been concentrated on 'ideal' habitats, where dormice were easy to find. Uncommon and in decline, they are one of the key species adopted by English Nature's Species Recovery Programme (Bright *et al.* 2006) and are apparently scarce in Worcestershire and Shropshire, although all possibly suitable habitat has not been surveyed.

Efforts to assess their distribution nationally, including the 'Great Nut Hunts' of 1993 and 2006 (Bright *et al.* 2006) organised by the People's Trust for Endangered Species (PTES), have provided valuable information, but were mainly restricted to traditional ancient woodlands containing Hazel *Corylus avellana*. They provided a snapshot of the distribution of dormice in Britain: discovering them in other habitats has usually been a chance finding and Wyre is no exception.

An unlucky dormouse that came to grief in Ribbesford Wood during verge mowing operations in the late 1980s was the first inkling of their presence (Rudlin 2000–2014). Its discovery was doubly surprising since most of the Wood was clear-felled in the mid-1970s and replanted with conifers, including Corsican Pine *Pinus nigra* and Scots Pine *P. sylvestris*. When this animal was found the conifer crop was at thicket stage with a variety of young broadleaved trees among the conifers, most too young to flower or fruit: significantly Hazel was almost absent.

Ribbesford Wood is 2 km south of the main Wyre Forest block, although Rock Coppice (which also has

dormice) lies between the two. Farmland and roads probably restrict movement of dormice between these woodlands. Ribbesford is a large wood of over 200 ha and, although mainly a Plantation on Ancient Woodland Site (PAWS), it retains ancient semi-natural woodland characteristics. Was this mouse an unlucky pioneer or part of a thriving population? Following discussions with the Nature Conservancy Council (now Natural England) and local ecologists, in June 1993 30 dormouse boxes were placed near the site where the unfortunate dormouse had been found. In October 1994 seven fresh nests were found in the boxes, along with 12 dormice, including ten juveniles (Rudlin 2000–2014). This remarkable revelation confirmed a strong breeding population, but also raised questions. How did the dormice get here after clear-felling? How did they cope with coniferisation and what were they eating? And, importantly, what management could help them in the future? To try and answer these questions this project began and is continuing.

By dividing the woodland into 17 areas, and surveying each for possible food plants, we found that plantation edges were rich in broadleaved trees, including oak, birch, Alder *Alnus glutinosa*, Rowan *Sorbus aucuparia* and Holly *Ilex aquifolium* (Rudlin 2000–2014). Further into the crop pure conifer dominated the woodland. The stream valleys and adjacent hedgerows seemed more typical dormouse habitat, with many broadleaved trees and an understorey of Hazel. Hedgerows on the western edge of the woodland contained oak, hawthorn *Crataegus* spp., Rowan, Cherry *Prunus avium*, Holly, Crab Apple *Malus sylvestris* and Hazel. Could these areas be a source of colonisation? Bramble, an important food source and safe nesting habitat, was found throughout, but was very sparse and did not flower or fruit under

The Hazel Dormouse *Muscardinus avellanarius* hibernates throughout the cold winter months and is known in some places as the seven-month sleeper. Strands of Honeysuckle bark are often collected as nest material as seen here. [FR]

Hazel Dormouse *Muscardinus avellanarius* feeds on a variety of fruits, seeds, nuts, pollen and insects [JR]

conifers. Honeysuckle *Lonicera periclymenum*, valuable for food and nesting material, was widespread and abundant.

In July 1995 a further 270 boxes were erected throughout the woodland at approximately 20 m intervals around the edges of the ride system in similar habitat to the first discovery (Rudlin 2000–2014). Others were placed in broadleaved areas of streamside and hedgerow. Since then every box has been checked between May and October, and the data collected.

Dormice were soon found in boxes throughout the whole of Ribbesford Wood. Some boxes have been used on a regular basis, others only once. By 2000, 42% of boxes had been used throughout the woodland at some time or another, but only 19% in the broadleaf valleys and hedgerows. The mice generally seemed to prefer the mixed broadleaved trees and conifer edges along forest tracks (Rudlin 2000–2014).

Conifers provide a warm, safe environment for nesting and the horizontal, interconnecting branches create an arboreal motorway system, but they are poor in flowers and fruit. They do however harbour a variety of invertebrates throughout the year, which could in turn support the dormice.

Ribbesford Wood became a key research site in a national project initiated in 2000 when the Forestry Commission Research Branch began studying dormice occurring in PAWS woodlands. Thousands of boxes were erected throughout England and Wales including, in March 2001, 60 boxes in Ribbesford Wood where mice were also radio-tracked and micro-chipped to establish their movements and population density. The project is co-ordinated by Dr Roger Trout (Mammal Specialist at the Woodland Ecology branch of Forest Research), who is licensed to carry out these activities. Most of the radio tracking was carried out by Darren Smith, a Zoologist from Northumberland, with various assistants, including Lorna Bousfield, a Biology undergraduate from Liverpool University, as well as other Forestry Commission staff (Trout *et al.* 2012).

Because the radio-tracking of dormice through thickets of young conifers was almost impossible, it was decided to take bearings on the animals from three points along the surrounding rides in order to pinpoint them. This helped to build a picture of how far animals moved over time and gave an idea of territory sizes in coniferous woodland.

Preliminary analysis indicated that dormice in the 17 ha study site ranged over an area of about 1 ha during the course of a month, a result similar to findings in more traditional habitats (Trout *et al.* 2014). Some mice travelled up to 200 m during an active period, often moving quickly. Little was known about daytime nest sites in conifers and it was assumed the habitat would be of little value. The mice confounded researchers by preferring conifers: a staggering 73% of all daytime positions were found in conifers compared with under 4% in broadleaves. It was a revelation to find tight nests made of pine needles, lined with grass usually close to the ground within the swathes of fallen

needles caught in lower branches. One dormouse occupied six such nests within one metre of the ground along with four other nests, including two in boxes.

It was difficult to confirm feeding preferences because following the mice in dense conifers without disturbing them was impossible. However, the virtual absence of flowering or fruiting plants within the plantation led researchers to conclude that insects were an important food supply. In late May and June however, dormouse droppings were often bright yellow with the pollen from pine flowers, an unexpected food source probably eaten in quantity over the short flowering period.

Dormice usually enter hibernation with the first substantial frosts, but body weight is a more important factor than temperature. They make a small tightly woven nest under logs, in thick hedges or at the base of coppice stools, just below ground where the temperature remains cool and stable (Bright *et al.* 2006). All the hibernation sites identified in Ribbesford were at, or below ground level and would have been impossible to locate without the use of the radio-tracking receiver. Their locations seemed to be random, with some under pine needles away from any trees or stumps. These would be quite vulnerable and pose problems for management: it is impossible to predict where these nests are likely to be and therefore they are difficult to protect during forestry operations taking place in the winter. One nest was found on the edge of an animal track within 4 m of the Forest road.

Dormice can live up to five years (Bright *et al.* 2006). It can be difficult to determine age, unless the animal was chipped as a juvenile. However, chipping suggests that their mortality rate is fairly high and a mouse four years old or older is quite rare. The oldest animal followed so far only used three boxes over a five year period (Rudlin 2000–2014) and was only found in boxes on five occasions. He wasn't recorded at all in one year. However, some animals recorded for only one or two seasons were found far more often and in more boxes. This chipping has also shown movements of animals within the research area. Although some animals do travel reasonably large distances, up to 300 m using different boxes (Trout *et al.* 2014), it seems that their home ranges are similar to those of dormice which inhabit the more traditional broadleaved woodland: about 1 ha thus confirming the earlier radio tracking work.

Woodland management for dormice

Since 2002 the Ribbesford project has focused on finding methods of reverting this 17 ha PAWS site back to native broadleaves, whilst maintaining dormice populations during the work. The results from these experiments could then form best practice guidance to the Forestry Commission and private woodland owners on how to carry out forestry operations with the least detrimental effects on dormice (Trout *et al.* 2005).

A further 140 boxes were erected in the research area in 2002 creating a 'grid' system, and in spring and summer of 2003 38 dormice were 'chipped' with an 8 mm microchip placed between the shoulder blades of each animal weighing over 12 g (Rudlin 2000–2014). In future inspections these animals were traced by using a microchip reader.

In autumn 2003 radio tracking took place again as a prelude to trialling experimental management techniques during the autumn and winter of 2003/2004 (Rudlin 2000–2014). Four different forestry operations or 'treatments' were then carried out:

- *Treatment 1: Hand cut with chainsaws and forwarder extraction (autumn).* Small areas of conifers were felled (approximately 20 m × 20 m) to create small glades within the crop, with the aim that these would regenerate naturally providing viable dormouse habitat by the time of the next operations in five years.
- *Treatment 2: Harvester operation with forwarder extraction (winter).* As treatment one.
- *Treatment 3: Harvester operation with forwarder extraction (autumn).* Two larger areas of conifers were felled (approximately 0.3 ha). This replicates the normal coppice size in the broadleaf scrub habitat, which dormice favour. Again this should regenerate naturally in years to come and provide viable habitat for dormice by the time of the next operations in five years.
- *Treatment 4: Harvester operation with forwarder extraction (winter).* A normal thinning operation removing 30–35% according to standard thinning tables.

Although a huge machine like a harvester might seem catastrophic in the Forest, especially in winter, when dormice are hibernating on or just below ground level, this machine can fell a tree approximately 6 m away from itself. Using a harvester causes less ground damage than a person with a chainsaw accompanied by a trailer on which to stack the timber. Autumn or winter timing was vital. Traditionally conservation work for dormice has always been undertaken during winter, while the animals are hibernating. Part of the experiment however, was to find out how dormice behaved while felling took place (Trout *et al.* 2012). One radio-tracked animal seemed quite happy in his box while chainsaws were working around him. In autumn the dormice can and will move away, but once hibernating they have no escape.

The most important aim in the operations was to maintain as much aerial connectivity as possible between trees and shrubs. Dormice avoid travelling on the ground where possible so it was vital to maintain aerial routes and links between small clearfells after the operations. Inevitably there were gaps where crops had failed, so where aerial connections were lost the forwarder driver pulled a tree across the rack on his last sweep to provide an aerial walkway.

In April 2005 a further 50 boxes were erected in an area of larch *Larix* spp. and Corsican Pine which was planted in 2000. This plantation (known as 'New Plantation') had grown well and provided a thick, mixed habitat of conifers, bramble and bracken. Dormice had been tracked to the edges of the plantation a few years previously but nothing had been done about finding animals in the rest of the impenetrable plantation. Fifteen boxes were erected in May 2008 in the adjacent conifer plantation (known as 'unthinned area') as a prelude to repeating the experimental work of 2003/04. This was intended to see if any of the chipped animals moved over the Forest road during or after the operations. One of these boxes was occupied by two juveniles in October of the same year.

During September 2009 the second phase of experimental work began. With the aid of local volunteers, we removed 279 boxes from the 17 ha site. The only boxes which remained were those in the 16 mini clear-fells created during the 2003/04 felling, (treatments 1 and 2) and in the two larger 0.3 ha clear-fells (treatment 4) in the sites known as Sausage and New Plantation.

The aim of the project was to replicate the treatments in each area over three phases to remove all conifer from the site. Treatments 1 and 2 were combined and worked with a harvester, and the other two treatment methods were repeated. In late September the machines moved, and work in the research area took less than a week, a short but intense period of disturbance. Most of the mini clear-fells remained connected as the harvester operator weaved his way skilfully through the woodland, although the method is far too fiddly when using large machinery and is not practical on a large scale.

Although the experiment is not yet complete and it will take a further ten years to remove all the conifers from this site, much has been learned. All areas of the site still have resident dormice in them and therefore none of the treatment methods have eliminated them completely. However, treatments one and two (small clear-fells) proved impracticable using big machinery and it became more difficult to avoid destroying good habitat after the first round of operations in 2003. This method may work in small woodlands, using small machinery or horse extraction. Treatment four (standard thinning) is the easiest to manage on a large scale, but does not create good habitat for dormice in the short term. Much of the connectivity is lost because about 30% of the trees are removed and the space between the trees increases.

Treatment three (0.3 ha clear-fells) seems to be the best option for long-term dormice management when removing conifers from a PAWS site. This operation replicates the more traditional coppice management in broadleaved woodlands. The areas are large enough to be practical using machinery, yet there is plenty of woodland left undisturbed. The key to the success of any of these operations is not to fell the whole site in one go, and leaving undisturbed 'buffer' zones around areas of operations to act as donor sites is vital. Working in late summer / early autumn, when the animals are active also seems to give them an advantage as they can move away from operations if necessary (Trout *et al.* 2005).

A more detailed account of this work is given in The Worcestershire Mammal Atlas (Green *et al.* 2012) and through the Wyre Forest Study Group Reviews (Rudlin 2000–2014).

Other dormice records in Wyre

Historically dormice have been considered quite common in parts of Wyre, especially along Dowles Brook and the old railway line. The first known record was of a nest and young at Dowles Manor in June 1911 (Worcestershire Biological Records Centre database). Most records are of accidental discoveries, such as in bird boxes. In 1987 the first purpose-built dormice boxes were erected near to Park House and Dry Mill Lane by Michael Taylor and Paul Bright. Records from these boxes are limited but they were certainly occupied on both sites. Nest boxes erected in various parts of Wyre along the Dowles Brook valley since 1995 have also attracted a few animals, but population levels seem low and the animals elusive. The only population that has been recorded regularly is in woodland towards the western end of Dowles Brook, where they were first found in Pied Flycatcher nest boxes in May 1987 by the late Helen Mackaness (H. Mackaness pers. comm.) and latterly by David and Brenda Rea, who now monitor the site. They erected dormouse boxes in 2005 and still find the mice occasionally in both bird and dormouse boxes (Rudlin 2000–2014).

Away from the main forest block, a garden in Bliss Gate, separated from the Forest by a main road but with good hedgerow links to other woodland fragments, has recorded a number of dormice since December 1998. Dormice boxes erected there in 2001, attracted single nests in November 2001 and again in April 2003 (Worcestershire Biological Records Centre database).

In March 2008, approximately 1.5 km from known sites, a nest was found in bracken litter near a young Corsican Pine plantation at Button Oak. Dormouse boxes placed in nearby pines attracted a nest and two youngsters in 2010 and the boxes are now in regular use. A local resident reported that his dog brought back two dormice, and was able to confirm this from corpses kept in a freezer. Since then he has seen dormice feeding regularly from peanut feeders outside his kitchen window (Rudlin 2000–2014).

In 21 years of dormouse monitoring and research, it has become clear to the author that dormice may have been under-recorded because of their complex ecology and the difficulty in finding evidence of their existence where populations are low or unexpected. In recent years dormice have been 'discovered' in a wide range of habitats, including Blackthorn *Prunus spinosa* scrub in Dorset, pure beech woods in Wales, willow carr and reedbeds on the Isle of Wight and conifer plantations in several areas (Bright *et al.* 2006).

Despite these 'new' findings dormice are still local. They must remain protected due to their fragile existence in certain habitats and their susceptibility to further decline. These records do, however, suggest that perhaps these attractive and mysterious animals will continue to surprise us all.

Dormouse boxes have a hole facing the tree trunk so that the dormice can access it easily from above. Tits use these boxes occasionally for nesting. [PR]

Deer

The scuffle of hooves in otherwise silent woodland, or dark shadows which slip unobtrusively between tree trunks are thrilling signs of Wyre's deer. Four species have been recorded in the Forest in modern times: Roe Deer *Capreolus capreolus*, Sika Deer *Cervus nippon*, Reeve's Muntjac *Muntiacus reevesi* and Fallow Deer *Dama dama*. Only Fallow and, much more recently, Muntjac, have established breeding populations. Red and Roe were the only deer species native to the British Isles in the post-glacial period, and both would have been present in prehistoric times, but there is little mention of them in historical documents, suggesting Red Deer at least have been absent since medieval times.

Fallow Deer

The deer most visitors are likely to see and hear in the autumn rutting season are Fallow. Although it is widely stated that they were first brought to Britain by the Normans in the late eleventh century, recent research suggests that the Romans may have introduced small numbers of this species, perhaps a thousand years earlier, for captive breeding to provide fresh meat (Sykes *et al.* 2011). It is highly unlikely that any of these animals survived long in a feral state.

In medieval times several deer parks were established in Wyre, for example the Old Park at Rock, Tickenhill (Bewdley Park) and Cleobury Park (Bradley 1996). When these were disbanded it is thought that few, if any, deer survived. However, a new park, stocked with Fallow Deer, was created during the early or mid-19th century at the present Mawley Hall (Bradley 1996). There is little mention of Mawley Park by contemporary writers, although in 1889 the Rev. Josiah T. Lea, Vicar of Far Forest, wrote "In the severe winter of 1880 and 1881, all the Deer slept on the ice of the river [Rea] which was covered with snow, instead of on the ground which was also covered with snow". This was presumably because it was slightly warmer.

Around this time a mass escape took place from Mawley Hall when a fallen tree apparently breached the outer wall (Bradley 1996). The surviving deer and their descendants established themselves in Wyre,

forming the basis of the modern herd. Fallow are now the most common species in the Forest and, although far less numerous than in the recent past, the winter population is still in excess of 250.

The male, or buck, Fallow Deer grows antlers which are shed each year in the spring and regrown in the summer months. A mature buck may weigh between 53 and 90 kg, and stands just short of a metre at the shoulder. By contrast the doe is about 10 cm shorter and weighs between 35 and 55 kg (Langbein & Chapman 2003). The mating season peaks in mid-October and, after a gestation period of about eight months, a single fawn (twins are virtually unknown in Wyre) is born in June or July, very occasionally into September.

Fallow Deer in Wyre exhibit a wide range of coat colours from white (not true albinos), menil (those retaining their spotty appearance during the winter months) and various shades of chestnut brown (known as 'common') through to black. The 'common' variety constitutes 55% of the herd, and another 40% are black. These 'common' forms are heavily spotted in summer, but lose their spots in autumn when the thicker winter coat develops. They are readily identified by a distinctive 'target area' on their rump and their white underbelly. White and menil deer are much rarer; although at least ten white deer were present in the Forest in October 2014, among them a mature buck without antlers.

The natural life span of a Fallow Deer is 12 to 15 years, largely determined by wear to their molar teeth, leading to malnutrition and ultimately death (Bradley 2000). In practice however the main factors determining their life span in Wyre are culling, illegal shooting, road accidents, and entanglement in discarded wire or stock fencing. Vehicle collisions involving deer are all too frequent and each year at least 40 animals are killed on the Forest roads and many others are badly injured. In the winter of 2006/07, according to the Wyre Forest Deer Management Society's data, 25 deer were killed on just one short stretch of the A456 at Long Bank. Campaigns to raise awareness of the issue, and the installation of reflectors and warning signs, have had only limited success.

After the Fallow Deer *Dama dama* rut, rivalry between the bucks ends, and they spend the winter in small male groups. The deer seen here are both the 'common' colour variety which have the white rear end under the tail known as the 'target'. [JR]

Fallow Deer fawn [PC]

Fallow Deer gather in herds for much of the year, but especially during the winter and early spring. Bucks and does usually form distinct herds, except during the autumn rut. Does and fawns use traditional areas at the heart of the Forest, whilst bucks prefer quieter private woods on the periphery where they graze on adjacent farmland. In July 1977 no fewer than 70 deer, comprising bucks, does and young fawns, were seen feeding in a potato field at Callow Hill. Such gatherings can represent the entire deer population from surrounding woods. In 1988 the summer population may have approached 800, with a winter herd in excess of 500.

The crowning glory of Fallow bucks is undoubtedly their palmate antlers, the mature head being particularly impressive. It is much larger in comparison to body size than that of a bull Moose *Alces alces*. However, as it takes seven or eight years to produce full size antlers, few of these are found in Wyre today (due to mortality before they reach that age). Antlers are cast each spring from early April, mature bucks shedding first, followed in early May by their younger brethren. Antlers are normally cast separately, hours or days apart, which explains occasional 'one-horned' specimens. As there is plenty of food in the Forest, deer tend not to gnaw their own cast antlers, though wood mice *Apodemus* spp., voles and Grey Squirrels *Sciurus carolinensis,* have no such inhibitions, since the bone provides a valuable source of calcium.

Growth of new antlers starts immediately; those discarded are soon replaced by an even larger and more impressive set encased in protective velvet. By early August these are fully grown although still soft, and it takes a couple of weeks for them to harden completely, a process known as ossification. Only then will a buck finally remove the velvet by rubbing his antlers on overhanging branches and young saplings: birch is a particular favourite for this. The often frenzied clacking of antlers during fraying is a sound reserved strictly for the late summer season.

Once the velvet is gone, the bucks prepare for the forthcoming rut. Their testosterone levels rise rapidly, the girth of their neck increases greatly and there is a very substantial enlargement of the larynx, this being most noticeable in mature animals. Around mid-September, having spent the summer months in small bachelor herds, the bucks return to their traditional rutting grounds deep in the Forest. However, as a result of culling and increasing public pressure, most of the does now seek sanctuary on private land around the Forest edge. In 2008, for example, the greatest concentration of does was found not around the old familiar ruts, but rather in small woods and gardens near Far Forest, where a herd of some 40 does and followers was frequently seen. This same pattern was repeated in following years.

Rutting stands are often established in beech or oak woodland, presumably to take advantage of the ready supply of acorns and beech mast in the autumn. Many of the major rutting stands are on the permanently blackened soils of old charcoal hearths, which appear to be much prized by the master bucks for their rutting scrapes. They often urinate in them before lying down in the smelly mixture, although they do not actually wallow as Red Deer stags often do. By definition, such habitats are necessarily open, providing only limited cover for deer, which are easily disturbed by the approach of people and dogs. Therefore, nowadays most mating activity takes place at night.

At the peak of the rutting season a master buck will repeat his intimidating belching call, known as groaning, for many hours on end. This attracts receptive females to his stand, which is defended vigorously, and warns rival males of his presence and status. Bucks rarely rut on their home ground, and some individuals travel many miles from their summer quarters to court the does. In the 1970s and 80s, antlered masters from Arley Wood, Chorley Covert, Deuxhill and Billingsley regularly 'came in' for the rut (Bradley 1996), holding stands on New

Fallow Deer bucks lock antlers in a fight in Wimperhill during the rut [SC]

Parks, Longdon Wood and Wimperhill. At the same time, well to the south of the main block, bucks from Wissetts Wood, Gaudywood Park and the Mawley Estate found their way to the major ruts at Coachroad and Bell Coppice.

The crack of antlers colliding in combat (Bradley 2007a) was once, along with vociferous groaning, a sound evocative of the autumn wildwood, but is now rarely heard in Wyre. By mid-November the mating season is essentially over for another year, and the Forest is strangely quiet. The bucks gradually recover their weight and condition, helped by the crop of acorns and beech mast, before dispersing to their winter quarters where they reform into small bachelor herds. Their glossy summer pelage is now replaced by a duller, thicker coat in preparation for the rigours of winter which not all will survive.

Roe Deer

Roe Deer sightings are few, but always noteworthy. They include a young buck in June 1977 at Hall of Hammonds Coppice, another buck in 1992 feeding on Winwoods Farm, and a fine six-pointer (buck with antlers having six tines or branches) in 1994 on New Parks. In early 1995 another young buck was seen to the north-west in Maxfields Coppice, and then later in Malpass Wood. In August 2002 a mature buck was seen mating with a young doe in Chamberline Wood, the first confirmed report of a Roe doe in Wyre Forest. There were though no further sightings of these deer or any offspring. However, Roe are still present in small numbers and bucks have been seen quite recently in Ribbesford Woods and, in October 2013, near the remnants of the once mighty Mawley Oak. There are frequent records to the south of Wyre in the Dunley and Abberley areas and a good population can be found in the Mortimer Forest west of Ludlow. But thus far a breeding herd has not established itself in Wyre Forest's main block.

Sika Deer

In 2005 a young Sika stag was encountered following a group of Fallow does in New Parks during the October rut, although the two species cannot successfully interbreed. This animal was later filmed by a local deer watcher and subsequently shot on Forestry Commission land at Brand Wood. The antlers were of exceptional quality, suggesting that while it was most probably an escaped animal it had been living wild for some time. There are few other records of Sika in the main Forest area. Some years ago, a yearling stag (brocket), an escapee from Shatterford Lakes Wildlife Park just north of the Forest, became trapped in a Bewdley car park. In 2012 other individuals from the same park took up residence in nearby woods at Arley and Spring Coppice. Since then there have been several sightings of stags and also a hind with a male calf. It is not known if any of this group survives, but in the winter of 2013/14 there were reports of a hind and a calf on the Mawley Estate.

Young Reeve's Muntjac *Muntiacus reevesi* [JR]

Reeve's Muntjac

Since numerous escapes from the Woburn Abbey estate in the early 1900s Muntjac have become increasingly widespread, especially in south and east England (Harris & Yalden 2008). They were first seen in Wyre in 1980 at Longdon Orchard, although there were no further sightings until July 1986 in New Parks. Since then, and particularly over the past ten years, their barrel-shaped forms and raucous barks have become increasingly common within the main forest block and in most of the outlying woods. But, due to their small size, about the same as a Labrador dog, and preference for dense undergrowth, they often go largely unnoticed. These elusive deer graze forest plants, especially ground flora, and can cause significant damage in coppiced areas. Management policy is to reduce their numbers wherever possible. Fenced areas (designed to keep Fallow Deer out) can provide refuges for Muntjac which are adept at squeezing under the fences. More are also being killed on local roads, which suggests a major population expansion. They are also seen occasionally in urban and suburban areas in neighbouring Bewdley, Stourport-on-Severn and Kidderminster (Rudlin pers. comm.)

Deer management

As ruminating herbivores, Fallow Deer help to shape the Forest. Although they are primarily grazers, they also browse the shoots of many broadleaf species and, if their favoured forage is not readily available, they will also resort to Heather *Calluna vulgaris*, Holly *Ilex aquifolium*, and even bark. In autumn they feast on acorns, beech mast and fungi. In winter, particularly in severe and snowy weather, bramble leaves provide a welcome source of nourishment. Nevertheless short, sweet grass is preferred above all else, especially in spring. They have no natural predators (Bradley 2007b), and if numbers become excessively high there may well be unacceptable damage to young coppice and ground vegetation, and major depletion of associated

Fallow Deer like to eat the succulent new leaves of Holly and other trees often leaving a browse line showing the height to which they can reach. Small Holly bushes can look like forest topiary. [RW]

invertebrates, so to maintain the population at a reasonable level culling is undertaken annually.

The Wyre Forest Deer Management Society was formed in 1977 to encourage landowners to manage the deer of the Forest in a collaborative manner. The main aims of the society are to study, conserve and protect from abuse the deer of the Forest whilst undertaking humane control measures. An annual census of the Fallow Deer has been carried out in March each year since the Society was first formed. During the mid-1990s damage to farmers' crops and to the Forest ecosystems became a major issue. In 1997 the Society decided to reduce the population to a level most landowners felt acceptable, not an easy task as each landowner has a different opinion on what constitutes acceptable damage. However, it was agreed that a spring population of 300 was about right. (This gave a summer population, after the fawns are born of approximately 450.) Since then the population has fluctuated, as would be expected, but has not increased dramatically at any stage. In 2013 this figure was reduced once again to 250 following deer impact assessments, and Site of Special Scientific Interest condition assessments, which showed unacceptable levels of damage in many places. Natural regeneration of oak was being suppressed by a combination of poor light levels and deer browsing, so in areas of dedicated oak coppice fencing became necessary, and many deer exclosures have been erected since the turn of the century to help protect vulnerable sites (Southcott 2007). Woodland managers have been encouraged to improve light levels beneath broadleaved trees to boost this process. It is hoped that a combination of a reduced deer population and improved light levels will result in an increase in food availability, and a decrease in the impact deer have on oak regeneration. Ultimately that should lead to an improvement in the structure and diversity of Wyre's ancient woodland.

Visitors to Wyre enjoy seeing deer roaming the Forest, but one of the major management challenges for the future is to balance the remaining deer population with the aims of long term woodland management, and the requirements of the key native flora and fauna (Green *et al.* 2012).

Other mammals

After deer, Fox *Vulpes vulpes* and Badger *Meles meles* are the largest native mammals in Wyre. Live individuals are only seen occasionally but they are often recorded as road casualties, or from signs of their presence. The shallow Forest soils are mostly unsuitable for excavation by Badgers and the established setts tend to be around the edge of the woodland and in the dingle valleys. Badger latrines and tracks provide information on territories and diet. With their links to bovine tuberculosis, Badgers are not popular with livestock farmers, and the owners of neighbouring strawberry fields are certainly not keen on their nightly visits. In some years, and usually in early spring, local lawns, meadows and school playing fields are regularly dug over by badgers as they search for soil invertebrates, especially leatherjackets, the larvae of craneflies.

In 2006 Rosemary Winnall obtained night-time footage of badgers frequenting a garden in Bliss Gate and this provided some information about behaviour away from the sett. When two or more badgers met, the dominant animal would raise its tail and scent-mark the backs of others from the subcaudal gland below the base of the tail. This marking was repeated on some of the garden plants such as lavender bushes.

A reference to the find of 250 golf balls in a Badger sett (MacDonald & Barrett 1993) resulted in some experiments using peanuts, hen eggs (raw and hardboiled), ping pong balls, and golf balls. Whenever a golf ball was present, the badger immediately ignored everything else including the food, collected the golf

Fox *Vulpes vulpes* [JR]

Badger *Meles meles* [JR]

ball and went off with the trophy. Moving the remote camera around the garden, showed this was taken out of the garden, and although neighbours were alerted to look out for the labelled and dated balls none were ever recovered. Perhaps they are down inside a sett somewhere. When there were encounters between fox and badger the fox almost always gave way and slunk off, although on one evening a badger and a fox fed alongside each other for 20 minutes, both in relaxed mode with the badger lying down to feed.

A walk in Wyre will often cross the route of a Fox whose distinctive scent envelopes you as you pass. The animal's twisted droppings also provide clues to recent activity. Foxes and Badgers are regular visitors to Wyre's orchards in the autumn, scrumping the windfalls, especially plums and damsons, whose stones are telltale signs in their droppings. Wing feathers found from a predated bird that have been bitten off leaving jagged edges indicate a fox kill: a bird-of-prey plucks out the feathers (Harris & Yalden 2008).

Foxes do not live communally like Badgers, but dig their own temporary earths for shelter or as breeding dens, although occasionally a fox is seen curled up asleep above ground. Foxes are particularly evident in December and January during the mating season, when the shrill scream made mainly by the vixen reverberates in the darkness of the night, a hair-raising sound. Small cubs are sometimes seen playing in the sunshine outside the breeding den in April or May, and may be seen pouncing on pieces of bone, tossing feathers in the air, and playing chase with their siblings.

Otters, once common across the region, declined from the mid-1950s after the introduction of organochlorine pesticides (Birks and Robinson 1995). They are thought to have become extinct in the area in the early 1970s. Legal protection in 1978, the ban on the use of dieldrin and aldrin, and conservation efforts resulted in a gradual recovery and fresh Otter signs were found on Dowles Brook in the summer of

American Mink *Neovison vison* [JR]

1987 (Birks & Robinson 1995). Since then, numbers have slowly increased. Their nocturnal behaviour means that they are rarely seen, but their droppings or spraints, which have a distinctive sweet musky smell, are a sure sign of their presence. Otter spraints are now easily found at stream confluences or on prominent features along Dowles and its tributaries. In 2014 a mother and two cubs were filmed at night with Rosemary Winnall's infra-red remote camera on Lem Brook, proving breeding success in the locality. The presence of several fishing pools in and around Wyre must have had some influence on their successful re-establishment. Dissection of otter droppings collected on Baveney Brook in 2009 and 2013 showed the diet included Common Frogs *Rana temporaria* and Signal Crayfish *Pacifastacus leniusculus*. Otters wander widely, often away from water and two recent road casualties have occurred, one near the top of Bewdley bypass and the other on the Bewdley/Stourport Road south of Blackstone.

American Mink have been present along the River Severn for many years. There were a few escapees from fur farms in South Shropshire as early as 1939, but they were first recorded along the River Severn in 1967 and had reached the Dowles catchment by the mid-1970s

Otter *Lutra lutra* [BK]

(Birks & Robinson 1995). Live sightings have occurred frequently since then, both along the Severn and on Dowles and its tributaries. As Otters and Polecats increase, Mink numbers appear to be declining (J. Ford 2014 pers. comm.).

The familiar plop of a Water Vole *Arvicola terrestris* along a riverbank or streamside was a common sound along the Severn and at the lower end of Dowles Brook, at least up to the early 1980s (J. Bingham 2014 pers. comm.). But in line with a national decline, a survey by the Worcestershire Wildlife Trust in 1999 showed that they were extinct in and around Wyre, probably because of predation by Mink (Green *et al.* 2012). The voles' sedentary nature makes them easy prey for this carnivore which can wipe out populations in a short time. According to the Worcestershire Biological Records Centre there have been no known records of Water Vole along the length of the River Severn in Worcestershire since 1995. It is of interest to note that Muskrats *Ondatra zibethicus* were living in the river at Bewdley for a while after escaping from their fur farm near Shrewsbury in the early 1930s (Pickvance & Fincher 1957). A successful eradication programme across the UK halted their spread.

Polecats are thought to have become extinct in Worcestershire around 1900 following heavy persecution, although they survived in very low numbers in western parts of Shropshire and Herefordshire (Birks & Robinson 1995). From the 1950s however, when persecution decreased, they began to recolonise the Welsh Marches and the first animals were seen again in Wyre. Now, although they appear to be widespread, live animals are rarely seen and most records are from roadkills, particularly at one or two regular crossing places, such as at Blackstone, Lem Bank and Callow Hill. Escaped Ferrets *Mustela furo,* the domesticated form of the European Polecat, have occasionally been spotted and rescued from the Forest. Pine Martens have been extinct in Wyre since about

1850, and the nearest confirmed live sighting is in mid-Wales (J. Birks 2010 pers. comm.) Their return to Wyre cannot be discounted however as they are known to be able to travel long distances (Birks & Robinson 1995) and in the summer of 2015 a Pine Marten, thought to be a wild specimen was photographed in a wood in west Shropshire.

The sight of a Stoat *Mustela erminea* or a Weasel *M. nivalis* in Wyre is always a matter of luck, though Weasels are seen more often. Like the Polecat, the Stoat prefers to prey on rabbits, but will readily take small rodents and birds (Harris & Yalden 2008). The Common Buzzard *Buteo buteo* that has recolonised the area in recent times also competes for rabbits and this may possibly have influenced Stoat numbers as these mammals do not appear to be as common as they used to be (Birks & Robinson 1995). The desperate squealing of a rabbit can alert one to the sight of a Stoat killing its prey with a fatal bite to the back of the neck. The rabbit is much larger than the predator, but the Stoat is still able to drag it back to its den or to cache it for eating when food is short. Stoats are very occasionally seen in ermine—a white coat and black tail—in very cold winters. One was observed in Rock Coppice on 18 December 1983: a beautiful but rare winter sight in Wyre. Female Stoats are unusual by becoming sexually mature at two to three weeks when still blind, deaf and hairless (Harris & Yalden 2008). They are mated by adult males and are usually pregnant by the time they are weaned. Weasels do not demonstrate the same behaviour and females are not mature until they are about four months old (Harris & Yalden 2008). Weasel numbers are most probably influenced by the fluctuating numbers of small mammals in Wyre (J. Birks 2010 pers. comm.). In good rodent years they may be glimpsed running across roads, or busily twisting and turning through the undergrowth in their search of prey. Sometimes they become prey: there are several records of local cats catching weasels.

The Weasel *Mustela nivalis* feeds mainly on mice and voles, its size and shape enabling it to hunt through rodent tunnels and runways.
[JR]

The Brown Hare *Lepus europaeus* with its long black-tipped ears is most easily seen in winter on farmland close to the Forest, though it is occasionally seen in dense woodland. [JR]

Rabbits are mainly nocturnal or crepuscular, but their droppings are easy to spot and provide evidence of their presence. They are not very common within woodland but are more frequently found around the Forest fringe. Since myxomatosis reached the area in about 1954 (Pickvance & Fincher 1957), rabbit numbers have fluctuated according to the virulence of the infection within the population. When young rabbits start to come above ground, they can easily be seen feeding along the sides of the Bewdley bypass. From time to time black or sandy coloured individuals are present, presumably after a pet rabbit has cross-bred. Brown Hares *Lepus europaeus* are locally common around the edge of the Forest, mainly on farmland, including Heightington, Horsehill, Huntsfield, Eymore, Meaton and Trimpley. They are sometimes seen lolloping along the lanes, feeding, or chasing each other in the fields, especially at dusk. At Eymore Wood they are frequent in the younger plantations of conifers and amongst broadleaved trees.

Hedgehogs *Erinaceus europaeus* are not common within the Forest, although they used to be seen regularly in gardens close by, but records of live animals are now much less frequent. Occasional road casualties are recorded, but even these have decreased substantially around Wyre in the last few years, a worrying indication of the decline of this familiar prickly animal. Like other hibernating mammals, hedgehogs are vulnerable in mild winters during which they may wake, but will be unable to find sufficient food to survive, and so vital fat reserves are depleted.

Moles *Talpa europaea* are found throughout Wyre, especially where the soil is deeper and where earthworms, their main food, are abundant.

Hedgehog *Erinaceus europaeus* [JR]

Mole *Talpa europaea* [JR]

Water Shrew *Neomys fodiens* [RW]

Conspicuous molehills provide evidence of their presence, although these are not so easily noticed amongst the woodland ground vegetation. The animals themselves are seen only rarely and sightings are generally of juveniles in the autumn when they venture above ground to move off to establish territories of their own (Harris & Yalden 2008). A survey for the Worcestershire Mammal Atlas, that mapped the presence of molehills in fields around Wyre in 2006, showed that they rarely occurred in the bright green pastures that had been intensively managed.

Three species of shrew are found in Wyre. Common Shrew *Sorex araneus* is the most commonly recorded species and is often heard squeaking as it hunts among hedgerows or along forest rides. Only a very close encounter will allow a Pygmy Shrew

Common Shrew *Sorex araneus* [JR]

S. minutus to be distinguished from young Common Shrews, although adults of the latter are conspicuous by their larger size. Adult Pygmy Shrews weigh on average 5 g the same as a twenty-pence coin. Records for both species include animals found under reptile refugia, killed by cats, in dormouse boxes, alive in house lofts, and dead in abandoned drink cans. The larger and darker Water Shrew *Neomys fodiens* is a much rarer mammal, although it has been recorded from time to time along Wyre's streams, particularly where there are good numbers of aquatic invertebrates and riparian vegetation for cover. There have been several sightings at Knowles Mill in recent years. The shrews also occur on very small tributaries and away from water. The identification of their droppings from baited feeding tubes, as used in the Mammal Society's Water Shrew Survey 2004/2005 (Mammal Society website), is one way of establishing their presence or absence, and a survey using this method is continuing in Wyre (Winnall 2013a). The skulls of all three species are easily identified in owl pellets. Of 836 small mammal skulls identified in pellets collected from a Barn Owl *Tyto alba* box at Haye Farm near Bewdley in 2012, 118 were from Common Shrews, 25 from Pygmy Shrews and six from Water Shrews (Winnall 2013a).

Bank Voles *Myodes glareolus* and Field Voles *Microtus agrestis* are thought to be common and widespread in and around Wyre, although it is well known that numbers can fluctuate considerably from one year to the next (Harris & Yalden 2008). Field Voles prefer grassland and are an important ingredient in the diet of Barn Owls: their bones invariably turn up in the pellets and their skulls can, with practice, be

Field Vole *Microtus agrestis* [PR]

Yellow-necked Mice *Apodemus flavicollis* [JR]

distinguished from those of Bank Voles. Conversely, the Tawny Owl *Strix aluco*, which hunts more in woodland, catches more Bank Voles. Jannion Steele-Elliott may have been the first person to document this species in Wyre; he writes in 1894 "Bank Vole in Worcestershire and Shropshire. During the months of February and March I trapped the Bank Vole freely in the Wyre Forest, which covers a considerable area of both these counties. It has been recorded once before in Shropshire (Zool. 1888, p.184), at Eyton, some thirty miles distant, but, to the best of my knowledge, not in Worcestershire. If more naturalists would pay attention to the distribution of the mammals within their districts, this species would probably prove to be far from rare, if occasionally somewhat local." (Steele-Elliott 1894b.)

Two other common rodents, the Wood Mouse *Apodemus sylvaticus* and Yellow-necked Mouse *A. flavicollis* are not easy to tell apart without a close view. The latter, which is a little larger, has a yellow collar across the top of its chest. Although 'yellow-necks' have an uneven distribution in the UK, they are commonly found here, both in woodland and around houses. Although mouse bones are found frequently in owl pellets, the skulls of the two species cannot easily be distinguished. The animals have been recorded from live trapping, on remote camera footage, observed on bird feeders and under reptile refugia, and killed by cats. Both species have been found breeding in dormouse boxes and some of these boxes have occasionally been used for food caching. Phil Rudlin has observed boxes crammed full with either crab apples, holly berries, or acorns, but never a mixture. Wood Mice have been recorded on an infrared camera collecting Guelder-rose *Viburnum opulus* berries, bringing them to a feeding platform, extracting the seeds to eat and leaving the flesh behind.

The House Mouse *Mus musculus* with its associated musky 'acetamide' smell was introduced into Britain in the Iron Age (Harris & Yalden 2008) and used to be very common round habitations and on arable land in the district (Pickvance & Fincher 1957), but there has almost certainly been a decline due to changes

in agricultural practice. Records are now few and far between, but it has been identified from local houses, occasionally from owl pellets, and, like the shrews, found dead in empty drinks cans, lured in no doubt by the sweet-smelling residues.

Harvest Mice *Micromys minutus* are not often found, although they may be under-recorded. John Robinson found several nests in hedges and in a bean field on the northern edge of the Forest near Kinlet in the 1980s (Birks & Robinson 1995), but this is the only record we have for this species. Are they really that rare, or just overlooked? Brown Rats *Rattus norvegicus* are ubiquitous, although they are more readily found on agricultural land and near habitation. They have been seen on remote camera footage, on one occasion feeding on a dead Signal Crayfish along Lem Brook. Rats often have well defined runs and identifiable droppings that provide evidence of their presence around farms, houses and along hedgerows, especially near to where grain is stored or fed to animals. The popularity of feeding wild birds has increased the numbers of rats in some local gardens.

Grey Squirrel *Sciurus carolinensis* [RW]

Red Squirrels were still common in the area in the early 1900s (Tomes 1901b) and Norman Hickin remembered them from the Wyre Forest as a boy (Hickin 1971). They probably became extinct in the 1960s, the last official record being from Hawkbatch valley in 1955 (Pickvance & Fincher 1957). However, there is a reliable report of a Red Squirrel being shot near Chamberline Lodge in 1963 (E. George pers. comm.). They were displaced by Grey Squirrels, which were first introduced into Britain from America in the 1820s. The release of some in Birmingham in 1912 is thought to be the cause of their arrival in Wyre between 1930 and 1944 (Pickvance & Fincher 1957). Fred Fincher recorded them along the Dowles Valley in 1949 as far upstream as Baveney Brook. Grey Squirrels are disliked intensely by foresters because of the damage they do to trees, stripping the bark of broadleaved trees in the spring, perhaps to feed on the rising sap, and damaging the timber. In 2008 Steve Davies counted 30 Grey Squirrels in one monad in New Parks (Davies 2008). Attempts have been made to control them, but numbers remain as high as ever. They are not restricted to woodland, but readily take up residence in gardens and along hedgerows.

During the winter of 2012–2013, whilst the Severn was in flood and weirs overtopped, a Grey Seal *Halichoerus grypus* made its way up the river to Wyre from the Bristol Channel, probably following Atlantic Salmon *Salmo salar* swimming upstream towards their spawning grounds. It was first spotted near Powick by members of the Wychavon Kayak and Canoe Club on 17 November 2012 (Winnall 2013b) who named the animal Keith after the Scottish aristocrat and Royalist Commander Colonel George Keith. (He fought for Charles I against the Roundheads in the English Civil War, and his troops were eventually defeated as they tried to defend Powick Bridge in the Battle of Worcester in 1651.) Although the seal turned out to be a female, the name stuck. She was first seen in Bewdley

on New Year's Day 2013 and stayed until at least the 17 January, drawing in visitors to watch her swimming close to both onlookers and boats. She became quite a celebrity and gathered an internet following with her own Facebook page and Twitter feed. However opinion divided when she was seen eating Atlantic Salmon, Chub *Squalius cephalus*, Pike *Esox lucius*, Barbel *Barbus barbus*, and quayside Mallard ducks *Anas platyrhynchos* (Winnall 2013b). She stayed in the river for some months between Gloucester and Bewdley and caused a lot of interest during her stay, enabling many people to obtain a close encounter with this mammal in a most unexpected setting, a hundred miles from the sea. It is likely that prior to the construction of locks and weirs along the Severn, the arrival of seals would have been more frequent, but this animal's progress upstream was helped by exceptionally high river levels.

To conclude, greater Wyre is home to a large number of mammals, many of which go unobserved. When the wind is in the right direction we might even hear the unexpected, such as the roar of a lion or the howling of a wolf from the nearby Safari Park. There have been odd glimpses of what might have been a 'big cat' in the vicinity over the years too, for example Winwoods Farm, Sturt Common, Tiphouse Farm (C. Bradley pers. comm.) but no confirmed sightings. A few of the introduced species that have no natural predators can cause habitat destruction and may need to be controlled, whereas some of our indigenous mammals may be close to extinction. As Wyre is one of the largest connected areas of woodland in the country, it is big enough to provide habitat for many different mammal species, but with increased pressures on our countryside, changes in land use and agricultural practice, plus climate change, mammal populations are vulnerable. Recording their presence, and where possible surveying their status and distribution, is important if population changes are to be monitored.

Keith the female Grey Seal in Bewdley

Grey Seal *Halichoerus grypus* [RW]

Surprised onlookers watch Keith the seal close to the bank [RW]

Chapter 15

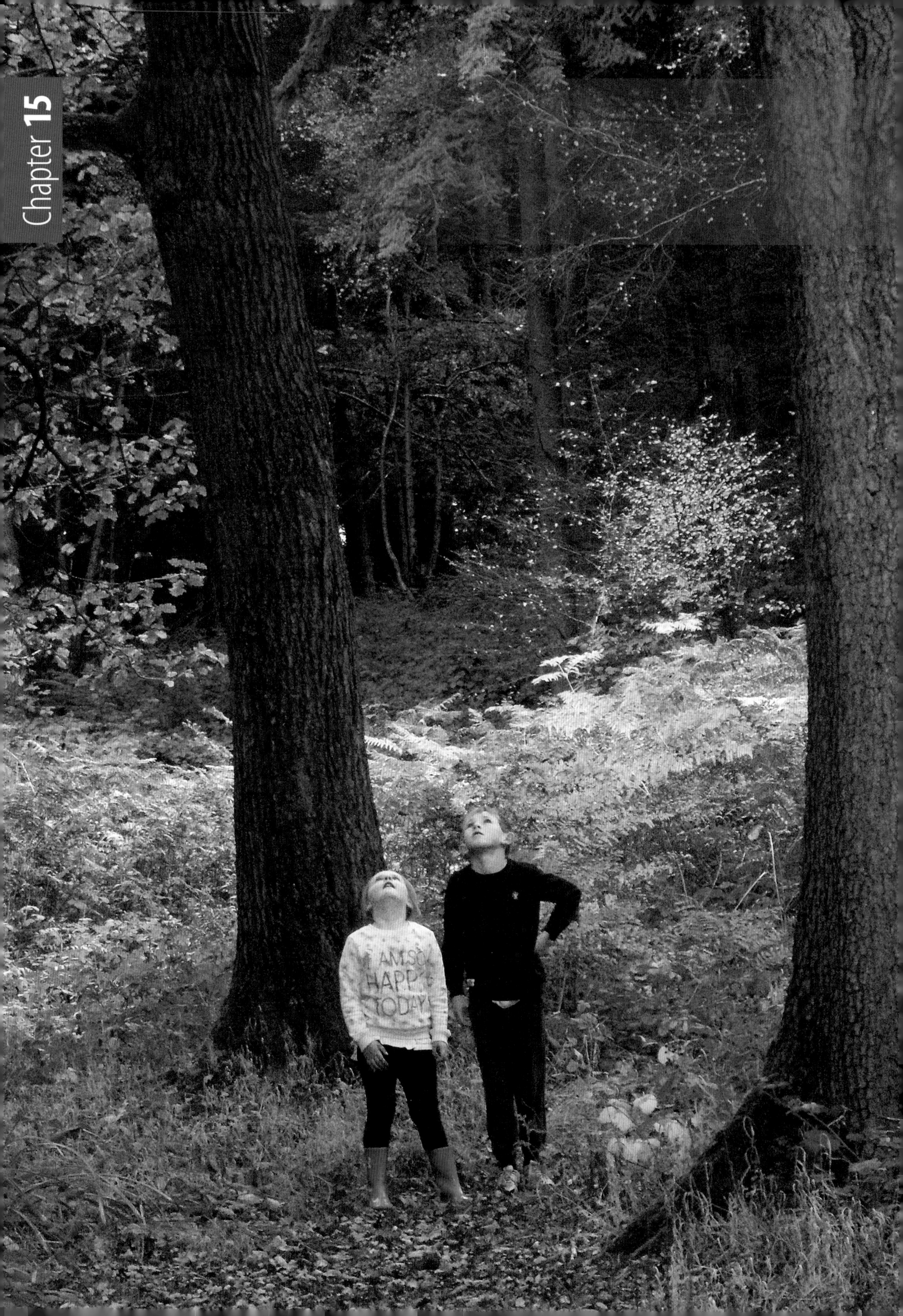

The Future of Wyre

The remarkable thing about the Wyre Forest is the fact that it is still here. As this book has shown, over time many factors have influenced its landscape and natural history and continue to do so. Past glaciations and subsequent floods and erosion have scoured the area, creating steep valleys and cutting a new path for the River Severn. More recently, and for many thousands of years, people have changed the vegetation, first as hunter-gatherers, and later as farmers, foresters and feudal lords who used the Forest for hunting, grazing, fuel and timber. However, large areas of woodland have survived because its underlying geology meant that much of Wyre was not worth clearing for farmland.

By medieval times small-scale clearances, settlements, patches of cultivation, coppice, timber cutting, deer parks and deer hunting had changed the nature of Wyre, but still much of the Forest remained wild. Mechanised industry created new demands: oak was cut on rotation to make charcoal to feed hungry furnaces, whilst the bark was stripped and used by tanneries to produce leather. In the 1900s, cycles of conifer planting created new woodscapes in the quest for speedy timber production. Now, in the 21st century, we have a fresh perspective on the Forest as we strive to balance timber production, nature conservation, recreation, and education.

Wyre Forest is valued by many people for many reasons and sometimes this can cause a conflict of use. Because of this potential conflict it is vital to have a sustainable vision so that recreation, forestry and nature conservation can be balanced. The Forest is clearly significant for the quality and variety of its plants, animals and fungi. It harbours a wealth of interesting and nationally scarce species and has an increasingly important role in sustaining populations of declining wildlife. Its central position in Britain at a bio-geographical junction makes it a 'stepping stone' site for plants and animals found in the south and north of Britain but very rarely in-between. Part of the woodland is a National Nature Reserve, most a Site of Special Scientific Interest. In short, it is one of the most important woodland ecosystems in England and as such deserves to be valued and protected.

Some of the more serious threats to Wyre's wildlife and habitats include introduced and problematic native species such as deer and bracken, and climate change, but the Forest's size may make it more resilient than smaller woodlands. For this reason it is vital to protect its scale and the integrity of its habitats. Its size will also help the Forest absorb more visitors.

Wyre is undeniably important to people and provides relaxation, exercise, inspiration and an escape from the hubbub of everyday life. Visitors enjoy the beauty, peace and tranquility, and their requirements have to be taken into account and balanced alongside the needs of wildlife. Open space in which to walk, jog, exercise dogs or ride a horse or a bicycle is at a premium in the modern British countryside. Access to Wyre is important but will need to be managed sensitively to allow people and wildlife to benefit from vital nature conservation work. This is not easy: more people mean more pressures. Paths are widened and eroded by mountain bikes and walkers, off-lead dogs can scare ground-nesting birds, and even well-meaning naturalists can disrupt the behaviour of Adders *Vipera berus* by seeking that

The Wyre Forest Community Discovery Centre is used by people of all ages and abilities [RW]

Wyre Forest Study Group birdwatching in the Forest [RW]

Worcestershire's Entomology Day is held in Wyre every year [RW]

perfect photograph. But of course its wildlife is why many people come to Wyre and so education and information are paramount for their enjoyment.

Even though visitor numbers have grown during the last decade, the same period has seen some remarkable changes to the landscape which have boosted special habitats and species. Grow With Wyre, a Heritage Lottery funded scheme has, among many other aims, targeted the conservation of key habitats such as orchards. It has also encouraged locally important species such as fritillary butterflies which have responded well as a result of the Back To Orange initiative. Changes in forestry and conservation management have reduced conifer cover, opened up clearings, widened rides and let light into the woodland which has boosted many insect and plant species: Common Lizards *Zootoca vivipara*,

Scarce 7-spot Ladybirds *Coccinella magnifica* and many butterflies are particularly welcoming the extra sunlight. These are exciting times and as we monitor the changes it is heartening to see species making a recovery here, even though they are declining elsewhere.

We must not be complacent though. The Wyre Forest Landscape Partnership is currently planning for a sustainable future where income through profitable forestry (with benefits to the local economy) goes hand in hand with management for wildlife, recreation and heritage. Education and information will be an essential part of the plans and we hope that this book will contribute by helping visitors and residents to celebrate the wonders of Wyre. If we succeed we will all feel, as one of Wyre's most ardent advocates Norman Hickin wrote, "*Forest refreshed*".

The Kentish Glory moth *Endromis versicolora*, became extinct in Wyre, its last English location, in 1972. If a suggested reintroduction project goes ahead, this beautiful moth may be seen again flying free in the Forest. [RWa]

References

Ainsworth, A.M., Cannon, P.F. & Dentinger, B.T.M. (2013) DNA barcoding and morphological studies reveal two new species of waxcap mushrooms (Hygrophoraceae) in Britain. *MycoKeys* 7: 45–62.

Alexander, K., Butler, J. & Green, T. (2006) The value of different tree and shrub species to wildlife. *British Wildlife* 18: 18–28.

Alexander, W.B. (1945) *The Woodcock in the British Isles*. Publication of the British Trust for Ornithology, based on a Report on the Inquiry, 1934–35. *Ibis* 87: 512–550.

Allan, A.A. (2005) The recent occurrence of *Sturmia bella* (Meigen) (Diptera: Tachinidae) in south-west England, including rearings from two host species of Nymphalidae. *British Journal of Entomology & Natural History* 18: 269–271.

Allen, G.W. & Archer, M.E. (1989) *Dolichovespula saxonica* (Fabricius, 1793) (Hym., Vespidae) found in Britain, with a key to British *Dolichovespula*. *Entomologists Monthly Magazine* 125: 103–105.

Altringham, J. (2003) *British Bats*. New Naturalist series. London: Harper Collins.

Altringham, J. (2011) *Bats, from Evolution to Conservation*. 2nd Edn. Oxford: Oxford University Press.

Amphlett, J. & Rae, C. (1909) *The Botany Of Worcestershire*. Birmingham: Cornish Bros Ltd.

Anderson, R. (2005) Annotated list of the non-marine mollusca of Britain and Ireland. *Journal of Conchology* 38(6): 607–637. [Online:] www.conchsoc.org/sites/default/files/MolluscWorld/Anderson-2008.pdf

Andrén, C. & Nilson, G. (1987) The copulatory plug of the adder, *Vipera berus* – does it keep sperm in or out? *Oikos* 49: 230–232.

Appleby, L.G. (1971) *British Snakes*. London: John Baker.

Arnold, N., Ovenden, D. & Corbet, G. (1979) *Collins Handbook to the Wild Animals of Britain and Europe*. London: Collins.

Ashe, P., O'Connor, J.P. & Murray, D.A. (In press) A review of the distribution and ecology of *Buchonomyia thienemanni* Fittkau (Diptera: Chironomidae) including a first record for Russia. *European Journal of Environmental Sciences*.

Atherton, I., Bosanquet, S. & Lawley, M. (2010) *Mosses and liverworts of Britain and Ireland. A field guide*. British Bryological Society.

Atkins, A.H. (1883) Geology of the Wyre Forest. *Midland Naturalist* 6: 31–33.

Averill, M. (2007) The great flood of June 2007. *Wyre Forest Study Group Review 2007* pp 10–12. [Online:] www.wyreforest.net

Averill, M. (2014) Identification of scorpion flies. *Worcestershire Record* 37: 4.

Averill, M.T. (2006) The Dragonflies of Wyre Forest. *Wyre Forest Study Group Review 2006* pp 45–47. [Online:] www.wyreforest.net

Bagnall, J.E. (1909) 'Mosses and Hepatics' In: Amphlett, J. & Rea, C. (Eds) *The Botany of Worcestershire*. Birmingham: Cornish Bros Ltd.

Baily's Magazine of Sports & Pastimes (1926) p 95.

Baker, J., Beebee, T., Buckley, J., Gent, T. & Orchard, D. (2011) *Amphibian Habitat Management Handbook*. Bournemouth: Amphibian and Reptile Conservation.

Baldock, D. (2008) *Bees of Surrey*. Woking: Surrey Wildlife Trust.

Baldock, D. (2010) *Wasps of Surrey*. Woking: Surrey Wildlife Trust.

Baldwin, M. (1994) Ironworking in Cleobury Mortimer. *Cleobury Chronicles* 3: 34–49.

Ball, S. & Morris, R. (2013) *Britain's Hoverflies. An introduction to the hoverflies of Britain*. WILDGuides. Woodstock, Oxfordshire: Princeton University Press (UK).

Ball, S.G., Morris, R.K., Rotheray, G.E. & Watt, K.R. (2011) *Atlas of the Hoverflies of Great Britain (Diptera, Syrphidae)*. Wallingford, Oxfordshire: Biological Records Centre, NERC Centre for Ecology and Hydrology.

Balmer, D.E., Gillings, S., Caffrey, D.J., Swann, R.L. Downie, I.S. & Fuller, R.J. (2013) *Bird Atlas 2007–2011: the breeding and wintering birds of Britain and Ireland*. Thetford: BTO Books.

Barber, A.D. (2008) *Key to the identification of British Centipedes*. Preston Montford: Field Studies Council.

Barnard, P.C. (2011) *The Royal Entomological Society book of British Insects*. Oxford: Wiley-Blackwell.

Barnard, P. & Ross, E. (2012) *The adult Trichoptera (caddisflies) of Britain and Ireland. Handbook for the identification of British insects*. Vol. 1, part 17. Preston Montford: Field Studies Council.

BAS data: British Arachnological Society (BAS) *Spider and Harvestmen Recording Schemes*. [Online:] srs.britishspiders.org.uk/portal.php/

Bat Conservation Trust, UK Bats. [Online:] www.bats.org.uk/pages/uk_bats.html

Beamish, A. (2008) Gannet rescue! *Wyre Forest Study Group Review 2008* p 35.

Beckwith, W.E. & Serjentson, R.M. (1882) *Centunculus minimus* and *Potamogeton plantagineus* in Shropshire. *Journal of Botany* 20: 347.

Bees, Wasps & Ants Recording Society, *Provisional atlas of the aculeate Hymenoptera of Britan and Ireland*. Wallingford, Oxfordshire: Biological Records Centre, Centre for Ecology and Hydrology. Part 1. Edwards, R. (Ed.) (1997) pp 32 & 84.

Part 2. Edwards, R. (Ed.) (1998) pp 30 & 90.

Part 3. Edwards, R. & Telfer, M. (Eds) (2001) pp 20, 108 & 110.

Part 4. Edwards, R. & Telfer, M. (Eds) (2002) pp 22, 32, 82, 100, 110, 112 & 114.

Part 5. Edwards, R. & Broad, G. (Eds) (2005) pp 48, 76 & 98.

Part 6. Edwards, R. & Broad, G. (Eds) (2006) pp 88.

Part 7. Edwards, R. & Roy, H. (Eds) (2009) pp 86 & 96.

Part 8. Collins, G.A. & Roy, H. (Eds) (2012) pp 54, 64, 66, 78, 80 & 118.

Bennallick, I. & Pearman, D. (2013) *Sorbus domestica* (True Service-tree) in Cornwall (v.c.2). *BSBI News* 125: 37–38.

Benton, T. (2012) *Grasshopper and Crickets*. New Naturalist series. London: Harper Collins.

Bingham, J. (2009) Longhorn Beetles of Wyre Forest (Coleoptera: Cerambycidae). *Wyre Forest Study Group Review 2009* pp 7–13. [Online:] www.wyreforest.net

Bingham, J. (2011) Two Interesting Longhorn Beetles from Wyre *Anoplodera sexguttata* (Fabricius, 1775) and *Asemum striatum* (Linnaeus, 1758). *Wyre Forest Study Group Review 2011* p 6. [Online:] www.wyreforest.net

Bingham, J. (2012a) A New Beetle for Wyre Forest and Shropshire *Epiphanis cornutus* (Escholtz, 1829). *Wyre Forest Study Group Review 2012* p 15. [Online:] www.wyreforest.net

Bingham, J. (2012b) Snow Flea *Boreus hyemalis* (L., 1767 Mecoptera: Boreidae) in Wyre Forest. *Worcestershire Record* 32: 13–14.

Bingham, J. (2012c) *Micrommata virescens*. *Wyre Forest Study Group Review 2012* p 24. [Online:] www.wyreforest.net

Bingham, J. (2013) Two Scarce Spiders recorded in the Wyre Forest. *Wyre Forest Study Group Review 2013* p 36. [Online:] www.wyreforest.net

Bingham, J. (2014a) Clubs, Spindles, Corals and Clavaroid Fungi of the Wyre Forest. *Wyre Forest Study Group Review 2014* pp 22–27. [Online:] www.wyreforest.net

Bingham, J. (2014b) Snow Flea, *Boreus hyemalis* (L., 1767 Mecoptera: Boreidae) found mating in Wyre Forest. *Worcestershire Record* 36: 7–9. [Online:] www.wyreforest.net

Bingham, J. & Taylor, M. (1991) An Annotated List of Macro Moths Recorded in Wyre Forest. Unpublished Report. Peterborough: Natural England.

Biodiversity Action Plan for traditional orchards (2007) [Online:] ncc.defra.gov.uk/default.aspx?page=2183&q=orchards

Birks, J. & Robinson, J. (1995) The Mammals of Wyre Forest. In: Packham, J. R. & Harding, D. L. (Eds) *Ecology, Management and History of Wyre Forest*. pp 85–95. Wolverhampton: University of Wolverhampton.

Blakeway, J. (1908) Notes on Kinlet (edited by Mrs Baldwyn-Childe). *Transactions of the Shropshire Archaeological Society 1908*. 3rd Series. 8: 83–150.

Blower, J.G. (1985) *Millipedes*. Synopses of the British fauna No. 35. London: Linnean Society of London.

Bloxham, M. (2006) The Blood-red Robber Ant *Formica sanguinea* (nationally scarce) in Wyre. *Wyre Forest Study Group Review 2006* p 40. [Online:] www.wyreforest.net

Blythe, M. (2010) *Ellipteroides* craneflies (Diptera: Limoniidae) in the Wyre Forest. *Wyre Forest Study Group Review 2010* pp 34–37. [Online:] www.wyreforest.net

Boardman, P. (2014) *A Provisional Atlas of the Shieldbugs and Allies of Shropshire*. Telford: Field Studies Council.

Boertmann, D. (2000) *Fungi of Northern Europe*. Vol. 1. *The Genus Hygrocybe*. Svampertryk.

Booth, T. (2010) Mills on Dowles Brook and its Tributaries. *Wyre Forest Study Group Review 2010* pp 10–11. [Online:] www.wyreforest.net

Both, C. & Marvelde, L. (2007) Climate change and timing of avian breeding and migration throughout Europe. *Climate Research* 35: 93–105.

Both, C. (2012) Insufficient adaptation to climate change alters avian habitat quality and thereby changes habitat selection. In: Fuller, R.J. (Ed.) *Birds and habitat: relationships in changing landscapes*. Cambridge: Cambridge University Press. pp 432–452.

Bouček, Z. (1972) On European Pteromalidae (Hymenoptera): a revision of *Cleonymus, Eunotus* and *Spaniopus*, with descriptions of new genera and species. *Bulletin of British Museum Natural History (Entomology)* 27 (5): 268–315.

Boycott, A.E. (1936) The relation of slugs and snails to man in Britain. *Proceedings of the Cotteswold Naturalists' Field Club* 26.

Bradley, C. (1996) The Realm of the Fallow Buck. In: Bradley, C. (1996) *The Deer of Wyre Forest*. Christopher Bradley (self-published).

Bradley, C. (2000) Fallow Buck Mortality in Wyre Forest 1999–2000. *Wyre Forest Study Group Review 2000* p 40. [Online:] www.wyreforest.net

Bradley, C. (2007a) Fallow Deer Battle for Dominance. *Wyre Forest Study Group Review 2007* p 8. [Online:] www.wyreforest.net

Bradley, C. (2007b) The Fallow Deer of Wyre Forest. *Wyre Forest Study Group Review 2007* pp 6–7. [Online:] www.wyreforest.net

Bradney, R.J. (1957) Black Stork in Worcestershire. *British Birds* 50: 348–349.

Brett Young, F. (1936) *Far Forest*. London: Heinemann.

Bright, P., Morris, P. & Mitchell-Jones, T. (2006) *The Dormouse Conservation Handbook*. 2nd edn. Worcester: English Nature.

Bristowe, W.S. (1958) *The World of Spiders*. New Naturalist series. London: Harper Collins.

British Bugs website: [Online:] www.britishbugs.org.uk/

British Marine Life Study Society website: www.glaucus.org.uk/Sturgen2.htm

British Trust for Ornithology (BTO) Trends website: blx1.bto.org/birdtrends/species.jsp?&s=piefl BTO BirdTrends data for Pied Flycatchers.

Brock, P.D. (2014) *A comprehensive guide to insects of Britain and Ireland.* Newbury: Pisces Publications.

Broughton, R.K., Bellamy, P.E., Hill, R.A. & Hinsley, S.A. (2014) Winter habitat selection by Marsh Tits *Poecile palustris* in British Woodland. *Bird Study* 61: 404–412.

Broughton, R.K., Hinsley, S.A., Bellamy, P.E., Hill, R.A. & Rothery, P. (2006) Marsh Tit *Poecile palustris* territories in a British broad-leaved wood. *Ibis* 148: 744–752.

Brown, A. (2010) Ground Beetles along the Banks of the River Severn 2010 (Coleoptera: Carabidae). *Wyre Forest Study Group Review 2010* pp 13–14. [Online:] www.wyreforest.net

Browne, S. & Aebischer, N. (2005) Studies of West Palearctic birds: Turtle Dove. *British Birds* 98: 58–72.

BTO Atlas 2007–2011: see Balmer *et al.* 2013.

BTO Mapstore: [Online:] www.bto.org/volunteer-surveys/birdatlas/results/mapstore

Bullock, J.M., Jefferson, R.G., Blackstock, T.H., Pakeman, R.J., Emmett, B.A., Pywell, R.J., Grime, J.P. & Silvertown, J.W. (2011) Chapter 6: Semi-natural grasslands. In: *The UK National Ecosystem Assessment Technical Report. UK National Ecosystem Assessment.* Cambridge: UNEP-WCMC.

Burton, A. (1985) Report of a field meeting to Wyre Forest during the BBS's paper-reading meeting at Birmingham, autumn 1984. *Bulletin of the British Bryological Society* 45: 13.

Cameron, R. & Riley, G. (2008) *Land Snails in the British Isles.* 2nd edn. Preston Montford: Field Studies Council.

Carrick, T. (2004) Spring field meeting 2004, Worcestershire. *Field Bryology* 84: 18–23.

Cefas and Environment Agency (2012) *Annual Assessment of Salmon Stocks and Fisheries in England and Wales (2011).* 136 pp. Bristol.

Cham, S., Nelson, B., Parr, A., Prentice, S., Smallshire, D. & Taylor, P. (2014) *Atlas of Dragonflies in Britain and Ireland.* Telford: Field Studies Council.

Chance, E. (1922) *The Cuckoo's Secret.* London: Sidgwick & Jackson.

Chance, E.P. (1940) *The Truth about the Cuckoo.* London: Country Life.

Charman, E.C., Smith, K.W., Gruar, D.J., Dodd, S. & Grice, P.V. (2010) Characteristics of woods used recently and historically by Lesser Spotted Woodpeckers *Dendrocopos minor* in England. *Ibis* 152: 543–555.

Charman, E.C. & Dodds, S. (2011) Seeing the Wood(peckers) for the Trees! Our experiences of studying Lesser Spotted Woodpeckers in the Wyre and surrounding woodlands 2007–2009. *Wyre Forest Study Group Review 2011* pp 59–62. [Online:] www.wyreforest.net

Charman, E.C., Smith, K.W., Dodd, S., Gruar, D.J. & Dillon, I.A. (2012) Pre-breeding foraging and nest site selection by Lesser-spotted Woodpeckers *Dendrocopus minor* in mature woodland blocks in England. *Ornis Fennica* 80: 1–15.

Charman, E.C., Smith, K.W., Dillon, I.A., Dobb, S., Gruar, D.J., Cristinacce, A., Grice, P.V. & Gregory, R.D. (2012) Drivers of low breeding success in the Lesser Spotted Woodpecker *Dendrocopos minor* in England: testing hypotheses for the decline. *Bird Study* 59: 255–265.

Cheffings, C.M. & Farrell, L. (Eds) (2005) *The Vascular Plant Red Data List for Great Britain.* Peterborough: JNCC.

Chinery, M. (2011) *Britain's Plant Galls, a photographic guide.* Old Basing: Wildguides.

Churchward, A.S., Hickley, P. & North, E. (1984) The introduction, spread and influence of the barbel *Barbus barbus* in the River Severn, Great Britain. *European Inland Fisheries Advisory Commission, Documents presented at the Symposium on Stock Enhancement in the Management of Freshwater Fisheries, Budapest 1982, Technical Paper* 42 (2): 335–343.

Claridge, M.F. (1962) *Andricus quercus-calicis* (Burgsdorff) in Britain (Hym: Cynipidae). *Entomologist* 95: 60–61.

Claxton, F. (1999) The Whitty Pear *Sorbus domestica* L. A Natural Pioneer Millennium Award Project – Work in Progress. *Worcestershire Record* 7: 28–30.

Clements, D.K. (1997) The Enemy Within: Conopid flies as parasitoids of bees and wasps in Britain. *British Wildlife* 8 (5): 310–315.

Conway, G., Wotton, S., Henderson, I., Langston, R., Drewitt, A. & Currie, F. (2007) Status and distribution of European Nightjars *Caprimulgus europaeus* in the UK in 2004. *Bird Study* 54: 98–111. DOI: 10.1080/00063650709461461.

Cramp, S. & Perrins, C.M. (Eds) (1993) *The birds of the Western Palearctic.* Vol. 7. Oxford: Oxford University Press.

Crimmin, P.K. (2008) The supply of timber for the Royal Navy, c1803–c1830. In: Rose, S. (Ed.) *The Naval Miscellany, VII.* Farnham: Ashgate. pp 200–201.

Crowther, E.M. (2003) A Living From the Forest; Bewdley Historical Research Group, Occasional Paper No. 8. Bewdley.

Csorba, G., Ujhelyi, P. & Thomas, N. (2003) *Horseshoe Bats of the World.* Bishop's Castle, Shropshire: Alana Books.

Dalton, S. (2008) *Spiders. The Ultimate Predators.* London: A. & C. Black Publishers Ltd.

Darlington, A. (1974) *The Galls on oak.* In: Morris, M.G. & Perring, F.H. (Eds) *The British Oak.* pp 298–311. Published for the Botanical Society of the British Isles by E.W.Classey Ltd., Farringdon.

Darlington, A. & Hirons, M.J.D. (1968) *The Pocket Encyclopaedia of Plant Galls in Colour.* London: Blandford Press.

Davies, C.E., Shelley, J., Harding, P.T., McLean, I.F.G., Gardiner, R. & Peirson, G. (Eds) (2004) *Freshwater Fishes in Britain, the species and their distribution.* Colchester: Harley Books.

Davies, N. (2015) *Cuckoo: Cheating by Nature.* London: Bloomsbury.

Davies, S. (2008) *Breeding Bird Survey notes, Wyre Forest 2008. Thetford*: British Trust for Ornithology.

Day, J.J. (2001) *Checklist of the Worcestershire Flora.* Hindlip: Worcestershire Wildlife Trust.

Denman, S. & Webber, J. (2009) Oak declines: new definitions and new episodes in Britain. *Quarterly Journal of Forestry* 103: 285–290.

Denman, S., Kirk, S. & Webber, J. (2010) *Managing Acute Oak Decline.* Practice Note. Forestry Commission.

Devignes, T. (1842) Description of *Pancalia grandis. The Entomologist* 1: 342.

Dietz, C., Helversen, O. & Nill, D. (2009) *Bats of Britain, Europe & Northwest Africa (English Edition).* London: A. & C. Black Publishers Ltd.

Dolling, W.R. (1991) *The Hemiptera.* Natural History Museum Publications. Oxford: Oxford University Press.

Donisthorpe, H.St-J.K. (1927a) *The Guests of British Ants, their habits and life histories.* London: Routledge.

Donisthorpe, H.St-J.K. (1927b) *British Ants, their life-history and classification.* London: Routledge.

Drayton, M. (1612) Poly Obrion, Song 7, lines 256–260. In: Hooper, R. (Ed.) (1876) *The Complete Works of Michael Drayton.* J.R. Smith publisher: 1, p 179.

Duke, T. (2015) *pers. comm.*

Duncan, J.B. (1911) Notes on the old collections of mosses in the herbarium of the Hastings Museum, Victoria Institute, Worcester. *Transactions of the Worcestershire Naturalists' Club* pp 75–77.

Edington, J.M. & Hildrew, A.G. (1995) *Caseless caddis larvae of the British Isles.* Ambleside: Freshwater Biological Association Scientific publication No. 53.

Eel Management Plans for the UK: Severn Basin District. Environment Agency (2010).

Environment Agency (2010) *Removal of in-channel structures.* [Online:] evidence.environment-agency. gov.uk/FCERM/en/SC060065/MeasuresList/M8/ M8T1.aspx

Evans, M. & Edmondson, R. (2005) *A Photographic Guide to the Shieldbugs and Squashbugs of the British Isles.* WGUK in association with WildGuideUK.

Everard, M. (2013) *Britain's Freshwater Fishes.* WILDGuides. Woodstock, Oxfordshire: Princeton University Press (UK).

Eyton, R.W. (1857) *Forest of Wyre, Antiquities of Shropshire, IV* pp 276–278.

Falk, S. (1991) *A review of the scarce and threatened flies of Great Britain. Part 1.* Nature Conservancy Council; Research and survey in nature conservation No. 39.

Falk, S.J. (1982) *Dolichovespula media* (Retzius) – a new British social wasp. *Proceedings and Transactions of the British Entomological and Natural History Society* 15: 14–16.

Falk, S. & Crossley, R. (2005) *A review of the scarce and threatened flies of Great Britain. Part 3, Empidoidea.* Nature Conservancy Council; JNCC, Species Status No. 3.

Farmer, G. (2005) An aquatic escape strategy of the Slender Groundhopper *Tetrix subulata. Bulletin of the Amateur Entomologists' Society* 6: 125.

Farmer, G. (2007) Have you seen the bathroom bush-cricket (aka the Oak Bush-cricket). *Worcestershire Record* 22: 32.

Farmer, G. (2012) Orthoptera and Allies – some observations of behaviour and Life-cycles. In Worcestershire Entomology Day report, *Wyre Forest Study Group Review 2012* pp 56–58. [Online:] www.wyreforest.net

Farmer, G. (2013a) Mapping Worcestershire's Orthoptera. *Worcestershire Record* 34: 10.

Farmer, G. (2013b) Christmas crossbills. *Wyre Forest Study Group Review 2013* pp 60–61. [Online:] www. wyreforest.net

Fletcher, J.E. (1869) Note on *Enoicyla pusilla. Entomologists' Monthly Magazine* 6: 61.

Fletcher, J.E. (1878) On the habitat of *Enoicyla pusilla. Entomologists' Monthly Magazine* 15: 204.

Fletcher, J.E. (1901) Trichoptera (Caddis-flies). In: *The Victoria History of the Counties of England: Worcestershire.* Vol 1. p 85. London: Dawsons.

Fletcher, S. (1981) *A Wyre Forest Diary.* Kidderminster: Kenneth Tomkinson Ltd.

Fowles, A.P., Alexander, K.N.A. & Key, R.S. (1999). The Saproxylic Quality Index: evaluating wooded habitats for the conservation of dead-wood Coleoptera. *The Coleopterist* 8: 121–141.

Fox, R., Brereton, T.M., Roy, D.B., Asher, J. & Warren, M.S. (2011) *The State of the UK's Butterflies 2011.* Wareham, Dorset: Butterfly Conservation and the Centre for Ecology & Hydrology.

Fraser, A., Green, H., Lake, S. & Neale, W. (1998) *Endangered Wildlife in Worcestershire, The County Red Data Book.* Worcestershire Biodiversity Forum Worcestershire Wildlife Trust.

Frazer, D. (1983) *Reptiles and Amphibians in Britain.* London: Collins.

Fuller, R.J. (Ed.) (2012) *Birds and habitat: relationships in changing landscapes.* Cambridge: Cambridge University Press.

Fuller, R.J., Smith, K.W. & Hinsley, S.A. (2012) Temperate western European woodland as a dynamic environment for birds: a resource-based view. In: Fuller, R.J. (Ed.) *Birds and habitat: relationships in changing landscapes.* pp 352–380. Cambridge: Cambridge University Press.

Garbett, A. (2011) Identification of individual Adders *Vipera berus* by their Head Markings. *Wyre Forest Study Group Review 2008* pp 16–17. [Online:] www. wyreforest.net

Gauld, I. & Bolton B. (Eds) (1988) *The Hymenoptera.* London: The Natural History Museum.

GB Non-native Species Secretariat (2015) *Help stop the spread of invasive plants and animals in British waters.* [Online:] www.nonnativespecies.org/ checkcleandry/

Gelling, M. (1984) *Place-names in the Landscape.* London: J.M. Dent & Sons.

George, E. (1987) *The Forest is my Life*. Countryside Publications.

Gerry, H. (2012) *Sorbus domestica*, the Woodward Family Connection in Worcestershire. *Worcestershire Record* 33: 67–68.

Gilbert, O. (2000) *Lichens*. The New Naturalist series. London: Harper Collins.

Girling, A. (2005) Nest distribution and other ecological aspects of the wood-ant (*Formica rufa*) in an area of the Wyre Forest. *Wyre Forest Study Group Review* pp 17–20.

Gissing, T.W. (1855) A Visit to Wyre Forest, Worcestershire. *Phytologist New Series* 1: 151–153.

Goulson, D. & Williams, P. (2001) *Bombus hypnorum* (Hymenoptera: Apidae). A new British bumblebee? *British Journal of Entomology and Natural History* 14: 129–131.

Green, G.H. (2007) The Hawfinch. *Worcestershire Record* 20: 25.

Green, G.H. (2009) Ants of Wyre Forest – A review. *Wyre Forest Study Group Review 2009* pp 28–39. {Online:] www.wyreforest.net

Green, G.H. & Westwood, B. (2005a) In search of the Land Caddis. *British Wildlife* 17: 21–26.

Green, H. (2007) A great cricketing summer: the invasion of Worcestershire by Long-winged Coneheads *Conocephalus discolor* and Roesel's Bush-cricket *Metriotera roeselii*. *Worcestershire Record* 23: 38–41.

Green, H. (2009) The Old Sorb Tree, Whitty Pear or The True Service Tree, *Sorbus domestica L*, Previously *Sorbus pyriformis*. *Wyre Forest Study Group Review 2009* pp 69–73. [Online:] www.wyreforest.net

Green, H. (2013) Planting the 2013 Whitty Pear. *Worcestershire Record* 35: 12–14.

Green, H., Birks, J., Schenke, J. & Trevis, G. (2012) *Worcestershire's Mammals*. Worcestershire Recorders & Worcestershire Biological Records Centre.

Green, G.H. & Westwood, B. (2005a) In search of the Land Caddis. *British Wildlife* 17: 21–26.

Green, H. & Westwood, B. (2005b) The Land or Terrestrial caddis (*Enoicyla pusilla*) and *Wyre Forest*. *Wyre Forest Study Group Review 2005* pp 3–9. [Online:] www.wyreforest.net

Green, G.H. & Westwood, B. (2006) The shining guest ant *Formicoxenus nitidulus* in Wyre Forest. *Wyre Forest Study Group Review 2006* pp 9–11. {Online:] www.wyreforest.net

Green, H. & Westwood, B. (2012) Sightings of adult Land Caddis *Enoicyle pusilla* and a mating pair, Worcestershire October 2012. *Worcestershire Record* 33: 39–40.

Green, J. (1982) *A Practical Guide to the Butterflies of Worcestershire*. The Worcestershire Nature Conservation Trust (now Worcestershire Wildlife Trust).

Green, S.W. & Clark, M.C. (1962) The bryophytes of the Wyre Forest. *Proceedings of the Birmingham Natural History and Philosophical Society* 20: 3–22.

Grundy, D. (2006) A List of Significant Species of Lepidoptera Recorded in the Wyre Forest. Unpublished report for English Nature.

Grundy, D. (2008) A List of Significant Species of Lepidoptera recorded in the Wyre Forest. 2nd edn. Unpublished report for the Forestry Commission.

Grundy, D.G. (2003) *A Study of the Common Fan-foot Moth* Pechipogo strigilata *in the Wyre Forest and other sites*. English Nature, Forestry Commission, and Butterfly Conservation (West Midlands Branch).

Gullett, P., Evans, K.L., Robinson, R.A. & Hatchwell, B.J. (2014) Climate change and annual survival in a temperate passerine: partitioning seasonal effects and predicting future patterns. *Oikos* 123: 389–400.

Haes, E.C.M. & Harding P.T. (1997) *Atlas of Grasshoppers, Crickets and Allied Insects in Britain and Ireland*. ITE research publication number 11. London: The Stationery Office.

Hammond, P.M. *et al.* (1989) Some recent additions to the British insect fauna. *Entomologists Monthly Magazine* 125, 95–102.

Hampton, M. (1996) *Sorbus domestica* L. – comparative morphology and habitats. *BSBI News* No. 73. pp 32–37.

Hampton, M. & Kay, Q.O.N. (1995) *Sorbus domestica* L., new to Wales and the British Isles. *Watsonia* 20: 379–384.

Hand, N. (2010) *A study using external telemetry attachment on two separate adder (Vipera berus) populations within the Wyre Forest March–June 2010*. Unpublished report for the Forestry Commission.

Hand, N., Watson, W. & King, P. (2006) *Amphibians and Reptiles of Herefordshire*. Herefordshire Biological Records Centre.

Harding, D.J.L. (1995) The Terrestrial Caddis *Enoicyla pusilla*. In: Packham, J. R. & Harding, D. L. (Eds) *Ecology, Management and History of Wyre Forest*. pp 108–113. Wolverhampton: University of Wolverhampton.

Harding, D.J.L. (1998) Distribution and population dynamics of the litter-dwelling caddis, *Enoicyla pusilla* (Trichoptera). *Applied Soil Ecology* 9: 203–208.

Harper, M.W. & Simpson, A.N.B. (2003, 2004) *The Smaller Moths of Herefordshire and Worcestershire*. Part 1 in 2003, Part 2 in 2004. Wareham, Dorset: Butterfly Conservation.

Harper, M. & Simpson, T. (2000) *Larger Moths and Butterflies of Herefordshire & Worcestershire*. West Midlands Branch of Butterfly Conservation.

Harris, S. & Yalden, D.W. (Eds) (2008) *Mammals of the British Isles: Handbook*. 4th edn. Southampton: The Mammal Society.

Harrison, M. (2006) Sixteen years and counting. The birds of Dowles Brook. *Wyre Forest Study Group Review 2006* pp 41–44. [Online:] www.wyreforest.net

Harrison, G. & Harrison, J. (2005) *The new birds of the West Midlands*. Studley: West Midland Bird Club.

Harrison, M. (2007) The Dippers of Dowles Brook in Wyre Forest. *Worcestershire Record* 22: 16–19.

Harrop, A.H.J., Collinson, J.M., Dudley, S.P. & Kehoe, C. & The British Ornithologists' Union Records Committee (BOURC) (2013) The British List: A Checklist of Birds of Britain. 8th edn. *Ibis* 155: 635–676.

Harthan, A.J. (1946) *The Birds of Worcestershire.* Worcester: Littlebury.

Harthan, A.J. (1961) A revised list of Worcestershire Birds. *Transactions of the Worcestershire Naturalists' Club* 11: 167–186.

Hastings, C. (1834) *Illustrations of the Natural History of Worcestershire.* London: Sherwood, Gilbert & Piper; Worcester: Lees, at the request of the Worcestershire Natural History Society.

Hatcher, J. (1993) *Towards the Age of Coal.* pp 32–55. Oxford: Clarendon Press.

Hawkins, D. (2003) *Shieldbugs of Surrey.* Woking: Surrey Wildlife Trust.

Hawksworth, D.L. & Rose, F. (1969) A Note of the Lichens and bryophytes of the Wyre Forest. *Proceedings of the Birmingham Natural History Society* 21(3): 191–197. [Online:] www.nhm.ac.uk/nature-online/life/plants-fungi/lichens/

Heaver, D. (2006) The ecology of *Ellipteroides alboscutellatus* (von Roser, 1840) (Diptera, Limoniidae) in England. *Dipterists Digest (Second Series)* 13: 67–86.

Heaver, D. (2014) Further observations on the ecology of *Ellipteroides alboscutellatus* (von Roser) (Diptera, Limoniidae) in England and Wales. *Dipterists Digest (Second Series)* 21: 41–54.

Herefordshire Woolhope Club on 25th August 1904. Wyre Forest. *Transactions of the Woolhope Naturalists' Field Club for 1902, 1903, 1904* issued September 1905. pp 312–315.

Hickin, N.E. (1965) *Forest Refreshed. The autobiographical notes of a biologist.* London: Hutchinson.

Hickin, N.E. (1967) *Caddis Larvae.* London: Hutchinson.

Hickin, N.E. (1971) *The Natural History of an English forest. The wildlife of Wyre.* London: Hutchinson.

Hill, A. (2011) *Dowles Brook Wyre Forest Crayfish Survey.* Report for the Wyre Forest Landscape Partnership Scheme – Grow with Wyre.

Hill, A. & Hill, G. (2014) Update on White-clawed Crayfish within Wyre Forest, 2014. *Wyre Forest Study Group Review 2014* pp 10–17. [Online:] www.wyreforest.net

Hill, G. (2011) The relationship of benthic macroinvertebrate assemblages to water surface flow types in British lowland rivers. Unpublished PhD Thesis, Coventry University.

Hillyard, P.D. (2005) *Harvestmen.* Synopses of the British Fauna No. 4. 3rd edn. Preston Montford: Field Studies Council.

Holditch, D. (2003) *Ecology of the White-clawed Crayfish. Conserving Natura 2000 Rivers Ecology Series No. 1.* Peterborough: English Nature.

Holloway, S. (1996) *The historical atlas of breeding birds in Britain and Ireland: 1875–1900.* London: Poyser.

Hooke, D. (1985) *The Anglo-Saxon Landscape: the Kingdom of the Hwicce.* Manchester: Manchester University Press.

Hooke, D. (1989) Pre-conquest woodland; its distribution and usage. *Agricultural History Review* 37: 126.

Hooke, D. (2007) The early medieval landscape. *West Midlands Regional Research Framework for Archaeology,* Seminar 4.

Hopkin, S.P. (1991) A key to the woodlice of Britain and Ireland. *Field Studies* 7: 599–650. Later reprinted as an AIDGAP key by Field Studies Council.

Hopkin, S.P. (2007) *A key to the Collembola (Springtails) of Britain and Ireland.* Preston Montford: Field Studies Council.

Horsáková, J. (2003) Biology and immature stages of the clam-killing fly, *Renocera pallida* (Diptera: Sciomyzidae). *European Journal of Entomology* 100: 143–151.

Horsman, F. (2000) Edmund Pitt (1613–1688) and *Sorbus domestica* in Wyre Forest. *BSBI News* 83: 22–24.

Inns, H. (2009) *Britain's Reptiles and Amphibians.* WILDGuides. Woodstock, Oxfordshire: Princeton University Press (UK).

Invertebrate Site Register (1997) *Wyre Forest (SO745760)* September 1997 (internal report extract). Joint Nature Conservancy Committee.

Ironbridge Gorge Museum. [Online:] www.ironbridge.org.uk/assets/Uploads/resourceriversevern.pdf

IUCN (2015) *Austropotamobius pallipes, conservation status.* [Online:] www.iucnredlist.org/details/2430/0

Jackson, R. & Dalwood, H. (2007) *Archaeology and Aggregates in Worcestershire; a resource assessment and research agenda.* pp 58–59. Worcester: University of Worcester.

James, N.D.G. (1981) *A History of English Forestry.* pp 207–225. Oxford: Blackwell.

Jeffrey F.R. (1916) The Wyre Forest Sorb Tree. *Transactions of the Worcestershire Naturalists' Club* Vol. VI, part III pp 250–257.

Jenks, P., Green, M. & Cross, T. (2014) Foraging activity and habitat use by European Nightjars in South Wales. *British Birds* 107: 413–419.

Jennings, F. (2005) The sorb tree of Wyre – the True Service or Whitty Pear (*Sorbus domestica*). *Wyre Forest Study Group Review 2005* pp 53–56. [Online:] www.wyreforest.net

Jones, D. (1983) *The Country Life Guide to Spiders of Britain and Northern Europe.* London: Hamlyn.

Jones, M.M. (1981) [Caption to the picture of the 1916 planting]. *Transactions of the Worcestershire Naturalists' Club.* New series, Vol. 1, part 2, pp 96–97.

Jones, N. & Cheeseborough, I. (2014) *A provisional atlas of the bees, wasps and ants of Shropshire.* Preston Montford: Field Studies Council.

Jorden, G. (1864) Flora Bellus Locus. Unpublished manuscript. Worcester City Museum.

Joy, J. & Ellis, S. (2012) The impact of management on Pearl-Bordered Fritillary populations in the Wyre Forest. In: Ellis, S., Bourn, N.A.D. & Bulman, C.R. (Eds) *Landscape-scale Conservation for Butterflies and Moths: lessons from the UK*. Wareham, Dorset: Butterfly Conservation. pp 30–35.

Kelner-Pillault, S. (1960) Biologie, Écologie d'*Enoicyla pusilla* Burm. (Trichoptëres Limnophilides). *Annals of Biology* 36: 51–99.

Kennedy, C.E.J. & Southwood, T.R.E. (1984) The number of species of insects associated with British trees: a re-analysis. *Journal of Animal Ecology* 53: 455–478.

Kern, M., Slater, F., & Cowie, R. (2014) Return rates and dispersal distances of Welsh Pied Flycatchers *Ficedula hypoleuca* and factors that influence them. *Ringing & Migration* 29: 1–9.

Kerney, M. (1999) *Atlas of the land and freshwater molluscs of Britain and Ireland*. Colchester: Harley Books.

Kidston, R. (1917) XXVII.—The Forest of Wyre and the Titterstone Clee Hill Coal Fields. *Transactions of the Royal Society of Edinburgh* 51: 999–1084.

Killeen, I., Aldridge, D. & Oliver, G. (2004) *Freshwater Bivalves of Britain and Ireland*. Preston Montford: Field Studies Council.

Knutson, L.V. & Vala, J.-C. (2011) *Biology of snail-killing Sciomyzidae Flies*. Cambridge: Cambridge University Press.

Lambourne, V. (2011) Wyre Forest Newt Survey 2011. *Wyre Forest Study Group Review 2011* pp 63–65. [Online:] www.wyreforest.net

Langbein, J. & Chapman, N. (2003) *Fallow Deer*. The Mammal Society & The British Deer Society.

Langton, T., Beckett, C. & Foster, J. (2001) *Great Crested Newt Conservation Handbook*. Suffolk: Froglife.

Lawley, M. (2013) *The Mosses and Liverworts of Shropshire*. Privately published.

Lawley, M. (2015) *Wildlife in The Marches*. Ludlow: Marches publications.

Lea, Rev. J.T. (1889) Personal Observations on the Natural History of the Wyre Forest. In: *Transactions of the Shropshire Archaeological and Natural History Society*. Second series, Vol. 1.

Lee, P. (2006) *Atlas of the Millipedes (Diplopoda) of Britain and Ireland*. Pensoft for the Biological Records Centre.

Lees, E. (1853) Wyre Forest, Mopson's Cross, Park Brook, Dowles Brook to Bewdley. *Transactions of the Worcestershire Naturalists' Club* pp 5–10.

Lees, E. (1856) *Pictures of Nature*. Malvern: H.W. Lamb.

Lees, E. (1867) *The Botany of Worcestershire*. Worcestershire Naturalists' Club.

Leighton, W.A. (1841) *A Flora of Shropshire*. Shrewsbury: John Davies.

Leisler, B. & Thaler, E. (1982) Differences in morphology and foraging behaviour in Goldcrest *Regulus regulus* and Firecrest *Regulus ignicapillus*. *Annales Zoologici Fennici* 19: 277–284.

Lever, C. (2013) *The Mandarin Duck*. London: Poyser.

Lindsay, D.C. (1985) Some Lichens from the Wyre Forest. *Proceedings of the Birmingham Natural History Society* 25 (3): 153–154.

Loudon J.C. (Ed.) (1829) Flocks of Crossbills near Worcester. *Magazine of Natural History* 2: 268.

Lowe, G. (2014) New Treecreeper nest box. *Worcestershire Record* 36: 22.

Macadam, C. & Bennett, C. (2010) *A Pictorial Guide to British Ephemeroptera*. Preston Montford: Field Studies Council.

MacDonald, D. & Barrett, P. (1993) *Collins Field Guide. Mammals of Britain and Europe*. London: Collins.

Mallord, J.W., Orsman, C.J., Cristinacce, A., Butcher, N., Stowe, C.J. & Charman, E.C. (2012) Mortality of Wood Warblers *Phylloscopus sibilatrix* nests in Welsh Oakwoods; predation rates and the identification of predators using miniature nest cameras. *Bird Study* 59: 286–295.

Mammal Society website: www.mammal.org.uk/sites/default/files/Shrew%20News%20Results%202006.pdf

Marsh, T.J. & Hannaford, J. (2007) *The summer 2007 floods in England and Wales – a hydrological appraisal*. Wallingford: Centre for Ecology & Hydrology.

Martin, J. (2000) Bird Surveys in the Wyre Forest in 2000. *Wyre Forest Study Group Review 2000* pp 33–34. [Online:] www.wyreforest.net

Martin, J. (2002) Bird surveys in the Wyre Forest 2001–2002. *Wyre Forest Study Group Review 2002* pp 46–46. [Online:] www.wyreforest.net

Martin, J. (2003) Woodcock survey in the Wyre Forest area. *Wyre Forest Study Group Review 2003* p 14. [Online:] www.wyreforest.net

Maskew, R. (2014) *The Flora of Worcestershire*. Worcestershire Flora Project. Published privately by R. Maskew.

Matthysen, E. (1989) Seasonal variation in bill morphology of Nuthatches *Sitta europaea*: adaptations or consequences? *Ardea*. 77: 117–125.

McGavin, G.C. (2001) *Essential Entomology. An order by order introduction*. Oxford: Oxford University Press.

McGee, K. (2004) The Noble Chafer – an observation of three freshly emerged adults. *Wyre Forest Study Group Review 2004* p 20. [Online:] www. wyreforest.net

McGee, K. & Whitehead, P.F. (2003) A collection of invertebrates assembled by the late Dr Norman E. Hickin. *Entomologist's Record and Journal of Variation* 115: 201–211.

McKenzie, A.J., Petty S.J., Toms, M.P. & Furness, R.W. (2007) Importance of Sitka Spruce *Picea sitchensis* seed and garden bird-feeders for Siskins *Carduelis spinus* and Coal Tits *Periparus ater*: *Bird Study* 54: 236–247.

McLachlan, R. (1868) Occurrence in England of a terrestrial trichopterous insect; probably *Enoicyla pusilla*, Burmeister. *Entomologists' Monthly Magazine* 5: 43–44, also *Enoicyla pusilla*, a trichopterous insect, bred in England p 143; and Further note on *Enoicyla pusilla* p 170.

Meiklejohn, J. (2007) Yet another RDB2 beetle from Defford. *Worcestershire Record* 20: 8.

Middleton, R. (2009) Joseph Hesselgrave Thompson (1811–1889) Obituary. University of Hull. [Online:] www.herb.hull.ac.uk/herbarium/thompson.htm

Mitchell, G.H., Pocock, R.W. & Taylor, J.H. (1961) *The Geology of the Country around Droitwich, Abberley and Kidderminster* (Explanation of Sheet 182). Memoir of the Geological Survey of Great Britain. London: HMSO.

Morse, D.H. (2007) *Predator upon a Flower: Life History and Fitness in a Crab Spider.* Cambridge, MA: Harvard University Press.

Mountford, G. (1957) *The Hawfinch.* London: Collins.

Müller, C. & Schmid-Hemple, P. (1993) Exploitation of cold temperature as defence against parasitoids in bumblebees. *Nature* 363: 65–66.

Mustin, K., Amar, A. & Redpath, S.M. (2014) Colonisation and extinction dynamics of a declining migratory bird are influenced by climate and habitat degradation. *Ibis* 156: 788–798.

Nash, T.R. (1781–1782) *Collections for the history of Worcestershire.* London. The plate can also be seen in Tomkinson, K. & Everett, E. (1984) *Selections from Nash's Worcestershire.* Kenneth Tomkinson Ltd.

National River Flow Archive (2012) 54001 – Severn at Bewdley. [Online:] www.ceh.ac.uk/data/nrfa/data/time_series.html?54001

National Archives *Calendar of Inquisitions Post Mortum,* Vol 4, No 235; Inquest on Edmund de Mortimer, 1304.

National Archives *Calendar of State Papers (Domestic)* 13 April, 1537.

National Archives *Calendar of the Patent Rolls* (Cal Pat Roll), Edn I Vol. 3, 421.

Natural England website: www.sssi.naturalengland.org.uk

Natural England (2009) SSSI Citation, Wyre Forest. [Online:] www.sssi.naturalengland.org.uk/citation/citation_photo/1004198.pdf

Natural Environment Research Council (NERC) (2003) Hydrological Data UK, *Hydrometric Register and Statistics 1996–2000.* Wallingford: Centre for Ecology & Hydrology.

National Orthoptera Recording Scheme – Orthoptera and Allied Insects. [Online:] www.orthoptera.org.uk

NBN Gateway [Online:] data.nbn.org.uk/ National database and maps.

New, T.R. (2005) *Psocoptera (booklice, barklice).* 2nd edn. *Handbooks for the identification of British insects.* Vol. 1, part 7. Preston Montford: Field Studies Council.

Newell Arber, E.A. (1913) On the Fossil Floras of the Wyre Forest, with Special Reference to the Geology of the Coalfield and its Relationship to the Neighbouring Coal Measure Areas. *Philosophical Transactions of the Royal Society of London* 204: 363–445.

Newton, I. (2006) Movement patterns of Common Crossbills *Loxia curvirostra* in Europe. *Ibis* 148: 782–788. [Online:] onlinelibrary.wiley.com/doi/10.1111/j.1474–919X.2006.00585.x/pdf

Newton, I. (2013) *Bird Populations.* New Naturalist Series, Vol. 124. London: Collins.

Nimis, P.L., Scheidegger, C. & Wolseley, P. (Eds) (2000) Monitoring with Lichens – Monitoring Lichens. *Proceedings of the NATO Advanced Research Workshop on Lichen Monitoring Wales.* 16–18 August 2000.

Oates, M. (2003) The ecology and dynamics of the Pearl-bordered Fritillary *Boloria euphrosyne* in a Gloucestershire woodland. *Butterfly Conservation Report SO3–12.* Wareham, Dorset: Butterfly Conservation.

Oliver, M. (1995) The Soil. In: Packham, J.R. & Harding, D.L. (Eds) *Ecology, Management and History of the Wyre Forest.* pp 33–35. Wolverhampton: University of Wolverhampton.

Orange, A. (1994) *Lichens on Trees.* British Plant Life Number 3. National Museum of Wales, Cardiff.

Packham, J.R., Harding, D.J. & Hilton, G.M. (1992) *Functional Ecology of Woodlands and Forests.* pp 316. London: Chapman & Hall.

Paton, J.A. (1960) Weekend Meeting at Birmingham. *Transactions of the British Bryological Society* 3: 789–791.

Pearson, E. (2007) In: Jackson, R. & Dalwood, H. (Eds) *Archaeology and Aggregates in Worcestershire; a resource assessment and research agenda.* p 61. Worcester: University of Worcester.

Peay, S. (2001) *Eradication of alien crayfish populations. R&D Technical Report W1-037/TR1.* Bristol: Environment Agency.

Peirson, G. (2011) Fish Sampling Day at Uncllys Reservoir. *Wyre Forest Study Group Review 2011* pp 40–41. [Online:] www.wyreforest.net

Perry, W.G. in Leighton (1841) *A Flora of Shropshire.* Shrewsbury: John Davies.

Phillips, R. & Rix, M. (1985) *Freshwater Fish of Britain, Ireland and Europe.* London: Pan Books Ltd.

Pickvance, T.J. & Fincher, F. (1957) Mammals of Worcestershire: a Revised List. *Proceedings of the Birmingham and Natural History and Philosophical Society Vol. XIX.* p 9.

Piper, R. (2009) The Large Timberworm Beetle, *Hylecoetus dermestoides* in Shrawley Wood. *Worcestershire Record* 26: 36.

Pitt, E. (1678) Extract of a Letter from Mr Edmund Pitt, Alderman of Worcester, a Very Knowing Botanist; Concerning the *Sorbus Pyriformis. Philosophical Transactions* (1665–1678) Vol. 12, 1677–1678, No. 139 April, May & June 1678, pp 978–979.

Plant, C.W. (1997) A key to the adults of British Lacewings and their allies (Neuroptera, Megaloptera, Raphidioptera and Mecoptera. *Field Studies* 9: 179–269.

Plantlife (2003) *Important Fungus Areas (IFAs).* Plantlife, British Mycological Society, and Association of British Fungus Groups.

Pontin, J. (1996) Ant nests, sun and shade – their measurement and significance for invertebrate conservation. *British Wildlife* 8: 21–27.

Poulton-Smith, A. (2003) *Worcestershire Place Names*. Stroud: Sutton. pp 136–137.

Poyner, D. & Evans, R. (2000) *The Wyre Forest Coal Field*. Stroud: Tempus.

Preston, C.D., Pearman, D.A. & Dines, T.D. (2002) *New Atlas of the British and Irish Flora: An Atlas of the Vascular Plants of Britain, Ireland, The Isle of Man and the Channel Islands*. Oxford: Oxford University Press.

Pryce, D. (2004) River-fly survey results 2004. *Wyre Forest Study Group Review 2004* pp 38–42. [Online:] www.wyreforest.net

Pryce, D.J. (2006) Trichoptera from the Roxel Malaise trap. *Wyre Forest Study Group Review 2006* p 31. [Online:] www.wyreforest.net

Rald, E. (1985) Vokshatte som indikatorarter for mykologisk vaerdifulde overdrevslokaliteter. *Svampe* 11: 1–9.

Ratcliffe, D. (1997) *The Raven*. Poyser: London.

Rea, C. (1910) Additions to the Botany of Worcestershire. *Transactions of the Worcestershire Naturalists' Club* pp 273–293.

Rea, C. (1922) *British Basidiomycetae. A Handbook to the Larger British Fungi*. British Mycological Society. Cambridge: Cambridge University Press.

Rea, C. (1923) The Fungi of Wyre Forest. *Transactions of the Worcestershire Naturalists' Club* Vol. 8, 1923–1931. pp 16–40.

Rea, C. (1929) The Flora of our Charcoal Heaps. *Transactions of the Worcestershire Naturalists' Club* Vol. 8. pp 312–318.

Rea, C. & Fletcher, J.E. (1901) *Lepidoptera*. In: *The Victoria History of the County of Worcestershire* Vol. 1. pp 100–124. London: Dawsons.

Redfern, M., Shirley, P.R. & Bloxham, M. (2011) *British Plant Galls*. 2nd edn. Shrewsbury: Field Studies Council.

Redhead, S.A., Ammirati, J.F., Walker, G.R., Norvell, L.L. & Puccio, M.B. (1994.) *Squamanita contortipes*, the Rosetta Stone of a mycoparasitic agaric genus. *Canadian Journal of Botany* 72: 1812–1824.

Reed, C. (2014) Parrot Crossbill *Loxia pytyopsittacus* – a First for Wyre. *Wyre Forest Study Group Review 2014* p 28. [Online:] www.wyreforest.net.

Rich, T.C.G., Houston, L., Robertson, A. & Proctor, M.C.F. (2010) *Whitebeams, Rowans and Service Trees of Britain and Ireland. A monograph of British and Irish Sorbus*. BSBI Handbook No. 14. London: Botanical Society of the British Isles.

Ricketts, J. (2001) Wyre Forest Lichens. *Wyre Forest Study Group Review* pp 45–47. [Online:] www.wyreforest.net

Ricketts, J. (2005) Worcestershire lichens. What a Difference a Century Makes. *Worcestershire Record* 19: 55–60.

Riley, A. (1991) *A Natural History of the Butterflies and Moths of Shropshire*. Shrewsbury: Swan Hill Press.

Roberts, M.J. (1995) *Spiders of Britain & Northern Europe*. London: Harper Collins.

Robinson, J. (2011) Smooth x Palmate Newt Hybrid in a Wyre Forest Garden pond. *Worcestershire Record* 30: 30.

Robinson, J. (2014) Wildlife photography, how it all began. *Wyre Forest Study Group Review 2014* pp 5–8. [Online:] www.wyreforest.net

Robinson, J.R. (2007) Hawfinches – getting the shot. *Worcestershire Record* 20: 23–24.

Rodwell, J.S. (Ed.) (1991a) *British Plant Communities, 1. Woodlands and scrub*. Cambridge: Cambridge University Press.

Rodwell, J.S. (Ed.) (1991b) *British Plant Communities, 2. Heaths and mires*. Cambridge: Cambridge University Press.

Rodwell, J.S. (Ed.) (1992) *British Plant Communities, 3. Grasslands and montane communities*. Cambridge: Cambridge University Press.

Rotheray, G.R. & Gilbert, F. (2011) *The Natural History of Hoverflies*. p 334. Cardigan: Forrest Text.

Rowson, B., Turner, J., Anderson, R. & Symondson, B. (2014) *Slugs of Britain and Ireland. Identification, Understanding and Control*. Telford: FSC Publications.

Rudlin, P. (2010) Wyre Forest balloon trip. *Wyre Forest Study Group Review 2010* pp 58–59. [Online:] www.wyreforest.net

Rudlin, P. (2014) Dormice and Conifers in Wyre updates. *Wyre Forest Study Group Reviews 2000–2014*. [Online:] www.wyreforest.net

Russ, J. (2012) *British Bat Calls, a Guide to Species Identification*. Exeter: Pelagic Publishing.

Salisbury, E.J. (1925) The Vegetation of the Forest of Wyre: A preliminary account. *Journal of Ecology* 13: 14–321.

Savory, T.H. (1933) Arachnida of Worcestershire. *Transactions of the Worcestershire Naturalists' Club* Vol. IX p. 87.

Saproxylic Quality Index: Evaluated sites ranked by SQI. [Online:] khepri.uk/main/

Sawyer (1380a) quoted in Hooke, D. (1990) *Worcestershire Anglo-Saxon Charters* pp 235–239.

Sawyer (1380b) quoted in Hooke, D. (1990) *Worcestershire Anglo-Saxon Charters* pp 120–125.

Scott, J. (2014) New Sites in Wyre for Strawberry Spider *Araneus alsine*. *Wyre Forest Study Group Review 2014* pp 44–45. [Online:] www.wyreforest.net

Shaw, G. (1990) Timing and fidelity of breeding for Siskins *Carduelis spinus* in Scottish conifer plantations. *Bird Study* 37: 30–35.

Sheldon, S. & Bradley, C. (1989) Identification of individual Adders (*Viperus berus*) by their head markings. *Herpetological Journal* 1 (9): 392–396.

Sheldon, S., Bradley, C. & Garbett, A. (2014) Annual Reviews of Herpetofauna behaviour correlated with Weather. *Wyre Forest Study Group Reviews 2000–2014*. [Online:] www.wyreforest.net

Shirt, D.B. (Ed.) (1987) *British Red Data Books: 2. Insects*. Peterborough: Nature Conservancy Council.

Simpson, A.N.B. (1996) *Caryocolum junctella* (Douglas) in Worcestershire (VC37) in 1994. *The Entomologist's Record and Journal of Variation* 108: 145–146.

Simpson, T. (2012) A Weevil Parasitoid. *Wyre Forest Study Group Review 2012* p 6. [Online:] www.wyreforest.net

Smart, M.J. & Winnall, R.A. (Eds) (2006) *The Biodiversity of three Traditional Orchards within the Wyre Forest SSSI in Worcestershire: a survey by the Wyre Forest Study Group*. English Nature Research Report Number 707. Worcester: English Nature.

Smith, M. (1951) *The British Amphibians and Reptiles*. London: Collins.

Smith, K.W. & Charman, E.C. (2012) The ecology and conservation of the Lesser Spotted Woodpecker. *British Birds* 105: 294–307.

Southcott, A. (2007) The Impact of Deer Browsing on Coppiced Vegetation at the Wyre *Forest*. A Summary of a BSc Independent Study, Worcester University, May 2007. *Wyre Forest Study Group Review 2007* pp 42–46. [Online:] www.wyreforest.net

Southwood, T.R.E. (1961) The number of species of insects associated with species of trees. *Journal of Animal Ecology* 30: 1–8.

Spencer, A. (2009) Bird boxes in the Wyre Forest. *Wyre Forest Study Group Review 2009* pp 48–49.

Steele-Elliott, J. (1894a) Palmate Newt in Worcestershire and Shropshire. *Zoologist* 3 (10): 154.

Steele-Elliott, J. (1894b) Bank Vole in Worcestershire and Shropshire. *Zoologist* 3 (18): 233.

Steele-Elliott, J. (1901) Nightjar hawking mayflies. *Zoologist* 4 (15): 70.

Steele-Elliott, J. (1904) Cirl Bunting in Worcestershire and Shropshire. *Zoologist* 1 (8): 457.

Steele-Elliott, J. (1905) The Red-backed Shrike (*Lanius collurio*) and its prey. *Zoologist* 1 (9): 309.

Steele-Elliott, J. (1908) Nesting of the Wryneck. *Zoologist* 4 (12): 393.

Steele-Elliott, J. (1911) Former occurrence of Black Grouse in Wyre Forest, Shropshire and Worcestershire. *Zoologist* 4 (15): 387–388.

Steele-Elliott, J. (1912) Some notes on the nesting of the Tawny Owl (*Syrnium aluco*). *Zoologist* 4 (16): 293–297.

Steele-Elliott, J. (1919–20) Grey Wagtails nesting at a distance from water. *British Birds* 13: 81.

Steele-Elliott, J. (1936–37) Tawny Owl taking prey during the day. *British Birds* 30: 47.

Stephens, B. (2006a) Damsons & Dyeing. *Wyre Forest Study Group Review 2006* pp 52–55. [Online:] www.wyreforest.net

Stephens, B. (2006b). *The Fruit Trade in the Area of Bewdley and Wyre Forest*. Unpublished report commissioned by English Nature.

Stephens, B. (2008) Orchards in the Manor of Bewdley in 1749. *Wyre Forest Study Group Review 2008* pp 32–34. [Online:] www.wyreforest.net

Stephens, B. (2009) Orchards near Bewdley and the Wyre Forest 1749–1870. *Wyre Forest Study Group Review 2009* pp 50–53. [Online:] www.wyreforest.net

Stephens, B. (2011) The Hurricane at Bewdley. *Wyre Forest Study Group Review 2011* pp 52–56. [Online:] www.wyreforest.net

Stephens, B. (2012) John Rea, Florist of Kinlet, 1605(?)–1677. *Wyre Forest Study Group Review 2012* pp 44–45. [Online:] www.wyreforest.net

Stephens, B. (2014) Cherry varieties in the 17th Century. *Wyre Forest Study Group Review 2014* pp 40–43. [Online:] www.wyreforest.net

Stostad, H.N. & Menéndez, R. (2014) Woodland structure rather than tree identity determines the breeding habitat of Willow Warblers *Phylloscopus trochilus* in the north-west of England. *Bird Study* 61: 246–254.

Stubbs, A. & Drake, M. (2014) *British Soldierflies and their Allies*. 2nd edn. British Entomological and Natural History Society.

Sykes, N., Baker, K.H., Carden, R.F., Higham, F.G., Hoelzel, A.R. & Stevens, R.E. (2011) New Evidence for the Establishment and Management of the European Fallow deer (*Dama dama dama*) in Roman Britain. *Journal of Archaeological Science* 38: 156–165.

Taylor, M.N. (1989) *Linyphia (Neriene) marginata* C.L. Koch: new record for England. *Newsletter of British Arachnological Society* 54: 4.

Thompson, R., Humphrey, J., Harmer, R. & Ferris, R. (2003) *Restoration of native woodland on ancient woodland sites*. Edinburgh: Forestry Commission.

Thompson, R.D. (1986) *Rock*. pp 4–6. Kenneth Tomkinson Ltd.

Trevis, G.H. (2004) A taxonomic revision of the ants of the genus *Lasius*. *Worcestershire Record* 16: 29–30.

Tomes, R.F. (1901a) Reptiles and Amphibians. In: *The Victoria History of the Counties of England: Worcestershire*. Vol. 1. p 138. London: Dawsons.

Tomes, R.F. (1901b) Mammalia. In: *The Victoria History of the County of Worcester* Vol. 1. p 176. London: Constable.

Trout, R.C., Brooks, S. & Rudlin, P. (In press) *The advantages of permanent marking, such as microchipping, during long term monitoring of the Hazel dormouse (Muscardinus avellanarius)*. International Dormouse conference Denmark 2014.

Trout, R.C., Brooks, S.E., Rudlin, P. & Neil, J. (2012) The effects of restoring a conifer Plantation on an Ancient Woodland Site (PAWS) in the UK on the habitat and local population of the Hazel Dormouse (*Muscardinus avellanarius*). *European Journal of Wildlife Research* 58 (4): 635–643.

Trout, R.C., Brunt, A. & Rudlin, P. (2005) *Dormice: preliminary recommendations for Best Practice forest operations in broadleaved and conifer woodlands*. Dormouse Best Practice Guidance 2007. Edinburgh: Forestry Commission.

Twinn, P.F.G. & Harding, P.T. (1999) *Provisional Atlas of the Longhorn Beetles (Coleoptera, Cerambycidae) of Britain*. Huntingdon: Biological Records Centre.

UK Biodiversity Action Plan (1994). Department for the Environment, HMSO.

Vesterholt, J., Boertmann, D. & Tranberg, H. (1999) 1998 – et usaedvanlig godt ar for overdrevssvampe. *Svampe* 40: 36–44.

Walker, C.I. (1994) The Roman fort at Walltown Farm. *Cleobury Chronicles* 3: 26–33.

Wallace, I. (2006) *Simple key to caddis larvae*. Preston Montford: Field Studies Council.

Wallace, I.D. (1991) *A Review of Trichoptera in Britain*. Peterborough: Nature Conservancy Council.

Wallace, I.D., Wallace, B. & Philipson, G.N. (2003) *Keys to the case-bearing caddis larvae of Britain and Ireland*. Ambleside, Cumbria: Freshwater Biological Association.

Wardle, P. & Quayle, C. (1989) *Ruskin and Bewdley*. Sheffield: The Guild of St George.

Warr, A. (2007) The irruption of wintering Hawfinch in Worcestershire. *Worcestershire Record* 20: 24.

WBRC from Data provided by Worcestershire Biological Records Centre, 2014.

Wernham, C., Toms, M., Marchant, J., Clark, J., Siriwardena, G. & Bailie, S. (2002) *The Migration Atlas. Movements of the birds of Britain and Ireland*. London: Poyser.

Westwood, B. (2010) White Mandarin Duck at Trimpley. *Wyre Forest Study Group Review 2010* p 33. [Online:] www.wyreforest.net

Westwood, B. (2013) A Surfeit of Lampreys? *Wyre Forest Study Group Review 2013* pp 48–49. [Online:] www.wyreforest.net

Wheeler, A. & Jordan, D.R. (1990) The status of the barbel, *Barbus barbus* (L.) (Teleostei, Cyprinidae), in the United Kingdom. *Journal of Fish Biology* 37 (3): 393–399.

Whitton, B. & Lucas, M.C. (1997) Biology of the Humber Rivers. *Science of the Total Environment* 194/195: 247–262.

Wilde, N. (1973) Nuthatch assuming camouflage posture. *British Birds* 66: 230–231.

Wilde, N. (2001) Wyre Forest, Cuckoos and the secret. *Wyre Forest Study Group Review 2001* pp 3–10. [Online:] www.wyreforest.net

Wilde, N. (2002) Tawny Nights: observations at the nest sites of Tawny Owls in Wyre Forest. *Wyre Forest Study Group Review 2002* pp 2–7. [Online:] www.wyreforest.net

Wilde, N. (2004) A Wyre Forest Woodcock. *Wyre Forest Study Group Review 2004* p 2. [Online:] www.wyreforest.net

Wilson, P. (2011) Wood Ants of Wyre. *Wyre Forest Study Group Review 2011* pp 17–22. [Online:] www.wyreforest.net

White, G. (1789) *The Natural History of Selborne*. London: Benjamin White.

Whitehead, P.F. (1998) Extraordinary numbers of *Polyxenus lagurus* (L) (Myriapoda) in the Shropshire Wyre Forest. *Entomologists' Monthly Magazine* 134: 266.

Whitehead, P.F. (2008) Observations on the ecology of *Corizus hyoscyami* (Linnaeus, 1758) (Hemiptera, Rhopalidae) and the British influx of 2006. *Entomologists' Monthly Magazine* 144: 163–176.

Whitehead, P.F. & Key, R.S. (2010) Observations on British *Issus* (Hemiptera, Issidae) with reference to development, periodicity and ecology. *Worcestershire Record* 29: 23–27.

Whitehead, T.H. & Pocock, R.W. (1947) *The Geology of the Country around Bridgnorth and Dudley (Explanation of Sheet 167)*. Memoir of the Geological Survey of Great Britain. London: HMSO.

Willis, K.J. & McElwain, J.C. (2014) *The Evolution of Plants*. 2nd edn. Oxford: Oxford University Press.

Winnall, R. (2001) Woodpeckers of Rock Coppice. *Wyre Forest Study Group Review 2001* pp 25–31. [Online:] www.wyreforest.net

Winnall, R. (2003) The Common Frog (*Rana temporaria*) and its breeding status in Wyre. *Wyre Forest Study Group Review 2003* pp 3–8. [Online:] www.wyreforest.net

Winnall, R. (2004) Fascinating Frogs. *Worcestershire Record* 16: 22.

Winnall, R. (2005) Waxwings come to Wyre. *Wyre Forest Study Group Review 2005* p 16. [Online:] www.wyreforest.net

Winnall, R. (2007) Wyre Forest Woodcock. *Wyre Forest Study Group Review 2007* p 59. [Online:] www.wyreforest.net

Winnall, R. (2009a) Creatures of the Dark! *Wyre Forest Study Group Review 2009* p 74. [Online:] www.wyreforest.net

Winnall, R. (2009b) Harlequin Ladybirds *Harmonia axyridis* in Bewdley. *Wyre Forest Study Group Review 2009* p 80. [Online:] www.wyreforest.net

Winnall, R. (2009c) Snow Fleas *Boreus hyemalis* (Linnaeus, 1767) (Mecoptera: Boreidae). *Wyre Forest Study Group Review 2009* p 42. [Online:] www.wyreforest.net

Winnall, R. (2012) *Nereine radiata*. *Wyre Forest Study Group Review 2012* p 25. [Online:] www.wyreforest.net

Winnall, R. (2013a) The Water Shrew Project. *Wyre Forest Study Group Review 2013* pp 74–78. [Online:] www.wyreforest.net

Winnall, R. (2013b) Grey Seal in Bewdley! *Wyre Forest Study Group Review 2013* pp 6–8. [Online:] www.wyreforest.net

Winnall, R., Blythe, M. & Finch, R. (2012) In search of canopy invertebrates. *Wyre Forest Study Group Review 2012* pp 46–53. [Online:] www.wyreforest.net

Winnall, R. & Farmer, N. (2013) A New Harvestman in Wyre Forest *Sabacon viscayanum*. *Worcestershire Record* 35: 16–17 and *Wyre Forest Study Group Review 2013* pp 21–22. [Online:] www.wyreforest.net

Winnall, R. & Hall, S. (2009) Glow-worms at Pound Green Common. *Wyre Forest Study Group Review 2009* p 66. [Online:] www.wyreforest.net

Withers, P. (1989) Moth Flies (Diptera: Psychodidae) *Dipterists' Digest* (old series) 4.

Worcestershire Biological Records Centre [Online:] www.wbrc.org.uk

Worcestershire Naturalists' Club (1853) Wyre Forest, Mopson's Cross, Park Brook, Dowles Brook to Bewdley. 24th August, 1853. *Transactions of the Worcestershire Naturalists' Club 1847–1896* pp 5–10.

Worcestershire Naturalists' Club (1860) Kidderminster, Bewdley and Stourport. Friday, 21st September, 1860. *Transactions of the Worcestershire Naturalists' Club 1847–1896* pp 61–62.

Worcestershire Naturalists' Club (1869) Cleobury Station, Wyre Forest, Mawley Hall, Old Forge and Cleobury. Tuesday, 28th September, 1869. *Transactions of the Worcestershire Naturalists' Club 1847–1896* pp 142–144.

Worcestershire Naturalists' Club (1895) Wyre Forest Station to Bewdley. Fourth Half-day Walk, Thursday, 18th July, 1895. *Transactions of the Worcestershire Naturalists' Club 1847–1896* pp 408–409.

Worcestershire Naturalists' Club (1932) Wyre Forest. Saturday, 2nd July, 1932. *Transactions of the Worcestershire Naturalists' Club Volume IX 33* p 13.

[Online:] www.youtube.com/watch?v=dN8FU51kgmo Many aerial images of Wyre Forest.

[Online:] www.youtube.com/watch?v=cqHQfm2mVDg The Grow with Wyre documentary.

Wyre Forest Study Group website: www.wyreforest.net

Yapp, W.B. (1956) The Theory of Line Transects. *Bird Study* 3: 93–104.

Yapp, W.B. (1962) *Birds and Woods*. London: Oxford University Press.

Yapp, W.B. (1969) The bird population of an oakwood (Wyre Forest) over eighteen years. *Proceedings of the Birmingham Natural History Society* 21: 199–216.

Zwarts, L., Bijlama, R.G., van der Kamp, J. & Wymenga, E. (2009) *Living on the edge: wetlands and birds in a changing Sahel.* Zeist, The Netherlands: KNNV Publishing.

Index

Page numbers to species mentioned in the text are shown in Roman type, page numbers to pictures are shown in **bold** type